C000292123

The Public Sector
Climate Change Series

A Guide to
Solar PV Projects

in Local Government
and the Public Sector

Second Edition

By Stephen Cirell LLB, Solicitor

In association with:
British Solar Renewables

Peer Reviews of A Guide to Solar PV Projects in Local Government and the Public Sector

"It is unusual to use the words inspirational and Local Government in the same breath. Stephen Cirell has done a remarkable thing in drawing together everything you need to know about Solar PV projects in Local Government and the Public Sector. This is a hugely important work because it is full of practical examples and approaches the issue from the perspective that one day the whole world will be doing this – so why wait? Stephen has long been a champion for solar projects and saw many years ago the returns that the public sector could make on its investments, describing them as long as four years ago as being 'no brainers'. Evidently the rest of the world has taken a while to catch up, but now there is no excuse. Any far-sighted Council in the country has here a blueprint for the future. The green technology revolution isn't so much on the horizon as in our lap. Essential reading for all those charged with looking after and developing the common wealth in an emerging low carbon world."

Tim Smit, *Eden Project.*

"Nationally, the debate about climate change, renewables and solar power is muddled, polarised and deeply problematic in terms of building real momentum behind the vision of the low-carbon Britain. By contrast, at the local level there's a lot of dynamism – but it's patchy and vulnerable to poor policy making at the national level.
Stephen Cirell's book is therefore particularly timely – pitched unapologetically at people 'on the front line', striving to make real progress on the ground in terms of both local renewables and energy efficiency. It provides an authoritative account of how it all fits together, from the big picture stuff about accelerating climate change, all the way through to ideas about new financing and investment models. This is complex and contested territory, which means that well-informed and insightful guides are therefore going to become more and more important. Stephen Cirell's 'guide to solar PV projects' sets an impressive benchmark in that regard."

Jonathon Porritt, *Founder Director, Forum for the Future.*

"This book is a must for every local authority or pubic body contemplating a solar PV scheme. It will help convince the political and managerial leaders to go down the solar route, dispel the myths about solar PV, guide the officers tasked with the project and ensure that no time or money is wasted. No stone is left unturned in Steve's thorough and easily understandable analysis. A unique publication for the public sector."

Ray Noble, *Solar Trade Association.*

"Climate Change is impacting us at a national and local level. National policy continues to fail at the same time local authorities are required to bear the greater burden in combating this change. Steve's book for local authorities provides the first practical and realistic guide for forward thinking local organisations to take steps to implement renewables effectively. This is a must for all involved in local government who want to stop talking about climate change and start doing something about it."

David Owen, *Chief Executive Officer, Solar Media Ltd*

"As you'd expect, this book deals brilliantly with the nuts and bolts of setting up solar projects. Equally impressive, though, is Steve's grasp of the context for this vital work for local authorities: building a low carbon future after years of half-hearted action on climate change."

Warren Hatter, *Local Improvement Advisor on Climate Change.*

"This book comes at a perfect time. Despite rumours to the contrary, this is an excellent time for a local authority to embark on a solar PV programme, as demonstrated by the extensive project work that Steve has undertaken with APSE members. This book is unique in that there is no other work as comprehensive and authoritative to help guide a public body through the process. But over and above that, it should give every Council both the ambition to want to do it and the confidence to deliver."

Paul O'Brien, *Chief Executive, APSE.*

"Councils should take renewables seriously for environmental, financial and economic reasons. The damage done to Planet Earth by man in recent times is undeniable and renewable energy helps halt the tide of destruction. Renewables can also help address the financial challenge by cutting costs and insulating councils and communities from future price increases in high carbon electricity. And in many cases renewable energy also generates jobs which in turn creates wealth and, importantly, local taxes to fund local services!

So, it's a great idea but how do we make it happen? This is where Stephen Cirell comes to the rescue. His book provides an invaluable guide to the why, what and how to deliver solar energy. It is written in plain English and should be required reading for portfolio holders, chief officers and energy managers. Enjoy!"

Kevin Lavery, *Chief Executive, Cornwall Council.*

ISBN 978-0-9563131-7-1

Stephen Cirell has been a solicitor for over thirty years and all of that time has specialised in local government and the public sector. He has worked as an in-house lawyer in local government, led a large public law team in an international law firm and been a director of climate change in a large Council. He has worked as an independent consultant since 2010, advising on a range of different renewable energy and low carbon projects.

Contact Stephen on:

T: 07774 451 587

E: stephencirell@me.com

Tw: @stephencirell

Linked in: uk.linkedin.com/pub/stephen-cirell/24/90b/b39

Web: www.publicsectorenergy.co.uk

Stephen Cirell Consultancy Ltd

Dedication

The Climate Change Series is dedicated to John Bennett, without whom a lifetime of inspiration may never have been discovered.

A Guide to Solar PV Projects
in Local Government and the Public Sector

Contents

Foreword

Local government is on a path 'back to the future'.

The APSE Energy vision sees local authorities able to generate and supply electricity and heat to both their own operations and their domestic and commercial customers.

Doing so would turn the clock back 70 years to when local authorities were routinely involved in the supply of electricity, gas and water at local level. The civic landscape has changed radically since then – and is in a further period of rapid change however the challenge of on-going austerity may make the cost and revenue opportunity of distributed generation a commerical operative.

The UK is moving away from its historic, centrally generated/nationally distributed model for energy. Carbon dioxide and other greenhouse gases were not considered when todays' systems were built, but are now driving the move to renewable power. Local generation, often in far smaller capacities, is seen as preferable. Local need, met locally, in a way that promotes the local economy is the panacea to today's ills of the monopoly of the big six, grid problems and a faltering market.

Local Authories have a range of potential roles to play in this revolution. At the most simple, they can act as a channel between developers and local communities for investment and long-term returns. At the most involved, they can become asset owners and power retailers in their own right. Their choice will depend on circumstance and appetite, and can evolve over time.

I established British Solar Renewables on the back of experience gained in other commercial areas, and a long term interest in the renewable sector. I had no expectation of how rapid and interesting our trajectory as a business would be. We see a long term future for the business as a supplier of energy and a partner to organisations and with local communities. As long as we continue to innovate, to work with the right customers and to provide great value we see little prospect of any slowing of the pace of change.

I hope that this book helps to explain the opportunities which Local Authorities are now presented with, and that it spurs some new thinking in how to realise them.

Angus McDonald
Managing Director
British Solar Renewables

Acknowledgements

A book this size is the result of many hours of hard labour, but it also results from a wide variety of projects and canvassing the knowledge and understanding of many others. I am indebted to all the people in the public sector that have contributed to my own knowledge and understanding of solar PV over past years, and in particular, those that have attended the various talks that I have given on climate change and renewable energy.

However, the following people deserve special credit. Paul O'Brien and Mark Bramah are colleagues from APSE who provide constant help and guidance in this area. Always willing listeners to ideas and initiatives, it is with them that much of my thinking has been fine-tuned.

Ray Noble is also a friend and colleague, well known in the solar PV industry. It is through his unending efforts that solar PV has grown to enjoy the position it does today and I thank him for his technical assistance on the book and projects.

David Owen of Solar Media Ltd has been a friend and colleague since my Cornwall Council days and is a detailed source of information on the solar PV market. He is responsible for much of my general knowledge on solar PV and how it operates. Solar Power Portal keeps me up to date on developments, along with countless other information sources.

I would like to thank the Energy, Infrastructure & Government Group at Walker Morris LLP, who listened to my ideas with tolerance and good humour; I appreciate this particularly as all are under pressure themselves: David Kilduff, Partner and Richard Auton, Director who also provided guidance on the differences between England, Wales, Scotland and Northern Ireland.

Colleagues at Cornwall Council are always high in my gratitude. This is where I really worked out how all this fits together, having been invited to lead the council's Green Cornwall Programme by Kevin Lavery. They made me think harder and deeper about the issues and provided the challenges that these solutions are designed to meet. Many of the examples are from my time in Cornwall, where Peter Marsh continues much of the work I started. I salute Cornwall as an authority at the cutting edge of climate change still. Tim Smit, from the Eden Project, is a mentor on climate change and continues to offer the level of lateral thinking to which I aspire.

Various authorities have provided case studies, including Swindon Commercial Services and Swindon Borough Council, Wrexham County Borough Council, Lancaster City Council and Tandridge District Council. Creative Concerns Ltd also provided a case study on communications strategies. Thanks go to Clive Chamberlain, Jonathan Edwards, Mark Davies, Stephen Weigel, Andrew Peacock and Dr John Feltwell respectively.

Howard Barton is to be thanked for the drawing of the various figures used in this work and also undertook much of the production work on the book. His support and assistance was greatly appreciated. Thanks to Jamie Hailstone and Nicola Carroll for their editing skills.

Finally, the original proofs were meticulously read by Adam Davidson of Walker Morris, Ray Noble of the National Solar Centre, David Owen of Solar Media and Judith Barnes of Beachcrofts, and I am grateful to them. Despite their best efforts, I retain responsibility for any errors or inconsistencies in the text. If I could blame anyone else for them I would. Unfortunately I cannot. Any faults are mine alone.

Stephen Cirell
Leeds, January 2015.

I have practiced law for nearly thirty years now, all of it spent either working for, or specialising in, the public sector. After twelve years working in house in the legal departments of various local authorities, I joined the private sector, in the form of an international law firm that wanted to build a stronger public sector presence. I spent nearly twenty years building up a public law/ commercial practice, all the while advising public sector clients on the best strategic solutions to the issues that they faced.

During this time I also wrote a series of books on various aspects of local government contracting and procurement. My work here was undertaken with John Bennett and we always sought to explain complex legal structures in a straightforward manner, so they could be understood by non lawyers. My writing work has never been 'academic' in nature, but more practical guidance on how to do a project.

In 2009, my career took a different turn. I joined Cornwall Council, newly created after local government reorganisation in the region, as Director of the Green Cornwall Programme. I had been immersed in environmental work for a while and believed that the infrastructure to deliver the Government's ambitious green programme would be built by the public sector in-house over the following decade. The only way to be part of that action was to join a large public sector organisation. My time in Cornwall was indeed instructive, as I led the entire climate change function of this large authority. I dealt with all aspects of climate change, but energy efficiency and renewable energy projects became the main area of my work. The very first project I proposed in Cornwall was a solar power project.

Since leaving Cornwall, I have established a niche practice, advising local authorities and the public sector how to build strong climate change and renewable energy strategies. I have advised on a variety of different projects, across many technologies, including solar, wind, biomass and marine energy. This work has been illuminating. From it I have concluded what works and what doesn't work; what the secret formula is that some authorities posses and others search for restlessly. In many ways, this is no different to my practice over the decades: it is all about a clear vision, a strong strategy and the implementation of a commercial contract. What makes that work for an environmental project is exactly the same as for a Private Finance Initiative project, a Building Schools for the Future or urban regeneration project. I translated skills in relation to general public law commercial transactions to a new field and this has been solidly successful.

So it is entirely natural that I return to writing, this time focusing on the area of climate change that has so inspired me over the past few years. This book is the first I have written alone and was borne out of a large number of solar PV contracts I have worked on. I wanted to set down exactly how to go about a project, as experience shows not many public bodies seem to know how to do this. Such projects are not so difficult if approached properly and worked upon diligently, although external assistance is likely to be required. But its not just about putting up a few PV panels on the roof of the Town Hall: good work in this area arises from a clear strategy, clear vision, good corporate and political control of the process and a wider programme. Whilst fitting a solar installation is, of course, a move forwards, it can be so much more if approached corporately and strategically.

It is for this reason that the book does not just focus on the technical issues to do with solar energy, the feed in tariffs or the regulatory framework. Many such works are available elsewhere. Instead, it starts by discussing what climate change is, what it will mean to all of us and then charts its rise in importance, the introduction of Government policy and the development of a legislative framework. It considers how to develop a solid corporate strategy for renewable energy that will stand a public body in good stead for this and other renewable energy work in the future. Perhaps surprisingly, it also goes into some detail about how to sell that idea to the public. Some areas, such as how to fund a project, are fast changing but the basics are the same.

But, you might say, this is a terrible time to be contemplating a raft of environmental projects, when local authorities are subject to savage budget cuts and reducing services across the board. This point is dealt with in detail in Chapter 3. In short, this is precisely the time that we should be using the green agenda to drive the corporate agenda and to provide jobs, growth and income where they are very hard to find elsewhere.

Despite much-discussed changes to feed in tariffs during 2012, solar PV still remains an excellent prospect. It is important to look forwards to the benefits, both financial and non-financial, that a project will deliver and to the individual business case that supports it, rather than backwards to consider how financial incentives have reduced. As grid parity approaches (when a solar panel – without subsidy – costs no more than electricity taken from the grid) more and more buildings will have solar power. The more experience that can be developed in relation to it in the ensuing years, the better.

Having said that, it is not necessarily difficult to identify and deliver a solar PV project. Proper advice should always be sought, either internally or externally. This book is not intended to give specific legal or financial advice and should not be relied upon in the absence of such advice. Moreover, the position with feed in tariffs and other developing areas of the regulatory framework are correct at the time of publication, in summer 2012, but things can change quickly. The purpose of this book is to inform officers and members what solar PV is all about, to encourage the development of schemes – and most of all to confirm the important place such projects have in the 'bigger picture' of a climate change strategy.

If the result is more solar PV on public buildings, as part of such a strategy, then the time and effort taken in preparing this text will have been well worth it.

Stephen Cirell
Consultant Leeds
December 2012

Preface to the second edition

Over two years have passed since the original publication of this work in 2012. Back then, solar PV was still seen as relatively novel in many authorities. There were few completed projects and the Feed In Tariff regime was going through some turmoil.

The intervening couple of years have shown a transformation in this scenario. The budgetary pressures remain and are likely to worsen over coming years. While the Ten O' Clock News reports on 'green shoots' in the economy, all local authorities know that austerity is here for some considerable time to come. Indeed, it is the cumulative impact of the cuts that is most worrying, where even a modest further reduction heralds no easy solutions. So local authorities are looking for income generation like never before, as one of a range of potential action. Another, is to join forces - or even merge – with other authorities.

On the solar PV front, everyone seems to have become used to solar panels and installations. There is less mysticism about it and, dare I say, even less cynicism too, about how it might be 'too good to be true'. There are a small number of civic solar farms completed and others in planning; many authorities have some solar PV on their buildings, with more considering large projects on their social housing; and more authorities are actively looking at their assets to see what might be possible.

The financial incentives situation has calmed down, with a better certainty about Feed In Tariffs payable on installations. The surprising fact here is that the return on the FIT levels at the end of 2014 are, in fact, largely the same as those in 2011, such is the reduction in costs of panels.

So this seems to be an appropriate time to bring the book up to date. The second edition is merely an update on the original, but there are some new elements of material, such as on community energy, which has risen in importance.

The Feed In Tariffs chapter has also been updated, although this will need further attention once the post-election FIT 2 regime comes along.

But this is an area that is always changing and so the book's main purpose is to ensure that the basics are properly explained, so that the reader can look up on the internet the latest FIT rates or check panel prices on my website, www.publicsectorenergy.co.uk, and still be able to work out the current position.

5 January 2015

Solar energy has been around for hundreds of years and is one of the oldest forms of energy known to man. It is only recently, however, that the focus on solar energy has reached its current level. This is for two reasons: on the one hand, the modern world consumes energy with a voracious appetite and this predominantly uses fossil fuels (which are part of the earth's natural resources) that have a finite limit; and secondly, due to problems associated with global warming.

As indicated in the **Preface**, this book is written for local authorities and public sector bodies, and indirectly for those advising them or working with them to deliver projects. It is timely, because the public sector in general, and local government in particular, is under increasing pressure to reduce CO_2 emissions and generate more energy for its own use from renewable sources.

The text is organised to follow the same path as a local authority intending to pursue a project. **Chapter 2** starts by detailing climate change and its rising importance for the public sector. It is important to note – and is continually stressed throughout this publication – that solar PV projects should not be seen in isolation, but as part of a 'bigger picture' of work. To have a credible position on renewable energy, it is essential that every authority has a grasp of what climate change is, understands what impact it will have on the local area, and then develops a strategy to deal with that. This work will be undertaken against a backdrop of the Government's policy and legislative framework. This is examined in **Chapter 3** and will need careful consideration to ensure not only that the regulatory framework is complied with, but also that the council's aspirations are delivered.

Chapter 4 looks in more detail at the position of local authorities and, in particular, their financial situation during the current recession. This will be a consideration, but should not prevent any authority that recognises the benefits of a solar PV project, from progressing such a scheme. **Chapter 5** considers how to produce a sound climate change strategy.

These are not some old platitudes, stolen from another document or bland, generic sentences that could apply to virtually anywhere. This is a tailored plan that covers the authority in question and inspires confidence that it understands what is required, what the consequences are if it is not done and the benefits that will flow when it is. Part of the strategic work will be to decide whether to focus on energy efficiency or renewable energy; the requirement is for both, but the balance can be a careful judgement to make. **Chapter 6** considers this question.

It is necessary to detail what comprises solar energy and how it works and **Chapter 7** takes care of this. It should be made clear that there are other books with far more details about solar energy generally and its uses, such as The Solar Century by Jeremy Leggett. These should be consulted for a wider picture. This publication is associated only with the planning and execution of a solar PV project. What this shows is that the power available from the sun is particularly striking, as is the fact that solar energy is actually at the core of many other types of renewable energy (geothermal, wind, marine). Of course it goes without saying that solar energy also had considerable impact on the development of the fossil fuels relied upon so heavily today.

The reason that many authorities will go down this route will not be the non-financial benefits mentioned in **Chapter 5**, but the financial ones. The various financial incentives available from the Government are considered in **Chapter 8**, including those less likely to be relevant to solar schemes. Closely linked to the financial incentives is the business case, which is considered in **Chapter 9**. This Chapter looks at the important role of the business case and also what essential components are required to develop a strong case that will command extensive support, both internally and externally. It is highly likely that the business case will be the key persuasive factor for many officers and members. Experience suggests that earning valuable income for the authority matters a great deal more to many people than saving the planet.

Perhaps the key area is determining how any projects are to be funded. Smaller scale energy efficiency work can be accommodated more easily, via Salix funding or other financial wizardry. However, raising sums in excess of a million pounds for a larger scheme is more difficult. **Chapter 10** considers how funds can be accessed, including loans, joint ventures and even a public offering. It goes without saying that the Director of Finance and the relevant portfolio holder on the Cabinet have to be on side to ensure a large project gets off the ground. This Chapter is for them to consider.

It is impossible to look at this area properly without some consideration of the regulatory framework. The working of the national grid is a mystery to most people and is the subject of major proposed changes in any event. Distribution Network Operators can make or break a project, but need to be dealt with in the right way. Schemes to ensure the quality of fittings (such as the Micro-generation Certification Scheme) cannot be ignored. **Chapter 11** considers all of these issues.

One area not touched upon thus far is whether to have a buildings-based scheme (IE: solar panels on the roofs of council buildings) or a free-standing arrangement (such as a so-called 'solar farm'). Up to 2012, solar farms had been a difficult proposition for the public sector, due to changes in the financial incentives. However, with the gradual falling of solar PV prices and the wide availability of public land, these will certainly return to the agenda over future years. There are different issues to be addressed in relation to land-based systems (particularly planning consent and grid connections) and these are examined in **Chapter 12**.

It may be that not everyone agrees that environmental projects are the best answer to the current budgetary position, either on the council or outside of it. The debate on wind energy offers some interesting insights into other views. This analogy is apt for two reasons: firstly, people can be successfully 'wound up' by a small minority with a entrenched and negative view; and also that much of what is said can be entirely incorrect. It is for this reason that **Chapter 13** has been included to examine communications strategies.

Some might be surprised at a whole chapter dealing with communications strategies, but long experience has shown these to be essential. Generally speaking, the better the communications strategy and the more time, effort and resources put into it, the more chance that the project will succeed. The converse is also, sadly, true. Establishing a decent communications strategy is not difficult; assuming, of course, that public relations was not the target of a recent budget cut. Even if this is the case, external assistance can readily be identified. More important is persuading decision makers that this expenditure is not only required, but essential.

Chapter 13 has been extended in this second edition to include more material on community energy. This is another area that has come to the fore in later years. Relatively unheard of in 2011, except in some leading edge green communities, by 2015 community energy warranted a complete Government strategy. This is considered in this Chapter.

Assuming that an authority has made it this far - investigated climate change and formed a view on its importance, developed a good strategy, come forward with some suggested solar PV projects and supported them with business cases – the next stage is to actually deliver the project. **Chapter 14** is a microcosm of the whole process, charting all of the necessary steps, from scoping at the start of the project to commissioning at the end. Procurement issues, risk and project management will be key to ensuring that a scheme is delivered on time and to budget.

Finally, some closing thoughts on where it all goes next are included in the conclusion in **Chapter 15**, which looks to the future. Specific to this is the move towards 'grid parity' (when a solar panel – without subsidy – costs no more than electricity taken from the grid). At this stage it will probably make sense to have solar panels on virtually every suitable public building in the country, thereby going some way towards delivering the Government's vision of decentralised energy.

The jargon involved in climate change can be difficult to get to grips with. So the **Appendices** contain a glossary of terms that might be of some use for reference and also further reading and references.

This book is organised in a linear fashion to mirror the development of a project, so by the time the conclusions have been considered, the journey should be over. There is no more to know about how to approach, plan and deliver a solar PV project only the development of the commitment to do so. And there's the rub really – all the strategies and plans and policies in the world count for nothing if they are not followed up by delivery. The only things that count are kilowatt hours of energy produced, Feed In Tariffs earned, business cases delivered and CO_2 abated. Perhaps that is another lesson from experience: too much is made of plans and not enough of delivery. It is for this precise reason that the UK has so far to go to meet EU and intergovernmental targets that press so heavily upon it. And it is specifically why this book has been written.

Introduction

It is a very interesting facet of work in this area that much of it is not prompted by environmental considerations at all. Indeed, seeking to pursue projects on the basis of climate change would be futile in many authorities, as any mention of the subject would deem such a project certain to fail. It is therefore pointed out in **Chapter 9** that often the best way to garner support for a project is to focus on commercial and economic benefits such as jobs and income. This can be referred to as playing the 'economic' card, rather than the 'green card'.

However, not every authority is like this and many pursue projects for sound environmental reasons. It is therefore necessary to have at least a working knowledge of climate change and what it is all about. The area has been much maligned but is fascinating and one that offers much promise for local government. It also touches upon almost every function in which local authorities are engaged.

In this Chapter the basics of climate change are explained and some of the myths from highly inaccurate reports that appear periodically in the press are debunked.

Human Activity and Climate Change

The first term that needs to be addressed is anthropogenic climate change. This can be simply explained as changes that are caused by the activities of the human race (IE: not naturally occurring).

There are many scientists in many countries that study climate change and express scientific opinions on its causes and potential remedial action that is required. Over time, these views have converged and the number of those who do not accept that the earth's climate is changing, or that this had been caused by human activities, is declining. Some people, such as former Conservative Chancellor Nigel Lawson (now with the Global Warming Policy Foundation – a well-known climate change sceptic organisation) will never accept anthropogenic climate change is upon us, but the independent evidence is now overwhelming. It has got to the stage where there is no credible view to the contrary.

It is true that you still hear claims that this is part of the earth's 'natural cycles' and that it is nothing to do with human activity, although this is simply not the case. The views of those who support the majority view on climate change have also been the subject of one or two scandals: the so-called 'hockey stick' chart being used as the basis for the current position, although being heavily criticised for the data on which it was based and its assimilation; or the emails from the University of East Anglia abusing those with alternative views. However, these were mere hiccups in the incontrovertible progression towards a consensus that climate change is happening and requires urgent action across the world.

For the avoidance of doubt, it should be stated that this work is written on the basis that climate change is happening, is man made and is in need of urgent remedial action to avoid catastrophic effects in the future.

Global Warming

On a technical level, the issue is global warming. The earth's temperature rises and that has potentially catastrophic consequences for the fate of mankind, particularly the melting of ice caps and rises in sea levels. But there are also other effects, such as rising ambient temperatures making human inhabitation impossible, the inability to grow food and possible human conflict over resources and land.

Al Gore in his well known book An Inconvenient Truth puts it very simply and this is reproduced in **Figure 2.1** opposite.

"The sun's energy enters the atmosphere in the form of light waves and heats up the Earth. Some of that energy warms the earth and then is re-radiated back into space in the form of infrared waves.

Under normal conditions, a portion of the outgoing infrared radiation is naturally trapped by the atmosphere – and that is a good thing, because it keeps the temperature on earth within comfortable bounds….(and) the temperatures here have been just right.

The problem that we now face is that this thin layer of atmosphere is being thickened by huge quantities of human caused carbon dioxide and other greenhouse gases. And as it thickens it traps a lot of the infrared radiation that would otherwise escape the atmosphere and continue out into the universe. As a result, the temperature of the earth's atmosphere – and oceans – is getting dangerously warmer."

© Al Gore (2008) An Inconvenient Truth, Bloomsbury Publishing PLC

The International Perspective

Climate change is, of course, a global phenomenon and will need a global response. This point was strongly made by the Stern Report in 2007, as mentioned below. Stern pointed out that it is not sufficient for a few nations to do good things – every country needs to be part of a joint movement in order to combat damaging climate change.

In answer to this global need, the Rio Earth Summit was called in 1992 and was apprised in 2012 (Rio + 20). The original conference led to the establishment of the United Nations Framework Convention on Climate Change (UNFCCC). This is the world organisation that is leading on monitoring and recommending action in relation to climate change.

The creation of the UNFCCC led to intergovernmental conferences being held annually in different countries. These tend to be referred to by where they were held and one of the best-known recently was Kyoto (which was held in Japan in 2010).

The Kyoto conference is memorable because it led to the first legally-binding targets being accepted by signatory countries, which was seen as a huge step forwards. However, it has to be said that not all countries signed up, particularly some large emitters, including the USA and China. The following year's conference in Copenhagen was a disappointment, as the good work of Kyoto was not built upon and despite Barack Obama coming to the White House, no binding targets were agreed at that conference. Similarly, later conferences resurrected the notion of legally binding targets, but delayed them until later. More recently, the twin issues of agreeing a legally binding deal, and actually ensuring that all of the major nations are included, particularly the major current and future emitters of the USA, India and China, have been more pressing. Accordingly, it has been agreed that the intergovernmental conference in Paris in 2015 will finally achieve this aim. Considerable preparatory work has been undertaken to ensure that this is the case.

The United Nations also established the Intergovernmental Panel on Climate Change in 1990. It began gathering evidence and has issued reports in 1991, 1995, 2001, 2007 and 2014. This is a panel of more than 1,000 scientists from around the world, hence its reports are considered authoritative. The Fifth Report in 2014 was published from a position of even more world support for its work.

The most important fact to note is that the Intergovernmental Panel on Climate Change (IPCC) has said that the world needs to limit global temperature increases to no more than two degrees Celsius above pre-industrial levels in order to have any chance of reducing the risks of dangerous climate change in the future. The range under consideration is two degrees to six degrees, with the absolute minimum being achieved as two degrees and the worst-case scenario being six. For those interested in what the actual consequences of the higher limit are, Mark Lynas outlines some of these in his book Six Degrees, which makes fairly terrifying reading.

There is now overwhelming agreement amongst scientists from more than 130 countries around the world, under the auspices of the Intergovernmental Panel on Climate Change, that the warming of our planet has been caused by human activity.

The Committee on Climate Change in the UK was established under the Climate Change Act 2008 and is a highly respected independent body.

In its Fourth Carbon Budget report (December 2010) it summarised the position thus:

> "...our assessment of the latest climate science, including a review that we commissioned covering over 500 recently published peer-reviewed papers, confirms that the fundamental science remains robust:
>
> - Global climate change is already happening
> - It is very likely that this is largely a result of human activity
> - Without action, there is a high risk of global warming, well , with potentially very significant changes in regional climate
> - This would have damaging consequences for human welfare and ecological systems over the course of this century and beyond. If anything, our assessment is that risks have worsened since we advised on the 2050 target in 2008 ......"

Whilst many people might question the policies that are formulated by politicians, it seems that the scientific community is coming together on the facts of what is happening.

Levels of Greenhouse Gases

In a technical sense, it is parts per million (ppm) of harmful greenhouse gases in the atmosphere that count towards the totals considered by the scientists.

Greenhouse gases include carbon dioxide, nitrous oxide, and methane, amongst others. The normal way in which this is presented is CO2e – or carbon dioxide equivalent. This is a way of demonstrating what the potential damage of each gas is, based on an equivalent of a single gas, normally CO2. This recognises that some gases are more potent than others. Methane, for example is over 200 times more dangerous than CO2. This is illustrated in Figure 2.2 below.

> - **Carbon Dioxide** • **Methane** • **Nitrous Oxide** • **Hydroflurocarbons**
> - **Perflurocarbons** • **Sulphur Hexafluoride**
> Kyoto Protocol to the United Nations Framework Convention on Climate Change (1997)

According to the monitoring that is being undertaken, a level of 382 parts per million was reached in 2007. By 2011, 400 ppm was exceeded and the level is projected to rise above 500 ppm in the near future. Sir Nicholas Stern suggested in his report that emissions be stabilised at 550 ppm, recognizing that immediate savings of the required magnitude are impossible. But Al Gore points out in his book that at no stage in the last 650,000 years has the level of CO_2 in the atmosphere been above 300 ppm.

So it becomes clear that the chances of staying within a two degree increase in world temperature reduce radically as time moves on, if emissions are not stabilised (IE: stop rising) and are then put on a path of reduction. It becomes a game of risk management, but the risk of getting it wrong is "runaway global warming and the destruction of most of life on earth", as Mark Lynas puts it in his book Six Degrees.

Different people will have different views on this scenario, but there are other comments that could be added to this picture.

The first is that there is a long time lag. It is likely that between half and one degree of further warming is already in the pipeline due to the thermal time lag of the earth's systems. Temperatures will rise for the next 30 years, even if emissions were cut totally today, because of the massive amount of carbon that has already been released into the atmosphere. Moreover, once there, the CO_2 endures for over 100 years, before breaking up. But the scientific community has concluded that stabilisation within two degrees would avoid the worst of the problems. The evidence that two degrees is the final end stop has been increasing; indeed, there is some scientific belief now that this itself might be too high a level.

The second point is that no climate model is perfect. They relate to different parts of the climate system. But the whole of a complex and interacting system is not just a sum of the parts. As Mark Lynas points out in his comparison in Six Degrees, doctors cannot assemble a human body by stitching together limbs and other organs. The secret lies in the way all human chemical and biological components interact within a living organism. The same is true of the planetary organism of the earth.

Finally, emissions depend on a wide variety of factors, or in other words on lifestyle and other decisions that are yet to be taken millions of times over by individuals, corporations and countries of the world. This means that future emissions predictions are more a matter of economics and politics, rather than the more solid ground of science. For this reason, it is likely that the long-term emissions can probably never be accurately predicted. It also confirms that decisions are political, although based on science.

The Temperature Gains

So politically, decisions needed to be taken in the light of this scientific evidence. As a result, more than 100 countries have adopted a target limit of two degrees of warming relative to pre-industrial temperatures, to avoid dangerous climate change. A study by Meinshausen suggests that to have a 70% chance of staying below two degrees C, it will be necessary for global greenhouse gas emissions to peak before 2020, be cut by 50% by 2050 and approach zero by 2100 (see zerocarbonbritain2030). This is where the often-quoted dates of 2020 and 2050 come from.

This evidence raises a very interesting point. It is stated above that to have a 70% chance of it working, those targets need to be met. This means that there is a 30% chance that they will not, with potentially catastrophic consequences. Put another way, and with a personal slant, would you sail on a ship that had a 30% chance of sinking? Or fly in an aeroplane that had a 30% chance of crashing?

Every year CO_2 levels are allowed to continue to rise, the odds on keeping within the two degree level are shortening.

Measurement of Emissions Levels

There is also room for different views about the best way of measuring climate change. As Al Gore points out, in his well known slide show, if you measure it one way, it gives very different results to another. As an example, to measure per capita (ie: on heads of population) leaves China with a very low score (due to the vastness of its population), whereas if you measure on actual quantities of emissions, China's score is very high and rising.

India currently emits 1 tonne per person; China 4 tonnes per person; and the US 20 tonnes per person. So the way in which measurement is undertaken and on what basis it is presented is extremely important, particularly in a political sense.

There are two so-called 'elephants in the room' that need to be discussed. The first is that none of the emissions calculations currently undertaken take account of embedded carbon. This is a very interesting concept and revolves around the necessity to look at carbon wherever it arises. A simple example is a wind turbine – it is manufactured and commissioned to produce renewable energy that will, in turn, reduce the carbon footprint of the country. However, there is carbon in the manufacture of this piece of equipment and if that level of carbon is higher than the carbon actually saved by the operation of the equipment, then emissions will not fall. In the context of national emissions, though, the real issue is the responsibility for emissions in the supply chain of goods we buy and use. It is often referred to as consumption based emissions. The Energy and Climate Change Committee of the Government looked into this area and published a report Consumption Based Emissions Reporting in 2012. This claimed that the Government should be clear about outsourced emissions. Tim Yeo, the Committee's Chairman put it thus:

"The Department for Energy and Climate Change likes to argue that the UK is only responsible for 2% of the world's CO2 emissions, but the Government's own research shows this not to be the case. We get through more consumer goods than ever before in the UK and this is pushing up emissions in manufacturing countries like China."

What Tim Yeo is referring to, of course, is the practice of Western economies focusing on reducing their emissions from buildings and installing more renewable energy, but at the same time ignoring all of the carbon emissions that are embedded in all of the consumer goods that they buy and consume. In other words, they take a territorial view of emissions. It has to be true that this leads to at least an incomplete picture. Furthermore, if emissions can simply be shunted round the world, to countries that are not bound by the UNFCCC or have more room for growth, the global position will not improve.

The second issue is the fact that the problem of the accumulation of green house gases over many years has largely been created by the industrial revolutions of the advanced nations. This point is not lost on newly industrialised countries such as India. Still on a political level, the issue will only really be addressed when some form of agreement can be reached which allows the developing nations to still capture their new economic growth, whilst reducing emissions at the same time. Politically, it is a non-starter to suggest that everyone cuts emissions to the same extent, when some nations have already enjoyed their economic growth.

The solution to this particular problem that has been arrived at is called 'contraction and convergence'.

Contraction and Convergence

Having said that no one should expect cuts to be adopted uniformly across countries at different places in their industrial development, contraction and convergence has been put forward as a fair solution to this problem.

This is based on the notion that the rich countries created the problem by their industrial revolutions and so must agree to higher cuts to get poorer countries to participate in a global climate change solution.

Under contraction and convergence, all countries would work towards convergence on an equal 'per person' emissions basis by an agreed date, within the overall context of a global contraction of emissions to acceptable levels.

As Lynas describes it in Six Degrees, "it would be a historic bargain: the poor would get equality and all (including the rich) would get survival".

Fossil Fuels

It is not possible to consider the position under climate change without giving consideration to the role played by fossil fuels. There are two major problems with fossil fuels, the first is that their combustion causes CO_2 and other harmful greenhouse gases to be released into the atmosphere. The second is that the reserves of these hydrocarbons are not limitless and they are fast running out.

The main fossil fuels are oil, coal and gas. Each has a carbon footprint, with coal the worst and natural gas the best. These are shown in Figure 2.3. There are obviously different levels of supply in the world of each of the main fossil fuels.

Figure 2.3 – Carbon Footprint of Fossil Fuels

- Coal - >1,000 gCO2eq/kWh
- Gas - ~500gCO2eq/kWh
- Oil - ~650gCO2eq/kWh

The mainstay of current world energy supply is oil. However, the discovery of new oil fields has been on a downward trend since the 1960's and the world now consumes more oil than is found. Indeed, oil is very rare and is created by thousands of years of geology. It only exists in certain places and once it is gone, the resource has been lost forever.

The whole world has now been surveyed for oil and it is very unlikely that major new finds would happen. All of the biggest oilfields are already in production, for example in Saudi Arabia and neighbouring countries.

Peak oil is a term that is often mentioned. This is when the world's peak production rate for oil is reached; thereafter, it can only decline. Currently, over 80m barrels of oil per day are used across the world and it had been expected previously that this would continue to rise, perhaps to as high as 120m barrels per day. However, the International Energy Agency has now indicated that this is unlikely as existing oil fields are declining and not being replaced. It is a sobering thought to consider that four new Saudi Arabia sized oil fields would be required, just to keep oil production where it is now. The forthcoming crisis is being brought forward by ever increasing needs from developing economies, such as India and China. New oilfields are also getting deeper and more difficult to exploit. The BP disaster in 2011 cruelly exposed the risks of getting it wrong.

There are many theories on when peak oil will hit, spanning from those who believe that the point has already been passed, to those who consider that it will arrive in the next twenty or so years. Either way, oil supplies are finite and mankind is extracting it faster than ever before. It is a sobering thought that the next generation may grow up never having experienced oil-based energy, because it may simply have run out.

Natural gas has also been discovered across the world. The United Kingdom was fortunate enough to discover gas in the North Sea and has enjoyed many years of inexpensive energy supply as a result. However, those gas fields are now declining and more gas than ever is being imported from Russia and other countries. There are more supplies of gas than oil and estimates are that there is 10 to 80 years still available.

The latest trend in gas, however, is not from the traditional gas fields, such as those found under the North Sea, but instead from in land sources. Shale gas is found trapped in rock deep beneath the earth's surface and has been successfully harvested in the United States, helping to produce more gas and to reduce the prices charged for it. The United Kingdom Government has expressed some support for shale gas and its controversial method of harvesting – commonly known as 'fracking' – but local communities remain deeply anxious about the environmental consequences of this work. It seems unlikely that fracking will ever fully develop in the UK for these reasons and it is not covered under renewable energy anyway, as shale gas is simply another fossil fuel.

Finally, coal is the most polluting of the fossil fuels, as demonstrated above, but there is enough in the supply chain for at least another 100 years.

Solutions to the Climate Change Dilemma

There have been many suggestions as to the solution to this world dilemma. These include those featured below. However, there are many more, forwarded by Governments, the IPCC, academics, industry and so on. In many ways, the only one that is relevant to the UK is that proposed by our own Government, which is still being developed, as indicated below.

The place to start is a paper written by Robert Socolow and Steve Pacala of Princeton University in the USA on "wedges". Its official title was *Stabilisation Wedges: Solving the Climate Problem for the Next 50 Years with Current Technologies.*

The idea was to have a number of wedges – 7 in all – which would each be based on a technology and reduce emissions, until the combined effect of all of them would be to reduce emissions to no more than the current level by 2050. Moreover, they said that all the requisite technology was already available for this.

The wedges were:

- *Increase fuel economy*
- *Reduce reliance on cars*
- *More efficient buildings*
- *More efficient electricity generation*
- *Gas displaces coal in energy generation*
- *Carbon Capture and Storage for coal plants*
- *Carbon Capture and Storage for hydrogen plants*

(Science, Volume 305, 13 August 2004)

This would take the world to a 500 ppm trajectory, but that may still be too much for a 2 degree warming level, as seen above.

Zero Carbon Britain

This report was produced by the Zero Carbon Britain Project. Its second report was published in Autumn 2010 and is entitled *Zero Carbon Britain 2030 – A New Energy Strategy*, and forms an important contribution to the climate change debate. This report offers a fully integrated route map for addressing carbon emissions in the UK and goes beyond the most ambitious targets hitherto, to suggest 90% reduction in green house gases by 2030, together with carbon capture equivalent to the remaining 10%.

The contributors to the report, published by the Centre for Alternative Technology (CAT) in Wales, came from academia, industry and community involvement organisations. The report starts by looking at the context and the science, then moves through the 'powering down' phase by reducing heat and electricity demand and then 'powering up' through the use of renewable energy technology.

Looking at powering down first, Zero Carbon Britain believes that there is huge potential to decrease energy demand without decreasing the services that are provided.

Areas covered include:

- *Buildings are a key area, as these can be improved by better insulation and fabric, better design and improvements in heating technology (as explained in* **Chapter 6***)*
- *A 'whole house' approach is necessary for housing, with a consistent approach to retrofit and base standards on energy demand per square metre*
- *For transport, electric vehicles and biofuels where necessary. Also different models for transport, with car clubs and pay per mile driven*
- *Behavioural change in less driving and aviation*
- *Better town planning, as illustrated by exemplar places, such as Freiburg in Germany*
- *Better communication strategies*

- *Better land use and agriculture – particularly less imported food and more grown locally*
- *Reduced livestock and increased production of biomass*
- *A healthy diet for the population from only 29% of the land currently used for food production*

Turning to powering up, Zero Carbon Britain believes that 100% of the world's energy needs can be met from renewables by 2030. This is described as: "A sustainable, secure, efficient Britain [that] can be powered without relying on fossil fuels or nuclear power".

The mix involved includes major use of offshore wind and other technologies, including biomass. There would also be changes in the demand for electricity and use of non-peak times, such as overnight, with improvements in the grid and distributed generation.

The report recognises that this will require drastic policy intervention at both international and national level. At international level the first step is a global agreement aimed at reducing temperature rise to below 2 degrees C and setting a cumulative carbon budget that provides us with a sufficiently high change of meeting this goal.

Three road maps are then offered:

1. *An international agreement on carbon, ensuring that the true cost of fossil fuels is explicitly included in the pricing mechanism everywhere in the world.*
2. *An international agreement providing a framework, allocating cuts, but leaving it to national governments to implement policies to achieve that. This could include contraction and convergence to allocate between countries.*
3. *Regional carbon pricing schemes – by like-minded countries forming blocs with each other and forgoing a global framework.*

At national level, it is suggested that we need to complement the EU's Emissions Trading Scheme by the Carbon Reduction Commitment but go further. A Green Deal is also needed to provide investment for the large-scale renewable energy technologies.

In another interesting point, the report states that public money should be used as a guarantor.

The final area covered is employment. All estimations are in "job years". It is stated that the total deployment of wind energy alone in the UK will deliver 3.4m job years. Jobs will be lost in other industries but this will be compensated for by new jobs created.

The authors provide a "balance sheet" in the report summarizing all the provisions. They claim that the value of Zero Carbon Britain 2030 reaches far beyond emissions; it is a bold national endeavour that will provide a plethora of economic, environmental and social benefits, including a common sense of purpose. The actions will bring about a far brighter future, revitalise communities, renew British industry and provide a sustainable economy.

These are bold claims, but the depth of the study and the detail in the report (which spans over 350 pages) demonstrate the effort that is being expended to find solutions to a global problem. What solution is ultimately chosen, of course, will be a political decision.

The Economics of Climate Change

In July 2005, Gordon Brown MP (then Chancellor of the Exchequer) announced a review to provide a report to the Prime Minister and Chancellor, to assess the economics of moving to a low carbon global economy and the potential of different approaches.

Sir Nicholas Stern was invited to chair the review. It reported in 2006. His main conclusion was: "There is still time to avoid the worst impacts of climate change, if we take strong action now. The scientific evidence is now overwhelming: climate change is a serious global threat, and it demands an urgent global response."

He concluded that the benefits of strong and early action far outweigh the economic costs of not acting. This was a pivotal moment, as a respected party from commerce was effectively endorsing action now, to save further cost later, describing climate change as "the greatest market failure the world has ever seen …".

It may be cynical to say that more people are likely to be persuaded by an economic argument, rather than an environmental one, but it is probably true.

Stern also recognised that climate change will affect the lives of people around the world via access to water, food production, health and the environment; accordingly the action to combat it must be international, based on a shared vision of long term goals and built on a national, regional and international level.

It may be cynical to say that more people are likely to be persuaded by an economic argument, rather than an environmental one, but it is probably true.

Stern also recognised that climate change will affect the lives of people around the world via access to water, food production, health and the environment; accordingly the action to combat it must be international, based on a shared vision of long term goals and built on a national, regional and international level.

So far as the cost of action is concerned, all countries will be affected but the poorest will suffer the most, even though they have contributed the least to the problem; our actions now will have a profound effect on the second half of this century but will save a substantial amount of money that will otherwise be needed.

If no action is taken to reduce greenhouse gases now, it is virtually certain that a two degree rise in temperature from pre-industrial levels will be exceeded. However, the risks of the worst impacts can be substantially reduced if greenhouse gas levels can be stabilised between 450 and 550 parts per million CO_2e. At the time of the Stern report, the current level was 430 ppm CO_2e and was rising at 2 ppm per year. From an analysis of the scientific evidence, stabilisation requires that annual emissions be brought down to 80% below current levels (hence the targets in the Climate Change Act 2008).

The estimated costs of stabilising between 500 and 550 ppm are 1% of global Gross Domestic Product. This is an eye wateringly high amount of money. However, the sting in the tail is that if concerted world action is not taken, the global costs will be equivalent to losing 5% of Gross Domestic Product every year, now and forever; rising to 20% of GDP or more in the future, as the position deteriorates.

The views expressed by Stern mirrored others mentioned above, such as the view that developing countries should not be required to bear the full costs of this action alone (and will not). Another key point, which is underlined throughout this work is that the world does "not need to choose between averting climate change and promoting growth and development...Tackling climate change is the pro-growth strategy for the longer term".

Stern concluded that three elements of policy were required for an effective global response to climate change:

- *The pricing of carbon, through tax, trading or regulation*
- *Supporting innovation and low carbon technology*
- *Removal of barriers to energy efficiency and to educate people on what they can do to respond to climate change*

These are all mentioned above and are recurring themes: use less energy, improve energy efficiency, develop new renewable energy sources (using technology); focus on both education and behaviour change and on how politicians and commercial markets manage the situation.

Each country, however large, is just part of the problem. This report confirmed that it is essential to create a shared, international vision of long terms goals, and to build the international frameworks that will help each country to play its part in meeting these goals.

HM Government – 2050 Pathways Analysis

This paper was published in July 2010 and was a bold effort to try and engage the public and the community generally in the extremely difficult choices the Government will have to take under long-term energy policy. Against the backdrop of the comments earlier in this Chapter, the Government tried to be more transparent about the difficulties of the choices required to deliver the emission targets and to canvass both opinion and views.

It seeks to present a framework through which some of the different pathways can be considered, for example, increasing nuclear energy – or not doing so; introducing Carbon Capture and Storage – or not doing so; developing bio-energy – or not and so on. The DECC website included a Pathways Calculator for visitors to make their own choices and attempt to meet the stringent emissions targets required by 2050.

A variety of themes emerge from this work. These include; the need for ambitious reductions in per capita use of energy; a substantial electrification of heating, transport and industry; the need for electricity supply to be decarbonised; and the growing challenges of balancing the supply grid, where variable renewable energy generation forms a much higher part than previously.

A side effect of this enterprise is to demonstrate to the public just what a difficult job the Government has to try and develop and implement an energy policy that will deliver the huge cuts in CO_2 emissions required, whilst not constraining growth or jobs in a difficult financial period and the work not costing an unaffordable amount.

What is required is balance but there are very different views about this. Some believe that nuclear is the answer to all of the UK's problems and that it should simply embark on a large expansion programme of its nuclear capacity. The Zero Carbon Britain report discussed above took a non-nuclear line, believing that energy reduction, energy efficiency and renewables could deliver the targets. A small minority prefer the 'head in the sand' or do nothing approach. What is clear is that as this century unfolds, citizens and businesses are going to have to change their ways.

Behaviour Change

David Cameron has stated that the need for behaviour change is one of the biggest problems facing the Government. If it were easy to move away from fossil fuels, the UK would have done so already, or at least be heading in the right direction. Instead, it seems to be going in the wrong direction. The problem is that fossil fuels have come to occupy a central role in modern life.

So climate change is as much about behaviour change as anything else. The British need to condition themselves to think differently and to make different choices. Yet there is very little behaviour change work going on at any level.

In truth, the human race is good at fighting battles that require immediate attention; much less so with threats that might happen at some indeterminate point in the future. The old analogy about the frog and the pan of boiling water is apt here: if you put a frog in a pan of boiling water, it will jump out immediately; however, if the frog is in tepid water that is increasing in temperature, it will eventually boil to death.

One of the problems faced by the Government, in its quest to meet the targets and do so cost effectively, is that much of Western society is geared round a high fossil fuel consuming lifestyle, so changes require social courage. As Lynas notes in Six Degrees: "Those who make an effort are frequently dismissed as 'tree huggers' or 'sandal wearers' by the mainstream. A high energy lifestyle is often seen as a badge of social success."

Detailed work needs to be undertaken to get to the root of why people act as they do and what measures might be used to persuade them to think differently. A good example is loft insulation and cavity wall insulation. Both are heavily subsidized, meaning that the average loft and walls can be treated for under £500. This work will save thousands of pounds in energy bills in forthcoming years. Yet the public cannot be persuaded to do it.

There are many reasons why behaviour change has not happened. Looking at the macro issue of global climate change the following excuses were identified in a Swiss study and are illustrated in **Figure 2.4** below.

- *"I protect the environment in others ways, such as recycling" (the metaphor of displaced commitment)*

- *"I am not the main cause of this problem" (denial of responsibility)*

- *"You have no right to challenge me" (condemning the accuser)*

- *"I have done nothing wrong" (rejection of blame)*

- *"I don't know the consequences of my actions" (ignorance)*

- *"Nothing I do makes any difference" (powerlessness)*

- *"It is too difficult for me to change my behaviour" (comfort)*

- *"There are too many impediments" (fabricated constraints)*

Figure 2.4 – Excuses for Climate Change Bad Behaviour

These excuses have all been heard many times. But the researchers in that study found that the most powerful motivator was plain old selfishness – "I am not prepared to change and abandon my personal comforts and consumption patterns." That is what behaviour change work has to address.

The final key element of behaviour change is the so-called techno fix. Under this the white knight of technology rides over the hill and comes up with some form of solution, thus avoiding the need for any behavioural change. The signs so far, however, suggest that this is not going to happen. The investigation into carbon capture and sequestration technology (CCS) has illustrated that point very well. It is not clear that it will work or that it would offer an affordable solution, even if it did. In the meantime, the problems get worse.

Conclusions

The problem is the distance that needs to be travelled by the countries of the world in relation to stemming greenhouse gas emissions and the time in which to do it. To set too onerous targets would be counter productive in political terms and may turn the public off even more. This is why a balance needs to be struck between different countries in different parts of their development; between Governments and their people; and in ways and means to do it.

This leads us to the next Chapter, which looks at how politicians seek to solve this problem through the development of the policy agenda.

Key Learning Points

- *Climate change is happening, it is caused by humans and it is getting worse*
- *It is an international problem*
- *It will need an international solution*
- *'Contraction and convergence' is the fairest way to balance the needs of established and growing economies*
- *It is not a choice between environmental action or economic growth - both are possible*

Government policy and the legislative framework

3

Introduction

It is important when embarking on a renewable energy project to understand the policy and legislative context in which any such project takes place. This is particularly important to the commercial sector, where changes in policy can have damaging consequences, as seen with the changes to the feed in tariffs in 2011, mentioned in **Chapter 8**. There, a private sector developer might be faced with the situation where a project moves from a profitable venture to a loss-making one. But changes in policy are no less important for a local authority embarking on a scheme and can create similar difficulties. This is why it is important to have a good grounding in Governmental policy in order that clear foresight can be brought to bear.

The main elements of policy and legislation are examined in this Chapter, although in a work of this size, it can only be an overview. Further detail can be obtained from looking at each of the policy papers or statutes discussed below, if required.

A New Government

At the time of writing the second edition of this work (December 2014) the current Government is approaching the end of its Parliamentary term. It came to power in 2010 for a five-year term and is unusual in British politics in that it is a coalition. None of the political parties won the general election outright in 2010 and so the Conservative Party and the Liberal Democrats joined together to form a Parliamentary majority. Whilst many thought that this would be unlikely to last, it has demonstrated some longevity and looks likely to complete the Parliamentary term of five years from 2010 – 2015.

A coalition between the Conservatives and the Liberal Democrats is an interesting mix as both parties had published papers on green issues during the election process. Despite some – quite fundamental – differences in views (for example the Liberal Democrats do not support public subsidy for new nuclear energy and the Conservatives do) they have managed to find much common ground. One of the reasons for this is that there is indeed much consensus on 'green' politics, with the Labour Party expounding similar views as well.

However, having won power, the new Government prominently proclaimed that it was going to be "the greenest government ever" (David Cameron, 2010). Environmental campaigner Jonathan Porritt wrote a paper for Friends of the Earth in 2011, which was a critique on whether the Government had delivered on this promise. In a withering analysis, he concluded that it had fallen well short and that there was still much to be done.

After the election, the Government published a document The Coalition: Our Programme for Government, once the parties had agreed their respective roles in the new coalition. This document from the Spring of 2010 would be the cornerstone of the five year programme of action.

In the section on climate change it is stated that, "this is one of the gravest threats that we face …", requiring "urgent action" and therefore prompting a "full programme of measures".

That programme included introducing Feed In Tariffs for electricity generation, the creation of a new Green Investment Bank and introducing a floor price for carbon. These pledges have formed the foundations of the policy announcements made since.

Under the Coalition arrangements, the role of Secretary of State for Energy and Climate Change has gone to the Liberal Democrats. The first incumbent was Chris Huhne, and after he resigned over a personal matter in 2011 he was replaced by Ed Davey, who has continued in post for the remainder of the term.

The Department of Energy and Climate Change (DECC) is the main Government department. The Government has set up two offices: ORED is the Office for Renewable Energy Deployment. This is a newly created part of DECC and is tasked with driving forward the targets on renewable energy; the Energy Efficiency Deployment Office is the other one and, as the name suggests, is concerned with energy efficiency.

Aside from DECC, the Department of Food and Rural Affairs (DEFRA) also has environmental responsibilities, particularly in relation to climate change mitigation. The Department for Communities and Local Government (DCLG) remains the ministry for local authorities and of particular importance to local government. The Government Department for Business Innovation and Skills (BIS) is responsible for the Green Investment Bank and also has a role in relation to this agenda as there is a clear business element to climate change.

OFGEM is the Office for the Gas and Electricity Markets, the gas and electricity regulator. It has an important role in supervising the operation of the Government's financial incentives regime.

An Old Problem

The Government inherited a difficult financial situation. This arose due to a range of different factors, which are well documented, including the banking crisis, the recession and a steeply upward trend in public expenditure. In brief, the Government indicated that it needed to bring spending under control and embarked on an austerity package the severity of which had not been seen since the Second World War. The key elements are the Budget of June 2010 and the Comprehensive Spending Review (CSR) of October 2010. The Budget set out the level of spending for the four years from 2011/12 to 2014/15. The CSR said how and where the money was going to be spent.

There is no doubt that compared to other areas, the green agenda fared well and support was clear. Importantly, the green agenda is seen as part of the solution to the UK's problems.

The key parts of the CSR were:

- *Financial incentives*
- *Support for the low carbon economy*
- *Establishment of a new Green Investment Bank*
- *Changes to the Carbon Reduction Commitment Energy Efficiency Scheme*

DECC fared reasonably well in the departmental cuts, with then Minister Greg Barker, stating in a speech to the Micropower Council on 23 November 2010, that DECC, "had emerged from the Spending Review with its core mission fully resourced". In hindsight, this statement may have been a little premature.

North Sea oil and substantial gas supplies are now in terminal decline. The UK is still in an excellent position regarding potential renewable energy, however. This is fortunate indeed as a variety of different indicators do not bode well:

- *Peak oil may soon arrive, as discussed in* **Chapter 2***;*
- *Spiraling oil prices, for example oil reaching $140 a barrel, but also potentially limited supply*
- *Russia turning off the gas supply to the Ukraine emphasised the energy security implications for the UK in importing large quantities of gas*
- *The UK is also vulnerable to the effects of climate change, resulting from increased CO2 emissions, particularly flooding in lowland areas*

The UK's excellent position in relation to sources of renewable energy is therefore very positive:

- *As an island surrounded by sea, there is much potential for wave and tidal power*
- *The UK has the best offshore wind resources in the world*
- *The UK also has tidal rivers such as the Severn, Dee and Tay for tidal power*
- *There are many inland rivers suitable for hydropower*
- *Deep geothermal energy is a possibility with hot rocks deep in the earth's core*
- *Solar power may not be as strong as in other parts of Europe, but works effectively too*

Faced with a difficult world situation regarding energy, what Government would not want to progress renewable energy and free the country from the shackles of expensive, polluting imported energy?

The Aim of Policy

As mentioned in **Chapter 2**, climate change has both an international and world level of activity. Much of the science comes from the Intergovernmental Panel on Climate Change and the goals from the Intergovernmental conferences. This means that much of what is done in the UK is influenced from outside. Notwithstanding this, policy in the UK has been expansive and largely enjoys cross party support.

However, the question has to be asked – what is Government policy trying to achieve? It is the creation of a framework that will facilitate the introduction of a low carbon economy into the UK, resulting in lower CO2 emissions, more renewable energy, a share of the world renewable energy technology market and no lowering of prosperity?

Policy and legislation are, of course, intertwined. The legislation sets the targets and the framework within which the system will work and the policy maps how to get those targets. In the UK the main legislation is made by Parliament. Even though the UK is part of the EU block and also participates directly in the Intergovernmental Conferences, domestic legislation lays down the laws.

UK Emissions Targets

So the place to start when looking for the key targets for the UK is the Climate Change Act 2008. These are reproduced in Figure 3.1.

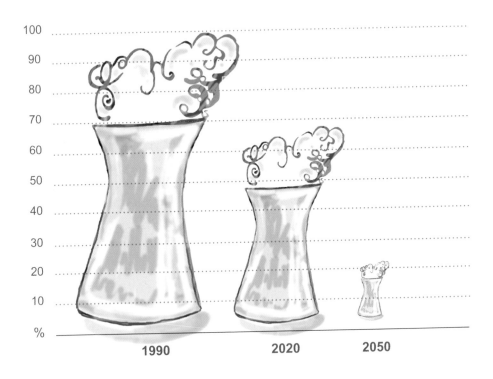

Figure 3.1 – Climate Change Targets

Section 1 of the Climate Change Act 2008 sets targets as follows:

80% reduction in greenhouse gases against a 1990 baseline by 2050 As an interim target, 34% reductions in greenhouse gases by 2020 has been set.

This was ground breaking legislation in that the UK was the first country in the world to introduce legally binding targets of this nature.

The 2008 Act is in sections, which are outlined in **Figure 3.2** below.

Part 1 - carbon targeting and budgeting.

section

1   *the Secretary of State is under a duty to ensure that the UK's carbon account for 2050 is at least 80% lower than the 1990 baseline*

4   *the Secretary of State is under a duty to set up a carbon budget for periods of five years. And to ensure that the UK's carbon account does not exceed that carbon budget*

11   *the Secretary of State has a duty to set a limit on the net amount of carbon that can be credited to the UK carbon account for each period*

13   *the Secretary of State is under another duty to prepare proposals and policies to enable the UK to meet its carbon budgets and these have to be reported to Parliament under s14*

16   *the Secretary of State is under a duty to lay before Parliament a statement each year, indicating the levels of greenhouse gases and to indicate if they are increasing or decreasing*

18   *the Secretary of State is under a duty to lay a final statement before Parliament, indicating the final amount of the UK carbon account*

     If the carbon budget has been exceeded, then the Secretary of State must put forward a report to Parliament with proposals for remedying the situation

Figure 3.2 – The Climate Change Act 2008 – Structure

It is immediately apparent that the Secretary of State at DECC has a sizeable number of statutory duties under this legislation, but others will do much of the work. It is also significant that the Climate Change Act created the Committee on Climate Change, an independent body to advise the Government on the targets and the carbon budgets that underpin them. The work of the Committee on Climate Change is well respected.

The innovation of the Climate Change Act was indeed the creation of those 'carbon budgets'. These last for five years each and the first three (2008-12, 2013-2017 and 2018 –2022) were completed around the time the Act came into force. The fourth carbon budget (2023–2027) was published a couple of years later in June 2011 and takes the proposals to a cut of 50% of emissions since the 1990 baseline.

The innovation of the Climate Change Act was indeed the creation of those 'carbon budgets'. These last for five years each and the first three (2008-12, 2013-2017 and 2018 –2022) were completed around the time the Act came into force. The fourth carbon budget (2023–2027) was published a couple of years later in June 2011 and takes the proposals to a cut of 50% of emissions since the 1990 baseline.

The key issue is whether carbon budgets will be devolved to geographical areas, such as regions or local authorities? The level of infrastructure below central government under the 2008 Act is not yet completed, but it seems certain that local authorities will have a role to play in it.

The government has also set a range of other targets, such as those relating to the energy performance of buildings (one of the most important areas for local government). These are discussed below but will see all new homes reaching zero carbon by 2016.

There is a range of other targets and these are widely confused. It is not just the main target that is misrepresented (for example it is often written that 80% of CO2 emissions is the target – when it is the wider greenhouse gases); the other confusion arises between the targets for emissions reduction and the targets for renewable energy. On the latter subject, the UK target is to have 15% of its energy from renewable sources by 2020. This is provided for by the EU Renewable Energy Directive, which itself has an overall target of 20%.

Whichever way the targets are looked at, they are very ambitious indeed. The UK was the first country in the world to have introduced domestic legislation to set a legally binding emissions target. This is a modern manifestation of the traditional position that the British will 'do their bit' to meet the goal. The statistic that UK emissions are only 2% of global emissions puts this in perspective (excluding embedded emissions, as identified in **Chapter 2**)

Key Policy Areas

So what policies has the Government put in place to meet those various targets? The answer to this question is in two parts. The first part is those elements of the policy framework put into place by the former Labour Government that remain in place. The second is the papers published by the Coalition since the Election in 2010, upon which greater emphasis is to be placed.

a) Policy Papers from the former Government

The Low Carbon Transition Plan

This was published in July 2009 by DECC and was presented to Parliament under sections 12 and 14 of the Climate Change Act 2008. Ed Miliband, then Secretary of State at DECC, described this Plan as the "route-map" for the UK's transition from here to 2020, with its importance in relation to targets. It is a comprehensive plan to move the UK forwards, through strategic action by the Government, covering a number of areas, including: energy from renewable sources; clarifying Governmental roles; focusing on households and funding improvements; helping the vulnerable; and developing green industry.

The Renewable Energy Strategy

This was published in July 2009 by DECC, as part of a suite of documents, including the Transition Plan above. The Government concluded that renewable energy was key to the targets for climate change and the Strategy had three component parts:

- *Financial support / incentives*
- *Creation of a new Office for Renewable Energy Deployment to co-ordinate delivery of renewables*
- *Development of a range of funds for investment and research for new technologies, such as wave and tidal power*

The Low Carbon Industrial Strategy

The third element of this policy related to jobs and employment. It was recognised that support for industry would be vital to climate change, as the UK did not just want to meet its targets, but wanted to benefit from the green jobs revolution too. The importance of the economic element of climate change at national level was recognized in this paper, which covered:

- *Local authorities are to be required to make local economic assessments*
- *Creation of low carbon economic areas*
- *Speeding up of the planning process*

The Heat and Energy Saving Strategy

Finally, the Government's Heat and Energy Saving Strategy, published jointly by DECC and DCLG. This was one of three consultations issued simultaneously, with the other two in relation to Carbon Emissions Reduction Target (CERT) and the Community Energy Saving Programme (CESP), which will now all be covered by Green Deal.

The Heat and Energy Saving Strategy relates mainly to housing and buildings. It is recognised that a huge element of the UK's emissions actually come from buildings and so if this situation can be improved, then the targets may be met.

The package of measures included the introduction of comprehensive home energy advice; moving from easier targets such as loft cavity wall insulation to a 'whole house' approach and changes to the Building Regulations.

Later Policy Papers

The change of Government in 2010 did not really herald a significant change in climate change policy, due to the consensus around green politics mentioned above. However, there have been some key papers subsequently published that have built on the foundations mentioned above.

The 2050 Pathways Analysis

This paper was published in July 2010 and is a bold effort to try and engage the public and the community generally in the extremely difficult choices that the Government will have to take under long-term energy policy.

It seeks to present a framework, through which some of the different pathways can be considered. The DECC website included a Pathways Calculator facility for visitors to make their own choices and attempt to meet the stringent emissions targets by 2050.

A variety of themes emerge from this work, including: the need for ambitious reductions in per capita use of energy; a substantial electrification of heating, transport and industry; the need for electricity supply to be de-carbonised; and the growing challenges of balancing the supply grid, where variable renewable energy generation forms a much higher part than previously.

The Carbon Plan

This follows on from the 2050 Pathways document, which looked at the different ways in which the emissions targets could be met. As mentioned above, a number of themes emerged from that work, and three areas are identified in this report in which change will be most critical. These are: generating more electricity from secure, low carbon sources (principally renewables, nuclear energy and fossil fuels with Carbon Capture and Storage); improving heating of homes and businesses (including renewable sources of heat and better insulation); and powering cars and vehicles differently.

The final plan was published in December 2011 and will be refreshed annually. It is a formidable document, spanning some 218 pages that sets out the way forwards. The Carbon Plan is summarized in Figure 3.3 overleaf.

The final part of the Carbon Plan shows how the fourth carbon budget can be met by a combination of these different approaches. As is to be expected, the plans become somewhat more vague, the more they stretch into the future.

- *Since 1990 there has been much progress. Emissions have fallen in buildings, transport, industrial output and agriculture*

- *However, to make much deeper cuts, there will have to be major changes in how electricity is used and generated across the economy*

- *There will be uncertainties about how this can be done but the sectoral plans in the Carbon Plan seek to reduce these*

- *In the next decade major progress will be made to install all cost effective technologies; all cavity walls will be insulated; fuel efficiency in transport will improve dramatically; more diverse energy sources will improve energy security*

- *Rather that picking a single winner, the Carbon plan sets out how the UK will develop a portfolio of technologies for each sector*

- *In electricity generation, this will be a three pronged approach: renewable power, nuclear power and carbon capture and storage (for coal and gas fired power stations still in operation)*

- *In transport, ultra low emission vehicles will come into operation, including fully electric cars*

- *In buildings, the technologies will include ground and air source heat pumps and using heat from power stations*

Figure 3.3 – Ingredients of the Carbon Plan

The UK Renewable Energy Roadmap

This was published in July 2011 and is the product of work by the Office for Renewable Energy Deployment (ORED) in DECC. Having determined that considerably more energy from renewable sources needs to be generated, the Government was keen to signpost how much energy it might be possible to generate by 2020 (a key date in the targets) and of what type. Identification of barriers to that development and effective action to remove those barriers was also deemed essential.

The Roadmap forms the heart of this plan and sets the UK on a path towards the 2020 targets. The tone of the paper is bullish with a clear statement that: "The UK can meet the target to deliver 15% of the UK's energy consumption from renewable sources by 2020."

The Government suggests that eight current technologies are capable of delivering more than 90% of the renewable energy that is needed. These are:

- Offshore and onshore wind
- Marine energy
- Biomass electricity and heat
- Ground source and air source heat pumps
- Renewable transport

Renewable electricity already has a pipeline of projects. Heat is more of a concern as the pipeline is much less developed and the total heat from renewable sources was little more than 1% in 2012. The introduction of the Renewable Heat Incentive, a financial incentive for the generation of heat from renewable sources, is seen as key to this.

Costs associated with these technologies are expected to fall over time as supply chains and technical difficulties are overcome and risk reduces.

The economic side to climate change is clearly illustrated in this paper too: "We want the UK to be the location of choice for inward investment and a world class centre of energy expertise…"

It is a point of particular interest in this book that solar PV did not feature on the original list of the eight favoured technologies. As discussed in Chapter 8, this reflected a prejudice against solar power, largely borne of the view that it is more expensive than other forms of renewable energy and therefore too heavily dependent on financial subsidy.

By 2014, however, over five GW (5,000 MW) of solar PV had been installed in the UK and costs of solar power had fallen consistently. In tandem to this, the Government had seen evidence of the creation of jobs and opportunities from solar power and therefore this view of solar energy was starting to change. The calls from the Renewable Energy Association and the Solar Trade Association to review the UK Renewable Energy Roadmap were heeded and in an updated version, published in November 2013, solar energy had been added to the favoured list of technologies

Greg Barker, formerly the Energy Minister and big supporter of solar power, indicated that the Government expected 20 GW of solar energy to be delivered by 2020, which was an extremely challenging target.

The Solar strategy

As mentioned above, the Government did not originally include solar PV in the UK Renewable Energy Roadmap. This was something of an oversight, as solar was already showing signs of considerable development in the UK. This growth in deployment meant that DECC had to change its mind about this and solar did subsequently feature. In the interim, the Government produced its own strategy solely for solar PV. The UK Solar PV Strategy Part 1: Roadmap to a Brighter Future was published in October 2013 and The UK Solar PV Strategy: Part 2 was published a year later in 2014.

Part 1 of the strategy was published when the extent of deployment of solar in the UK hit around 2.5 GW, far higher than had ever been expected by DECC. This was largely a statement of intent but did recognise formally for the first time that solar PV did have a role in the UK meeting its various targets. It was described as a vision of the strategic direction of solar PV in the UK, making sure that the Government's policies support appropriate deployment in a sustainable way.

To assist this it set out four guiding principles, as follows:

1. *Support for solar PV should allow cost-effective projects to proceed and to make a cost-effective contribution to UK carbon emission objectives in the context of overall energy goals – ensuring that solar PV has a role alongside other energy generation technologies in delivering carbon reductions, energy security and affordability for consumers*

2. *Support for solar PV should deliver genuine carbon reductions that help meet the UK's target of 15 per cent renewable energy from final consumption by 2020 and in supporting the decarbonisation of our economy in the longer term – ensuring that all the carbon impacts of solar PV deployment are fully understood*

3. *Support for solar PV should ensure proposals are appropriately sited, give proper weight to environmental considerations such as landscape and visual impact, heritage and local amenity, and provide opportunities for local communities to influence decisions that affect them*

4. *Support for solar PV should assess and respond to the impacts of deployment on: grid systems balancing; grid connectivity; and financial incentives – ensuring that we address the challenges of deploying high volumes of solar PV*

At the time this document was written, the Government was becoming anxious about the number and size of large-scale solar farms being planned and built in the UK and this was clearly starting to cause political problems. Hence, the third guiding principle above.

In the spring of 2014 the second part of the strategy was published. By now, the sector had planned or constructed almost 4 GW of capacity and showed no signs of slowing down. Following on from Part 1 of the Strategy, DECC wrote: "This document, which comprises Part 2 of our strategy, focuses on our ambition for the key market segments." It set out a series of actions, including the Government's plan to install 1 GW of capacity on the Government's own estate, clear guidance being provided to schools to encourage them to fit solar and proposed changes to the rules, such as on transferability of panels under FITs.

It was at this time that the Government's intention to slow down the solar PV marketplace for land based solar farms started to become apparent. It referred to the planning framework and in particular DCLG's planning guidance on large-scale solar farms and set up a DECC strategy group to consult with the industry.

As for the level of deployment, it quoted the EMR Delivery Plan, saying that indicated that 10 – 12 GW of solar PV could be deployed by the end of the decade. It seemed likely that at least that much was already built, planned or had the benefit of planning consent by the time this was written. Greg Barker, then the Minister for Energy and Climate Change, had already made clear that he wanted 20 GW of solar PV in the UK and this seemed eminently possible.

In tandem with wanting less solar farm development, the Government made clear that it wanted more social housing and development on more commercial or industrial buildings. As part of its plan for 1 GW of solar PV to be fitted to the Government estate, it wanted the country's 24,000 schools to benefit from solar and also some of the iconic buildings in public ownership.

The Strategy also looked forward to the future and considered what role technology and innovation could have in this. The two parts of the Solar Strategy were followed by a number of other papers amending the solar regime and changing the way that financial incentives were paid. These elements are dealt with in other chapters.

Financial Incentives

The government has introduced a series of financial incentives to help promote renewable energy. These are detailed in **Chapter 8**. They include the Renewables Obligation for commercial sized projects and feed in tariffs for micro-generation projects – both relating to electricity generation, plus the Renewable Heat Incentive, covering heat.

The various policy papers on feed in tariffs make clear the policy intent:

"The Renewables Obligation has mostly succeeded in encouraging investment from professional energy companies in large-scale renewables projects. A new system of feed in tariffs will provide support aimed at small low carbon generators. This will open up low carbon electricity generation beyond the traditional energy companies, making it more cost effective for communities and householders to take part."
(Consultation on Renewable Electricity Financial Incentives July 2009)

There is no doubt that this policy has been successful, particularly in relation to solar PV projects. It is unlikely that even a fraction of the current capacity would have been delivered without the intervention of the financial incentives.

The Green Investment Bank

The Green Investment Bank (GIB) is also a key part of government policy. Everyone accepts that a huge amount of investment will be required to deliver the green agenda, for example, an estimated £200bn is required just to regenerate the electricity network in the UK. The GIB will assist in finding the money required for various investment activities.

The Comprehensive Spending Review 2010 said that £1bn of funding would be allocated to the Bank, although there was general consensus that this was not enough. Accordingly, the government also said that it would provide more funds from asset sales.

The former Government set up a Green Investment Bank Commission. This was a fully independent group of individuals that was asked to look into this area and reported on 29 June 2010. The Commission concluded that £550bn could be required for green investment, in order to meet the Government's various targets.

The Commission recommended that the GIB be set up, by legislation, and with a clear mandate to sit alongside the Committee for Climate Change (also an independent body, created under the Climate Change Act 2008) and provide financial advice to the Government. The focus of the new Green Investment Bank would be on "reducing risk" for investors, rather than just providing capital. The new Coalition Government accepted the recommendations of the Commission and announced the finance in the Comprehensive Spending Review in October 2010.

In addition to the set up funds pledged above, the Government also said that it would provide funds from asset sales, bringing the total available to £3bn. This would help attract a further £15bn of private investment into the sector.

The independence of the Bank from the Treasury is seen to be critical in assuring developers and investors that the bank will not be subject to the excesses of party politics. This model has worked extremely well with the Climate Change Committee and is seen as vital.

Buildings Policy

The built environment is a very large contributor to CO2 emissions in the UK, with homes and non-domestic buildings comprising just under half of the total CO2 emissions (domestic properties forming around 27%, with non domestic buildings 17%).

However, only one in three homes that are occupied during 2050 will be built between now and then. This means that two thirds of properties in the domestic sector that will be occupied in 2050 were already built in 2012 and will need extensive retrofit work to bring them up to the zero carbon standard. This offers a huge challenge.

A number of targets have been set by the government in relation to the energy performance of buildings. These are featured below in Figure 3.4 below.

All homes to be zero carbon – *proposed in* Building a Greener Future *consultation paper, pubished in December 2006, and subsequently confirmed in the Government's Policy Statement of July 2007 from DCLG;*

All schools to be zero carbon – *announced in the Budget of 2008;*

All other buildings in the central government estate to be zero carbon – *announced in the Budget 2008;*

All non domestic buildings to be zero carbon – *announced in the Budget Statement of 2008;*

Figure 3.4 – Emissions Targets for Buildings

These targets are very ambitious. The UK Green Building Council described this policy as ..." perhaps the most ambitious environmental policy this government has ever introduced..." (about the former Government, when the targets were first introduced).
Zero Carbon Task Group Report – May 2008.

The base line is provided by the Building Regulations, made under the Building Act 1984 and periodically updated. Part L of the Building Regulations sets out the legal requirements for the conservation of fuel and power in buildings. Part L1 covers dwellings and Part L2 covers other types of buildings.

These are minimum standards required by law but buildings can be built to higher standards. The Government's main instrument used to be the Code for Sustainable Homes (see below) which proposed levels that are each based on the percentage that Part L standards are exceeded, leading to Code Level 6 (zero carbon). However, the Government changed its focus in 2014 and proposed a 'Building Regulations only' approach, with no optional additional local standards in excess of the provisions set out in Part L of the Regulations. This was done as part of the Housing Standards Review of 2013. The Government did, at the same time, reaffirm its commitment to implement the zero carbon homes policy for new homes from 2016. It decided that this will be best achieved through a strengthening of the energy performance requirements in Part L of the Building Regulations (incorporating carbon compliance, energy efficient fabric and services), and the delivery of allowable solutions.

There a vast number of papers on buildings and climate change and it would not be appropriate to consider them all here. This publication is predominantly concerned with the implications of fitting solar panels to land and buildings.

As well as the Code for Sustainable Homes as the original policy, there were also provisions for non-domestic buildings. In 2008 it released a paper Definition of Zero Carbon Homes and Non Domestic Buildings, which suggested a three fold hierarchy for all buildings as follows:

- A high level of energy efficiency in the fabric and design of the building
- "Carbon compliance" ie a minimum level of carbon reduction to be achieved from "on site" technologies
- And "allowable solutions" ie a range of measures available for achieving zero carbon beyond the minimum carbon compliance requirements

This is displayed in diagrammatic form in Figure 3.5 below.

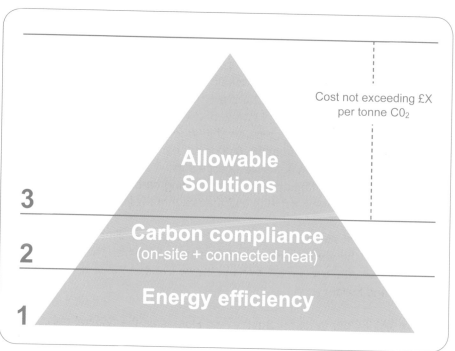

Figure 3.5 – The Government's Preferred Hierarchy

Definition of Zero Carbon Homes and Non-Domestic Buildings (DCLG , December 2008)

There have been many subsequent papers on this theme as it has developed. One of the most contentious issues has been the original requirement that renewable energy facilities must be provided "on site". It is often the case, particularly with inner city and urban developments that this is impossible and there was therefore considerable criticism of this requirement. However, the Government eventually removed this requirement, allowing local authorities to work with developers on Energy Services Company (ESCO) solutions and renewable energy infrastructure (such as heat networks) for the benefit of the wider community.

However, the Government's policy on zero carbon buildings was changed in the budget of 2011 and this attracted significant criticism. The change revolved around the treatment of 'unregulated' emissions. Regulated emissions are those emanating from the fabric of the building; whereas unregulated emissions are to do with use of appliances used in the house. The Government adjusted the definition of zero carbon to exclude unregulated emissions. In future, zero carbon will only measure heating, lighting, hot water and building services. Emissions from cooking, computers, TVs etc. will not be covered. The suggestion was that this was due to complaints from the building industry about building costs. The Government has been particularly sensitive to the cost issue during the recession, when the building industry has been decimated.

Whilst this change may sound minor, in fact it represented a major change in policy. The Government had always said that zero carbon meant zero carbon, in other words new homes would not add to the carbon footprint of the UK. The result of this change, in the eyes of many, was that zero carbon under the Government's definition would not actually mean zero carbon in reality. Put another way, it would be easier than before to reach the zero carbon standard.

So the Government policy is to meet strict targets for emissions, requiring challenging action from the built environment. New houses and buildings must be built to exacting new standards; and existing buildings must be retrofitted to reduce their emissions and improve their energy efficiency.

The problem with this latter strategy is cost. The vast majority of the owners of buildings in the UK cannot afford to pay for the necessary retrofit work. Those that can would probably not prioritise financing such works over and above other options. It was to meet this problem that the Government introduced the Green Deal.

The Green Deal

The Green Deal is another policy area about which reams has been written. It is not necessary to go into full detail here; instead, it is only necessary to explain Green Deal in the context of the Government's policy agenda. For these purposes it can be summarized as:

> *"a framework for private firms to offer consumers energy efficiency improvements to their homes, community spaces and businesses at no upfront cost, and recoup payments through a charge in installments on the energy bill."*
> **The Green Deal – A Summary of the Government's Proposals (October 2010).**

The need for Green Deal is considered above - the high carbon footprint from buildings in the UK, both domestic and commercial. The idea is that the Green Deal will be a private sector led scheme, with the market providing solutions to this problem, in the form of finance, building works and so on. However, it is more likely that there will be a significant public sector element to Green Deal too, either to kick start Green Deal or in parallel to private operators.

The scheme has been designed around consumers, according to the Government, and they will be protected throughout the process. Green Deal will be promoted by a greater awareness of energy efficiency and financial costs of energy wastage. The involvement of the market is also intended to be a spur for economic development, creation of new jobs and activities, which are badly needed in the current financial climate.

A new infrastructure will need to be created to accommodate Green Deal, from accreditation arrangements and oversight, to consumer protection measures, to skills and training and so on. The size of the task taken on by the Government Government illustrates the importance in policy terms that Green Deal has in its green agenda.

The Green Deal will operate as follows:

- *There will be an assessment of each property by an independent assessor*
- *This will lead to a report, recommending that 'measures' be undertaken to the house or building to bring it up to a better energy efficiency standard*
- *The measures recommended will all be costed and have the CO2 savings identified; it will also identify the bill savings on current costs*
- *The Golden Rule is that the cost of the works necessary to bring the house or building up to scratch should be met by savings in the energy bill*
- *The assessment report will be akin to an optician's eye test – once the eyes have been tested, the prescription can be taken anyway to buy appropriate eyewear; in the same way, the householder can choose any fitter to do the Green Deal work*
- *A Green Deal Provider will then be approached and will enter in to a Green Deal contract with the consumer or business to undertake work. The Green Deal provider will arrange for the finance and undertake the work, or arrange for it to be undertaken*
- *Payment for a Green Deal makeover will be via the electricity bill. The consumer or building owner will continue to pay the usual costs, but the saving is used to pay off the Green Deal finance*
- *There are a range of consumer protections necessary, from poor workmanship to Green Deal providers going out of business*
- *The system will be monitored and evaluated by an oversight body*

The detail of Green Deal is both voluminous and complex, even though the principle is relatively straightforward. As an illustration, the Consultation Paper The Green Deal and Energy Company Obligation, published in November 2011, was 235 pages long. The Green Deal is something of a gamble by the Government but indicates that urgent and radical action is necessary in order to comply with climate change targets. Notwithstanding the necessity of action, not everyone is convinced that Green Deal is the right policy instrument. Accordingly, the Government worked hard to ensure that the various elements could be completed and thought through before the launch of Green Deal in October 2012.

It is a source of great concern and potential embarrassment for the Government that in 2014 the Green Deal had not achieved anything like the success, which was expected. The criticisms of it are many and wide: it is too complex, it is too bureaucratic, the finance under the Green Deal Finance Company is too expensive, the public is not convinced etc. The list goes on and on. The consequence of that is that very few measures have been fitted under Green Deal as the end of 2014 approached, despite a growing number of Green Deal assessments having been carried out. This is certainly an area that will have to be addressed by the next Government in 2015.

It was always the case that if the Green Deal was not a success in its current form, the Government would amend the policy and press on. Successive Governments, of whatever political persuasion, have put far too much time and effort into Green Deal to abandon it entirely, and the pressing international targets get more burdensome by the year. It therefore seems likely that Green Deal will be fine-tuned over coming years – perhaps re-named or even re-launched - until it finds the success that is needed. Then its potential effect on CO2 emissions moving forwards will be much clearer to see.

Energy Performance of Buildings

Another strand of the Government's buildings policies is to require the energy performance of buildings to be measured and publicised. The requirement for an Energy Performance Certificate (EPC) was introduced from April 2008, via the *Energy Performance of Buildings Directive*. This EU Directive was implemented in England and Wales on a phased basis between 2007 and 2008 and required:

- *Energy performance certificates for all buildings when they are built, sold or rented*
- *Regular energy assessments of large public buildings and display of Display Energy Certificates so that users and visitors are aware of the energy use of the building*
- *Regular inspection of air conditioning / boilers and other installations*

The Directive was implemented in the UK by the Energy Performance of Buildings (Certificates and Inspections) (England and Wales) Regulations 2007. This is the first time that such data has been collected and it provides an increasing dataset of the energy efficiency of all types of buildings in England and Wales.

The Government believes that EPCs have a pivotal role to play in delivering its household energy management objectives, because they provide key information on a building's carbon emissions and the types of improvements that can be made.

One of the requirements of the Energy Performance of Buildings Directive is for all public buildings to display Display Energy Certificates (DECs) where they have a floor area of over 1000 m2. With DECs, the users of each public building can openly see what the energy efficiency of the building actually is, as transparency is seen to be an important driver to improvement.

Energy Performance Certificates have a further requirement in relation to solar PV projects. This is because in order to qualify for the highest rates under the feed in tariffs, a building to which solar panels are to be fitted has to reach a certain standard of energy performance. The rule is that to receive a full feed in tariff, a building would need to score at least a 'D' rating on the EPC. If it did not, then a very low baseline tariff (aligned with the rate for ground mounted solar or the lowest tariff available) would apply. This is a good example of the Government seeking to link the different parts of the climate change agenda and cross relate the benefits of the various incentives.

Planning Policy

Planning is another major strand of overall Governmental policy, but again, one that has a relevance to climate change and renewable energy. The essential point in relation to renewables is that the Government formed a view that obtaining planning permission was becoming too difficult, expensive and lengthy a process to deliver public policy adequately. Accordingly, it was determined that fundamental changes would be made to the system.

This is one area upon which the former Labour Government and the new Coalition Government did not agree. The last Government had determined that the answer to difficult planning issues, particularly in relation to major infrastructure, was to take them out of the hands of local councillors and place them with a central body. It passed the Planning Act 2008 to authorise the creation of the Infrastructure Planning Commission (IPC). Its role was to determine planning applications for major infrastructure and speed up the process. When the new Government took power, it announced the abolition of the IPC, which had only just started operating, and its replacement with a new team in the Planning Inspectorate (the National Infrastructure Directorate). More importantly, it promised the return of planning powers to local control.

In the document *The Plan for Growth*, issued alongside the Budget in 2011, the Coalition Government set out its plans for reform of the planning system. It published a draft of a new National Planning Policy Framework, which would have a presumption in favour of sustainable development that would influence both the plan making and decision taking elements of the planning process. The elements of the reform programme were to speed up planning applications and also to make the policy clearer and simpler.

The National Planning Policy Framework was published in March 2012 and replaced a significant volume of previous guidance and regulation, including all planning policy statements (PPS), all planning policy guidance notes (PPG) and all ministerial planning circulars. It now sets out the Government's planning policies for England and how these are expected to be applied.

The National Planning Policy Framework is only 50 pages long but provides a set of objectives which are designed to support growth, protect the environment and ensure that decisions are made at local level. The Framework is based on the concept of *sustainable development*, defined by the United Nations as, "meeting the needs of the present without compromising the ability of future generations to meet their own needs."

There are three key components to the new system: economic, environmental and social wellbeing. This is familiar to local authorities, following the passing of the Local Government Act 2000, which conferred general powers of wellbeing covering the same areas upon them.

Figure 3.6 summarises the notable areas of the Framework.

- *A presumption in favour of sustainable development*

- *Planning being based on local plans, drawn up in consultation with the community*

- *An aim to foster the delivery of sustainable development, not to hinder it*

- *Protection of green spaces, green belt and areas of outstanding natural beauty*

- *Specific mention of climate change and low carbon energy requirements, including the fact that "local planning authorities should recognize the responsibility on all communities to contribute to energy generation from renewable or low carbon sources..."*

Figure 3.6 – Key Areas of the National Planning Policy Framework

Those local authorities that already had a post 2004 Local Plan that is broadly in line with the Framework will be able to use those policies until March 2013. For those with no up to date plan, the National Planning Policy Framework came into force in March 2012.

Many believe that the introduction of the National Planning Policy Framework, with its substitution of broad principles over detailed policy, will not really change a great deal. Similar considerations will be at play and the hitherto objections to certain forms of renewable energy, particularly wind energy projects, are unlikely to fade away.

As mentioned above, the Framework does not contain policies for nationally significant infrastructure projects where specific national policy statements have been made. Energy is an important area of this latter system.

A series of energy National Policy Statements were prepared in draft and consulted upon extensively before their official designation by the Secretary of State for Energy and Climate Change in July 2011. The areas covered renewable energy generally, nuclear power, fossil fuel generation and gas, amongst others. These set out formal policy against which proposals for major energy projects would be assessed by the IPC, and latterly the National Infrastructure Directorate in the Planning Inspectorate, after April 2012.

The National Policy Statements will only affect very large renewable energy projects, including those over 50 MW in size. It is unlikely that a local authority would be promoting a project of that size and so their relevance to this sector will be limited.

The Localism Act 2011, discussed below, also makes changes to the planning system. The reason that these measures are under the localism banner, is that they are prompted by the 'Big Society' movement and the aim to decentralise more power to the people.

On a regional level, the Localism Act provided a mechanism to abolish regional strategies. The Government believed that these were "bureaucratic and undemocratic". However, the Regional Spacial Strategies formerly set out the targets for renewable energy. The Department of Communities and Local Government announced in the spring of 2013 the abolition of the last three remaining spatial strategies. It described them as unpopular and counter-productive and said that the new system reinforces the importance of councils' Local Plans produced with the involvement of local communities, as the keystone of the planning system. It is, according to the DCLG, this approach that will help deliver the homes, jobs and infrastructure the country needs. However, others thought that a major plank of planning policy built up over 30 years had been dismantled in just a few months.

Neighbourhood planning is also authorised by this Act. A local development plan is seen as a central document under the National Planning Policy Framework and provisions are included to facilitate their production and agreement, including referenda. However, whilst much vaunted, in reality such plans must be in conformity with local plans promoted by the local authority. It is not intended that they can restrict development.

For climate change the Community Infrastructure Levy (CIL) will be important, allowing a charge to be made when new houses, buildings or other developments are built. The Localism Act amends the CIL to make it more flexible, as indicated below.

Finally, on the subject of planning policy, Permitted Development rights will still apply to small renewable energy installations, meaning that specific planning consent is not required for them. The issue of Permitted Development rights is considered in **Chapter 14**.

The Community Infrastructure Levy and Section 106 Agreements

Planning obligations have been a feature of the planning system for some considerable time. Following the passing of the Planning Act 1990, these became known as s106 agreements. However, there had been sustained criticism of this system and the Government therefore sought to replace it with the new Community Infrastructure Levy in 2010.

The CIL allows qualifying authorities to raise funds from developers in relation to building projects in their area. This is to fund new infrastructure that is required as a result of the development. Whereas s106 agreements were project specific, the Government has now chosen a tariff-based approach, believing this to be fairer, faster and more certain.

The local authority will normally be the CIL authority (depending on area) and the Planning Act 2008 provides a wide definition of infrastructure. This can include renewable energy infrastructure, such as district heating networks or generation capacity. This is particularly important in the context of the definition of zero carbon for buildings, described in **Chapter 3**, as the proposals from the Zero Carbon Hub, which the Government has accepted in principle, are that "allowable solutions" should be permitted to top up the benefits from better design and fabric in building and available on-site generation capacity. The allowable solutions route effectively means a separate generating facility in the region of the new development and this might be a district heating network or a local renewable energy power station provided by an Energy Services Co (ESCO).

In order to bring in a Community Infrastructure Levy scheme, and to ensure that there is transparency, a detailed plan has to be followed. This includes advertisement and even a public inquiry, that is open to the public. Whilst this might be seen as something of a burden, in fact it is an excellent opportunity for the authority to publicise its green programme work and make clear what its aspirations are locally.

As mentioned above, the Localism Act 2011 amended the Community Infrastructure Levy system in order to make it more local. The Government's view seems to have been that if the benefits of a development can be kept in that area, the community is more likely to be in favour. This may play to the advantage of district heating networks where there would be a very distinct community benefit, from the Council funding the pipe-work infrastructure, which other users could then link into.

The Carbon Reduction Commitment Energy Efficiency Scheme

The Carbon Reduction Commitment Energy Efficiency Scheme – or the CRC as it is known – was introduced in April 2010 and is also an important area of Government policy. The scheme started out as a 'cap and trade' scheme loosely based on the EU Emissions Trading Scheme (EU ETS) to help reduce carbon emissions. The scheme was intended to target large non-intensive energy users that have at least one half-hourly electricity meter, together with an electricity consumption over 6,000 MWh per annum. This meant that only larger local authorities would be covered.

The reason that the CRC was introduced was to provide emissions coverage for a whole sector of society that had not hitherto been covered. The industrial and other sectors had been regulated under the EU ETS for some time, but medium sized organizations and the public sector had not. Originally 6,000 organisations, including a large number of local authorities, were to be covered. However, virtually from the time that the CRC was announced, its provisions have continually been reviewed and changed. Even after the scheme was introduced, further amendments were tabled, to ameliorate the impact on those covered.

In its original form, the CRC was in two phases, the introductory phase and the second phase. Each body covered by the scheme would need to purchase allowances in advance of each year to cover their anticipated emissions for the forthcoming year. In the Introductory Phase the allowances would be priced at a fixed price of £12 per tonne and be unlimited in availability. Following the end of that year, the body would surrender the correct number of allowances for emissions made. A complicated recycling payment would be made by the administrator to refund the allowances 'pot' to the participants, but on the basis of their performance, as indicated in a league table. Special rules were introduced for the first year of the scheme, where no actual performance figures existed.

The intention was that after the Introductory Phase, the price of carbon would be set by the market, allowances would be auctioned and there would be a finite number of allowances in the system. The intention of this system, mirroring the EU ETS, was to reward those bodies that had made improvements in their emissions, at the expense of those who had not.

Unfortunately, the CRC system was horribly complex and there were many complaints about its design and operation. As a result, the Government committed to make changes with the system to try and make it easier and more accommodating.

However, in 2010 the Government made a fundamental change that altered the whole remit of the CRC. The Chancellor announced in the Comprehensive Spending Review that it would not be making recycling payments to participants at all and would instead retain the allowances fund to assist with meeting the UK's budget deficit. This announcement was greeted with genuine shock, as for five years every consultation paper on the CRC had maintained the strict rule that the system was based on the cap and trade principle. It was difficult to see how the CRC could still be deemed a 'cap and trade' scheme thereafter and most considered bodies covered by the regime took the view that the Government had now changed it into a tax.

The first proposals for amending the system came forward in late 2011 and since then there have been several more attempts at radical surgery of the regime, culminating in a consultation in December 2012. This led to the CRC Energy Efficiency Scheme Order 2013, which came into force on 20 May 2013. The majority of the Government's proposals were introduced at the start of the second phase, in 2014 with the remainder coming into force later in 2014.

Since an early point in the tinkering with the CRC, it was rumoured that Chancellor of the Exchequer, George Osbourne, has grown tired of the problems thrown up by the CRC and the constant criticisms of it. Accordingly, the Budget in 2012 made clear that unless the CRC could deliver "very significant administrative savings" the Government would "bring forward proposals in Autumn 2012 to replace the CRC revenues with an alternative environmental tax". In some ways, that would be a considerably simpler option for all concerned.

The Legislative Framework

When considering policy, it is also necessary to look at the legislative framework. There has been a succession of legislation during the course of this Parliament, which has provided the legal authority to put into effect the Government's various policies. Of note in this programme are the Energy Act 2011, which permitted the Green Deal to finally be put in place, and the Localism Act 2011, which promised to change the whole way in which local government operates.

It should be borne in mind that much of the legislation that exists in the UK actually emanates from the European Union or the world order, as described in **Chapter 2**.

As the second edition of this work is published in 2015, the General Election approaches. For this reason, there is less legislation coming forwards than in the early part of the Parliament. This cycle will repeat itself later in 2015, when a new Government sets out its stall for energy and then brings forward the legislation to put this into effect.

The following is a brief summary of some of the key statutes that are relevant to climate change and the green agenda. Further materials are available on each legislative provision, should this level of detail be required.

The Climate Change Act 2008

This is the centrepiece of the legislative provisions and forms a unique legislative requirement to meet emissions targets. The Act has already been explained previously.

Essentially, it provides for the national emissions targets for the UK of 80% reduction in greenhouse gases by 2050, establishes the mechanism
.

for achieving this via carbon budgets and reporting to Parliament, and also establishes the Committee on Climate Change to advise the Government.

The Planning Act 2008

It was noted above that there were concerns about the planning system in the United Kingdom. The former Government was quoted as saying that a third of the UK's electricity needs to come from new infrastructure in the next few years and "the planning system is not able to cope..." The purpose of the Planning Act 2008 was intended to speed things up. The main element of the Act was the establishment of an Infrastructure Planning Commission, as discussed above. The idea behind this was very simple and was, effectively, to remove major planning decisions from local authorities and put them with the specialist IPC, thereby speeding them up considerably.

The act was passed and the IPC has just come into being at the time of the General Election in 2010. Interestingly enough, both of the Coalition parties had lobbied in opposition to scrap the IPC and return planning decisions to local control. When the Coalition parties took power it became apparent that as the IPC had been established by legislation, the Government did not have the legal power to abolish it without further primary legislation, eventually being found in the Localism Act 2011 as discussed below.

The Energy Act 2008

This act made changes to the Renewables Obligation for larger renewable energy schemes, such as the solar farms discussed in **Chapter 12**. As it turned out, the Government changed the rules again in 2014, to remove the Renewables Obligation completely from solar PV installations over 5 MW from April 2015. However, it is still available below this capacity.

This act is also the legal authority for the introduction of the new Feed in Tariff regime. This is examined in detail in **Chapter 8**, and is the main financial incentive from the Government to encourage the fitting of more renewable energy systems and technologies.

The feed in tariff was introduced from April 2010 by secondary legislation – The Feed in Tariffs (Specified Maximum Capacity and Functions) Order 2010 (SI 2010 No 678).

Finally, the Energy Act also includes legal authority for the Renewable Heat Incentive (RHI) to be introduced, which is effectively a feed in tariff for heat. This is also explained in **Chapter 8**.

The way that modern legislation works is for the statute to authorise the bringing into effect of a new provision, but the detail being provided in secondary legislation, in the form of Orders or Regulations.

The Planning and Energy Act 2008

Despite its name, this is a different Act from either the Planning Act 2008 or the Energy Act 2008, which is rather confusing.

This Act, which concerns renewable energy, started life as a Private Members Bill and it became law after it was adopted by the Government. It authorises a local planning authority in England or Wales to include in its local planning policies requirements for:

- *A proportion of energy used in developments in their area to be energy from renewable sources in the locality of the development*
- *A proportion of energy used in developments in their area to be low carbon energy from sources in the locality of the development*
- *Developments to comply with energy efficiency standards that exceed the energy requirements of Building Regulations*

This moves on the so called 'Merton Rule' to a statutory footing directly linked to climate change and renewable energy. Under the Merton Rule, the London Borough council had required applicants for planning permission to provide a fixed percentage of electricity (normally at least 10%) to be provided on site from renewable sources.

As mentioned above, the "on site" issue became problematic, as did the haphazard way in which planning authorities applied the rules. Accordingly, this Act puts the matter on a statutory footing, providing a discretionary power to introduce such rules and not constraining them to be produced on site but also the "locality" of the development.

However, in the Housing Standards Review of 2013 (considered above in relation to the Code for Sustainable Homes), the Planning and Energy Act was also proposed to be a casualty. The review focussed on removing red tape and the Secretary of State for Communities and Local Government, Eric Pickles, believed that this Act qualified for abolition. This view was heavily criticised by those in the renewables industry and others, including the influential House of Commons Environmental Audit Committee. As a result of considerable pressure, the Government relented and, whilst removing power from local authorities to set energy efficiency standards for new buildings, left in place powers to specify the sourcing of energy from on-site renewable technologies (such as solar panels) or connected renewable heat networks (using technologies such as biomass, geothermal or energy from waste). The REA said that this means local authorities can continue to specify the inclusion of renewable energy in new homes, helping reduce energy bills and carbon footprints for their occupants.

The Climate Change and Sustainable Energy Act 2006

This act is to enhance the UK's contribution to combating climate change. Under Section 3 of the Act, the Secretary of State has the duty to publish an "energy measures report" and every local authority must have regard to the most recently published report in exercising its functions.

The last Energy Measures Report was published in 2007 by the Department of Business Enterprise and Regulatory Reform. Whilst still on the statute book, few local authorities seem aware of this provision.

The Home Energy Conservation Act 1995

This is a short act that includes provisions in Section 2 placing local authorities under a duty to prepare an "energy conservation report".

The report sets out energy conservation measures that the authority considers practical, cost effective and likely to result in significant improvement in the energy efficiency of residential accommodation in the area.

As the new policy agenda described above developed, the Government indicated that it did not see a role for this legislation. However, it subsequently changed its mind and decided instead to retain and enhance the Act's provisions, in order to be part of the new Green Deal provisions, mentioned above.

The Government issued new guidance in July 2012, under the Home Energy Conservation Act 1995 (HECA), which required all English authorities with housing responsibilities to prepare a report by 31 March 2013 setting out the energy conservation measures that the authority considers practicable, cost-effective and likely to result in significant improvement in the energy efficiency of residential accommodation in its area. The reports, which numbered over 300, were subsequently published by DECC and need to be repeated every two years. In 2015, local authorities will approach their second duty to report on these matters.

The Electricity Act 1989

No work on any aspect of renewable energy can fail to mention the UK's electricity grid. This is like a tree, with the trunk being the transmission network (the carrier of electricity) and the branches being the distribution network (supply / sale of electricity).

The UK's infrastructure was built some considerable time ago and on the basis of fossil fuel power, emanating from a spine of coal fired power stations up and down the country. Needless to say, time has moved on. The problem is that the newer, renewable, forms of energy are all in the wrong places for the grid – off the western coast for offshore wind and distributed for many other technologies. The Government therefore has a major reform to embark upon to bring the grid up to the required standard for the 21st Century. This is discussed further in **Chapter 11**. The process is known as EMR (electricity market reform) and will be ongoing for a period of years.

In the interim, the Act that governs the old style grid remains in force – the Electricity Act 1989. Under this legislation, generation, distribution and supply of electricity requires a licence from OFGEM (The Office for Gas and Electricity Markets), issued under the 1989 Act.

The Energy Act 2011

The Energy Act 2011 was an important addition to the statute book and in particular authorized the introduction of the Government's flagship policy of Green Deal.

The Act is over 100 sections long and received Royal Assent on 18 October 2011. The main areas that the Energy Act covers are:

* *Introduction of the Green Deal; this will be the Government's flagship policy on energy efficiency for both domestic and non-domestic buildings*
* *The private rented sector, in particular the inability of a landlord to resist a tenant's reasonable request for energy efficiency improvements where a Green Deal or ECO package is available*
* *The Energy Company Obligation, which takes over from the current policy instruments of CERT and CESP which expire at the end of 2012. This targets households likely to need additional support, in particular those containing vulnerable people on low incomes and those occupying 'hard to treat' housing (normally solid wall)*

The Green Deal and ECO provisions are particularly relevant for Local Authorities.

The Localism Act 2011

The Localism Act 2011 is not about energy provision at all, but instead forms the backbone of another important Coalition Government policy. In the Foreword to the Plain English Guide to the Localism Act (DCLG November 2011), the Minister of State for Decentralisation, Greg Clark, stated:

"We think that the best means of strengthening society is not for central government to try and seize all the power and responsibility for itself. It is to help people and their locally elected representatives to achieve their own ambitions. This is the essence of the Big Society."

In constitutional terms, this is a very important piece of legislation, giving new powers to local authorities but also empowering communities to have more say in their own destinies.

Figure 3.7 outlines the key provisions of the Localism Act.

* *A new power of general competence. The legal powers for local authorities to engage in renewable energy projects are discussed in Chapter 14. Following the coming into power of this Act, it is certain that these powers will be used*

* *Greater control over business rates. These are key to attracting investment and creating jobs*

* *Giving communities the 'right' to challenge the local authority and ask for the transfer of a local authority service to community control. The community can also bid for assets (possibly relevant to energy generation assets held by authorities)*

* *Reform of the planning system (as discussed above)*

* *Reform of housing provision*

One of the most important changes made by the Localism Act 2011 is to local authority powers.

Taken together, the powers in the Localism Act are radical and will change the shape of local government over the next decade. Some of these changes, for example the introduction of an elected Mayor and changes to governance structures, have not been mentioned here has they have no relevance to climate change.

The Public Services (Social Value) Act 2012

This is a small Act but one worth mentioning for the public sector. It began life as a Private Members Bill in June 2010, put forward by Conservative MP Chris White.

The Act applies to all authorities that are subject to the EU public procurement regulations and applies to contracts for services above the threshold. It imposes a duty to consider how what is proposed to be procured might improve the economic, social and environmental wellbeing of the area (in other words, the 'social' value) and how the authority might act in conducting the procurement process to secure that improvement.

The wording of the duty is similar to the requirement of the 'community right to challenge', introduced by the Localism Act considered above. The duty is intended to operate within the confines of existing procurement law and authorities can only take into account social and environmental matters when deciding to award a services contract to the extent that they are directly relevant to the contract's subject matter. This means that evaluation criteria that are linked directly to economic, social or environmental matters are likely to become more common.

The Energy Act 2013

Finally, the Energy Act 2013, which establishes a legislative framework for delivering secure, affordable and low carbon energy and includes provisions many provisions, but is best known for introducing the 'Contracts for Difference' (CFD) regime. The Act is in two parts:

Decarbonisation

These provisions enable the Secretary of State to set a 2030 decarbonisation target range for the electricity sector in secondary legislation. A decision to exercise this power will be taken once the Committee on Climate Change has provided advice on the level of the fifth Carbon Budget, which covers the corresponding period (2028-32), and when the government has set this budget, which is due to take place in 2016.

Electricity Market Reform (EMR)

The Act puts in place measures to attract the £110bn of investment that is needed to replace current generating capacity and upgrade the grid by 2020, and to cope with a rising demand for electricity. This includes provisions for:

* Contracts for Difference (CFD): long-term contracts to provide stable and predictable incentives for companies to invest in low-carbon generation
* A Capacity Market: to ensure the security of electricity supply including provisions to allow Electricity Demand Reduction to be delivered
* Investment Contracts: long-term contracts to enable early investment in advance of the CFD regime coming into force in 2014
* Access to Markets: This includes Power Purchase A greements (PPAs), to ensure the availability of long-term contracts for independent renewable generators, and liquidity measures to enable the Government to take action to improve the liquidity of the electricity market, should it prove necessary
* Renewables Transitional: transition arrangements for investments under the Renewables Obligation scheme

Most of these provisions have now been acted upon and put into effect.

Conclusion

There can be no doubt that this is a bold policy agenda. The problem is that the UK has a reputation as being world class in developing policy, but perhaps something a little less in terms of actual delivery. The Climate Change Act 2008 puts the UK in a unique position, being the first country in the world to take climate change so seriously as to impose legislative targets moving up to 2050. The fact that those targets, and the carbon budgets that underpin them, are advised on by an independent body is also laudable.

The question then, is how to do we comply with this policy agenda and meet such strenuous targets? **Chapter 2** demonstrated what needed to be done to prevent global temperature gains in excess of 2 degrees Celcius; to deliver those changes is a very big ask.

The next Chapter considers the role of the local authority in the climate change scenario and how it can assist the UK to achieve its goals.

Key Learning Points

- *The Government needs to develop policy that will deliver progress on climate change targets*
- *It has introduced the Climate Change Act 2008, which is a world first legislative provision, to cut emissions*
- *The Carbon Plan and the UK Renewable Energy Roadmap are key policy instruments*
- *A whole range of policy and legislative provisions have been introduced in support of the climate change agenda*

The position of local government

Introduction

Having looked at the science behind climate change and the Government's policy for addressing those problems, consideration needs to turn next to the position of local authorities themselves.

Local authorities have suffered severe cuts in budgets, as discussed below, and seen many jobs lost and services curtailed. It is not an exaggeration to describe it as a 'crisis'. The next question is what impact has that crisis had on the green agenda and what does it mean for the future? Some might think that with so many problems to deal with, this would not be a good time to embark upon an environmental project. But nothing could be further from the truth. In fact, the green agenda might be an important saviour of local government in this difficult time. This Chapter explores the position of local authorities in relation to the green agenda.

The Current Position

As commented in **Chapter 3**, the Government came into power in the General Election of 2010. It inherited a poor financial state, largely caused by the banking crisis and the need for the former Government to step in and save the major UK banks from bankruptcy. As a result of this particular crisis, the indebtedness of UK PLC was raised from around £40bn, which was considered acceptable, to well over £100bn, which was not. The new Government was elected on a manifesto to deal with the deficit and whole of the Parliament saw action in that direction. This has proved unpopular, but the Government does not seem to be wavering from its central theme, which is to reduce the deficit as its main priority.

The knock-on effect of the austerity package has been felt keenly in public services. As large amounts of money had to be saved over the life of the Parliament, it was inevitable that local government would bear a large proportion of those cuts and so it has played out. The result has been an austerity package, the severity of which has not been seen since the Second World War.

This started with the Budget of June 2010 and was closely followed by the Comprehensive Spending Review (CSR) of that year. The budget set out the level of spending for the four years from 2011/12 to 2014/5 and the CSR indicated where the money was going to be spent. As pointed out in **Chapter 3**, the green budget fared reasonably well in comparison to other areas, including basic local government funding itself, where cuts in excess of 20% were common.

In the green area, the key parts of the CSR included the introduction of financial incentives to promote renewable energy and support for the low carbon economy. Money was also earmarked for the new Green Investment Bank.

As far as local authorities are concerned, there has been much said and written about the effect on local services and the day to day work of the councils themselves. Officers and members reacted angrily to the cuts and an almost palpable feeling of doom and gloom descended on local government. However, a survey by the Royal Society of Arts and the Local Government Information Unit in May 2012 found that most councils were, at this stage, doing better than expected, notwithstanding an average 27% of cuts being faced over the current Comprehensive Spending Review period. Over 90% of the 50 authorities polled had balanced their budgets in 2010/11 and 86% reported that they had protected frontline services by focusing on 'back office' functions when looking for savings. So it could be said that, as usual, the resilience of the local government sector has shone through. However, budget reductions are not over and as 2015 starts, further waves of cost cutting are planned by the Government. This may change the face of local government forever.

Little more needs to be said about the financial situation in local government, as everyone working in the sector and for the sector is familiar with this situation. Of more importance is what impact this is likely to have on the green agenda in local authorities.

The Impact on Green Programmes

The use of the term green 'programmes' is deliberate, in that it is a neutral phrase covering both strategy and delivery of renewable energy and energy efficiency measures. The impact on such programmes seems to have been extensive.

Evidence of this is to be found in a Green Alliance report, published at the end of 2011 – Is Localism Delivering for Climate Change? The most striking fact from the report is that 37% of local authorities questioned said that they were de-prioritising climate change work or claimed that it had never been a priority in the first place, see Figure 4.1 below. There are anonymous quotes such as: "Some services will be stopped completely eg: climate change work, work on renewable energy, natural environment policy and delivery..."

There are those who suggest that to do this is to completely miss the point. The green agenda in local government and the broader corporate agenda are now almost completely aligned, as discussed below. Therefore to undertake a 'green' project promises to deliver all of the core elements that the authority wants – income, cost reduction, jobs, growth and community leadership. This applies at almost any scale, and is not just confined to large or urban authorities. If an authority does not go down this route, where else is this growth going to come from? Put this way, it seems astounding that some local authorities are turning their backs on the very agenda that will save them.

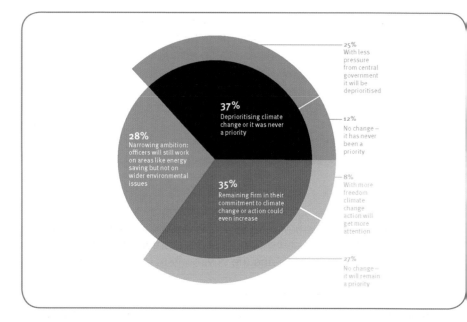

Figure 4.1 – *Green Alliance Report - Responses to the question:*
"How (if at all) do you think the priority afforded to climate change by your local
authority will change as a result of this new context?"
Taken from Is Localism Delivering for Climate Change? Green Alliance 2011

The Green Alliance report also confirms that climate change is a 'unique' challenge in the context of localism, as the Government has abolished targets, yet expects considerable action to be taken at local level – even in a very difficult financial climate. The report looked at the role of partnership working and whether community organisations can "hold local authorities to account" on their climate change work. It reported that: "these findings suggest that the foundations for a partnership approach to climate change are weak and raise serious questions about how the Government's localist approach can facilitate greater climate action."

It seems that by abolishing local government targets (such as the National Indicator set, including NI 185 and NI 186), the Government has made it more difficult to prioritise climate change at local level and has reated a huge diversity of approaches. As the report concludes: "… as long as opting out is possible, climate change will not be tackled with the consistency and level of ambition that is needed if national targets are to be met."

The tragedy about all this is that the financial incentives mentioned in **Chapter 8**, provide the finance for the funding of the climate change operation. A combination of cost savings from energy improvements and surplus income from renewable energy projects can easily be re-invested into a green programme to enable a holistic programme to be delivered.

The Role of Local Government in Climate Change

The evidence of the Green Alliance report mentioned above is even more surprising, when the potential for local government to have influence in the area of climate change and the environment is considered.

An analysis of the material in **Chapter 2** illustrates that there are seven levels of influence over combating climate change. These are reproduced in **Figure 4.2** below.

* *Intergovernmental level / world order, including the Intergovernmental Panel on Climate Change and other conferences*
* *The European Union, of which the UK is a part, based in Brussels*
* *The national UK Government based in London*
* *Regional government*
* *Local government*
* *Community level*
* *Individuals and businesses*

Figure 4.2 – Levels in Climate Change Influence

The role of the local authority is to influence as many of the other levels as it can. It is the only democratically elected body that is operational at local level and can influence widely.

Whilst influence on the world order might be stretching the point, most of the other levels can be reached. Examples might be lobbying the EU in

Brussels to influence EU policy making and legislation; discussions with DECC and other Government departments in relation to UK energy and climate change policy; negotiating with regional bodies such as Local Enterprise Partnerships; and then liaising with, and providing support to, communities and individuals. No other body has such a wide range of potential influence. A growing number of, certainly larger, local authorities in the UK have realised this and used it to their advantage. If local authorities do not take advantage of these areas of influence, they are missing an opportunity, to the disadvantage of their area.

The Functions of Local Government

It is not an exaggeration to say that climate change and the environmental agenda is relevant to virtually everything that a local authority does. Local government is constantly changing, but the basic tenets remain the same as they have for many years. In the 'two tier' system, the County Council undertakes strategic functions (transport, education, social services) whilst the District Council undertakes the local functions (housing, environmental health, leisure); in unitary and Metropolitan areas, the single authority enjoys all of the functions. Functions at both strategic and local level are affected by the climate change agenda, as indicated below:

• *waste management*

Waste management functions now have an increased importance. Here, the local authority is under a duty to collect domestic and commercial refuse (if requested) and to dispose of it. Duties now abound in relation to landfill. Landfill tax is rising quickly and has to be avoided at all costs. 'Waste to energy' plants using domestic refuse, food waste and the like are now seen as mainstream.

• *education*

Those local authorities that are education authorities will usually have a large number of schools in their area. The emissions from schools have now been added into the relevant Local Authority's CRC Energy Efficiency

Scheme calculations. This is problematic for many authorities. They are also involved in the energy efficiency of schools and often the procurement of energy. More to the point, the schools estate of an authority offers a huge expanse of roofs where solar PV can be exploited.

• *buildings and estates*

Most local authorities have a number of buildings from which to provide their functions. These include the civic hall, council offices right through to art galleries, leisure centres and homes for elderly people. All of these have energy and emissions issues related to them. DECC has confirmed that nearly half of all greenhouse gas emissions come from buildings and if the targets outlined in **Chapter 3** are to be met, the entire buildings estate needs to be carbon neutral by 2050. The buildings estate actually offers excellent opportunities in relation to renewable energy, as analysed in **Chapter 6.**

• *grounds maintenance*

Most local authorities have grounds maintenance functions, including parks and gardens, open spaces and playing fields. These can provide useful materials for use in climate change activities, such as biomass for wood burning boilers.

• *housing*

Social housing can be provided in three ways: directly via the council and the Housing Revenue Account; via arms length arrangements such as an Arm's Length Management Organisation (ALMO); or via a housing association or registered social landlord.

If the local authority is still the owner of the property, then energy issues are important. Again, there are vast expanses of roof that could be used to generate income. Wrexham County Borough Council's project to fit solar PV to 3,000 council houses is a good case in point. This project is the subject of a case study in this book.

• transport and vehicles

Local authorities have large vehicle fleets and the emissions from these will be significant. Many have already considered the move to electric vehicles and other forms of more environmentally friendly transport.

Local authorities may also transport people directly, for example elderly people to day care centres and so on.

Local transport policies, such as those relating to buses and trams affect millions of people across the country.

Local Carbon Budgets

The Climate Change Act 2008 sets down the system of carbon budgeting. One of the key planks of the legislation is the setting of five-year carbon budgets for the UK, with the budgets set three periods ahead. The first three carbon budgets, from 2008 to 2022 were adopted in May 2009 and the fourth carbon budget was adopted during summer 2011. This system means that the emissions targets for the following 15 years will be apparent.

The issue with carbon budgets is whether they will be devolved to regions, local authorities or communities in due course? It is something of a problem for the Government that under the national budgets, there is no infrastructure to ensure their delivery at local level.

At one stage it was thought that the Government might introduce measures to devolve these provisions by regulation. Instead, the Government reached an agreement with local government via the Local Government Association (LGA). After the General Election, the new Minister asked the LGA to outline its way forward for combating climate change. The document *Local Government's Offer on Climate Change* then formed the basis of a discussion between central and local government. The *Memorandum of Understanding* was finally signed in March 2011. It provided that local authorities would succeed in some of the demands they were making, and in return, would work in partnership with the Government to deliver national targets. The offer document is a detailed critique of what local government needs from Central Government to help address climate change.

In some ways, the Government is caught on the horns of a dilemma in relation to this. All of the thrust of modern policy since 2010 has been towards decentralisation and devolvement of power to local hands. Accordingly, the notion of setting targets or budgets nationally and imposing them on local authorities does not fit with this new way of working. However, there are those who argue that the delegation of carbon budgets to local level is, in fact, a localist measure. It seems difficult to agree with this approach, as the whole principle of localism, as discussed below, is to leave decisions to be taken at local level by the body best suited to take them.

The Localism Agenda

Local government has changed significantly during the course of the current Parliamentary term. The Coalition Government pledged to transfer power from central government down to local authorities and through them to the people. This is known as the 'localism' agenda and some aspects of it will have relevance to the green agenda.

The political aim was explained by Greg Clarke, Minister of State for Decentralisation, in A Plain English Guide to The Localism Act, as follows:

"We think that the best means of strengthening society is not for central government to try and seize all the power and responsibility for itself. It is to help people and their locally elected representatives to achieve their own ambitions. This is the essence of the Big Society."

The first change for local authorities under localism is in relation their powers. **Chapter 3** explained that new powers of general competence have been conferred and brought into effect. Instead of the old rule, whereby a local authority had to demonstrate that it had a legal power before it could act, new powers permit a local authority to do anything a person could do, provided that it is not prohibited by the civil or criminal law. This may be relevant to authorities seeking to act creatively around the establishment of Energy Service Companies (ESCO's) and Green Deal financing.

Greater control over business rates might also be important, in terms of the economic elements of a green programme. There is now power to offer discounts, to attract companies, promote investment and create jobs.

The new powers requested by the Core Cities Group for powers to be given from Whitehall to local government may also have an energy element to them. District heating networks and similar arrangements may require substantial changes to become established.

Finally, the community right to challenge services and take them over and the parallel right to bid for community assets might also be relevant. Local authorities may find that community groups consider some of the green programme work with interest; it should not be forgotten that many of the elements of green programme work could be undertaken as community arrangements.

It will take some time for the changes under the localism agenda to fully settle down and many are not relevant to the green agenda. The changes have been billed as fundamental, but only time will tell whether this is the case.

Bringing Projects Forwards

One of the issues relevant to levering in finance to local government projects is size and scale. In **Chapter 10**, the various ways that a renewable energy or energy efficiency project can be funded are considered. These include borrowing money from the Public Works Loans Board, or commercially, or finding equity partners. However, the scale of the projects that is required is so large that some think individual projects coming forwards are unlikely to ever meet the targets. This is when 'bundling' projects, creating larger funds and involving institutional investors, come to the fore.

There is a difference here between renewable energy projects and energy efficiency projects. The creation of renewable energy facilities is more than likely to be an individual authority issue and accordingly, will need individual councils to motivate themselves into action. The Feed In Tariffs and Renewable Heat Incentive should be strong enough to do this, particularly when put in the context of the non-financial benefits for a renewable energy project discussed in **Chapter 5**.

Energy efficiency is more difficult, however. Here, in order to make projects more cost effective, buildings need to be retrofitted together. A good example is housing, whether public or private. If the Green Deal is really to deliver the benefits intended, properties need to be retrofitted with energy efficiency measures on a house-by-house, and street-by-street basis. This takes a lot more resources to finance and plan. It would be difficult for a local authority to fund this work itself, bearing in mind the fact that it may stretch to hundreds of millions of pounds on its own (IE: without other elements of the green programme). Viewed in this way, it is likely to require outside funding.

In the area of energy efficiency, the Green Investment Bank is looking to provide funds for a 'pipeline' of qualifying projects. The funds available to the Green Investment Bank are at least £3bn, but need to be allocated in huge tranches, which are likely to be at least £25m, and match funded with private money. It is the same situation in relation to investment by pension funds. Again, they are looking for low risk projects that can receive large tranches of funding, often in £25m blocks.

This provides a problem for local authorities. There are nearly 500 authorities across the United Kingdom and each has legal powers and duties in relation to its own area. The notion of joint working has not been readily achieved in the past and whilst this is changing, it may be some time before collaboration of the extent needed can be realised. In simple terms, this means that local authorities will find it difficult to 'scale up' their own operations, to a sufficient size to benefit from these major blocks of funding. If the 'pipeline' of projects cannot be put in place, it may be that the funding moves elsewhere.

This means that if ever there was a need to accelerate the move towards joint working between local authorities, the climate change and energy agenda provides it.

Conclusion

It can be seen from the material above that the local government glass could be seen either as half empty or half full. The former perspective focuses on cuts to budgets, reduced services and low staff morale; the latter focuses on opportunities to pull local authorities out of this mess and how those might be captured.

Whilst the challenges facing local government should not be underestimated, it is important to look at the future from a positive perspective, rather than a negative one. The climate change agenda offers huge potential for a positive boost, both financially and non-financially. This starts with a process of realising that potential exists and developing a strategy to achieve it. This is considered in the next Chapter.

Key Learning Points

- Times are tough in local government and the public sector
- Does this mean that no environmental work should be done?
- No – the green agenda and the corporate agenda of a local authority are almost completely aligned; delivery of one delivers the other
- There is no area of local government that the green agenda does not touch
- A positive outlook is justified in terms of green programmes

Installation of a Solar PV Array by Tandridge District Council long before financial incentives were introduced

Considering the installation

In March 2004 Tandridge District Council's Resources Committee considered investing in a 25.5 KWh Photo-Voltaic array, to be installed to the south and west facing roofs of the council office.

Considering a scheme developed with BP Solar, the council debated the merits of investment which were detailed to:

* *Provide a source of free renewable solar energy of at least 25.5kWp, which will contribute directly to the electricity demand of the council offices for potentially the next 50 years*
* *Reduce the council's emission of greenhouse gases by 15 tonnes annually*
* *Demonstrate the Council's commitment to the generation of energy from sustainable and renewable sources*
* *Promote the concept of renewable energy to the residents of Tandridge*
* *Contribute to the Government's target for renewables to supply 10% of UK electricity by 2010*

It was noted that the array would develop between 5% and 10% of the council's energy requirements, and the paper lent heavily on the 2003 Energy White Paper, "Our energy future – creating a low carbon economy". The council noted the paper and requested a fuller financial analysis of the benefits, which was reported to the Committee in July 2004, where the scheme was approved.

At the time of approval, and in the early years of the installation, additional compensation was provided from schemes such as entitlement to Renewable Obligations Certificates, (ROCs), which gave exemptions from the Climate Change Levy and was estimated to provide cash benefits in excess to £1,000 per annum.

Following approval, planning permission for the scheme was sought and the installation planned. The installation was then installed in late 2005.

The installation was funded by the the council and the Department of Trade and Industry, which provided £73,125 of the total of £112,500. This left Tandridge to find £39,375.

Reviewing the Operation

Tandridge has been able to demonstrate its commitment to the green agenda throughout the period since installation. Our local MP at the time was Peter Ainsworth, who from 2003, chaired the Environmental Audit Select Committee before rejoining the Shadow Cabinet under David Cameron in December 2005 as Shadow Secretary of State for Environment, Food and Rural Affairs. The formal opening of the Tandridge PV array therefore gained significant support from the the local MP, and Tandridge was able to present itself as taking a lead role in environmental innovation.

The array has continued to attract interest as an early PV installation, and has caused the council no significant concerns. The undertakings at the time have largely been met, the array has proved to be effectively self cleaning.

Changes have also occurred which have benefited the council as subsidies for PV generation have improved, whilst the unit costs of electricity has also escalated. Further, the investment value of the funding used to install the array has significantly reduced. With these factors working in our favour, the array ought to justify itself financially. Only the amount of electricity generated has disappointed, which is at the low end of the forecast range. However, the rain which has reduced the output has at least kept the PC cells clean.

Does it pay?

In making our original assessment, the council made a number of financial assumptions. It estimated that it would achieve a future investment rate on the capital required of 4.5%, so the council would lose about £2,000 per year by committing £39,375 to the scheme. It assumed fuel price in inflation would range between 7.5% and 15% over the operational period of about 25 years, and that it would be able to achieve 10% of its electrical requirement from the photovoltaic cells.

Looking at the total energy requirements for the council since 2004/5, consumption has ranged between 467748Kwh (2004) and 550616Kwh (2008), and is currently since stabilising or reducing.

2004	2005	2006	2007	2008	2009	2010	2011
467,748	4 93,808	480,830	500,322	550,616	537,155	510,224	536,686

During this period, the PV cells have been generating electricity at a maximum rate of approximately 30 Kwh, and as this is not shown on the charged consumption, without the PV array these bills would have been larger.

We estimated that the PV array would generate between 5% and 10% of our requirement, and it has actually accounted for 139.35 Megawatt hours, or 139,350 Kwh, of the 2774350Kwh total energy consumption. The PV array has thus generated a little over 5% of the council's requirement. On average, the array generates a little more than 5Kwh during daylight hours, or 23225kwh per year, against its rated capacity of 25.5Kwh and maximum registered output of about 30Kwh.

So although the PV generation is lower than estimated, since installation financial investment rates have reduced, electricity costs have increased and we have been able to claim FITS instead of the ROCs current when we installed. These factors, in spite of the reduced energy production, have meant that Tandridge was well justified in investing £39,000 in the installation.

So although the PV generation is lower than estimated, since installation financial investment rates have reduced, electricity costs have increased and we have been able to claim FITS instead of the ROCs current when we installed. These factors, in spite of the reduced energy production, have meant that Tandridge was well justified in investing £39,000 in the installation.

The value of the PV electricity generated has been approximately £12,000 of electricity in six years, or £2,000 per year. However, at today's average prices, the value of the units is closer to £18,000, or £3,000 per year. The council estimated that fuel would escalate at between 7.5% and 15% per year on year, and the higher assumption has proved reasonably accurate in terms of market price. The council has previously been charged up to the current market average price of £0.13p, which is 260% of the price paid by the council in 2005, although the council is currently negotiating rates at less than £0.10p.

Equally, we made assumptions on the interest rates of 4.5%, on which the authority might have have generated interest of £11,500 on the capital invested in the PV cells. More recently, though, interest rates have dropped, and in the last year the capital would only have generated some £800, considerably less than the current energy value of the PV cells.

In addition to the value of the electrical units, the council now received a FIT subsidy payment, worth £2,400 in respect of last year's generation. In the last year, therefore, instead of a capital return of £800, the council obtained electricity and subsidies worth approximately £4,800. Had the current situation been current throughout the installed period, with low capital investment rates and high energy costs, the council would have made a gross profit from its investment in the PV array in under 10 years, with an annual return of some 12.0%.

Prices have, as expected, changed considerably over the years. The actual costs of the original installation was £112,500, not £39,000, and the council would not have invested had it had to fund the entire scheme. However, looking at the total investment, an annual return of 4.25% still looks reasonable in today's market, and would cost justify the installation if it meets its designed life of 25 years before any major re-investment. Further, the factors that make the equation work are still balanced in favour of the array, with low interest rates and high energy costs expected to continue.

On top of this, the onus of energy efficiency and the carbon agenda has increased, and the PV installation has put us ahead of that agenda. The array is a visible and public statement of our commitment to the environmental agenda. Tandridge's encouragement of energy efficiency, whether through insulation schemes or other alternative energy proposals, is given more weight by our early investment in our own offices.

Conclusion

In 2004 the council estimated three major financial factors in assessing the installation of its PV array; the generation capability of the array, the inflation in electrical energy costs and the financial investment value of its capital. Although the array generates less than expected, the value of electricity has significantly inflated and the return on financial investment diminished.

It was the council's 2004 assessment that the PV array investment was justified and that energy would become an increasingly valuable asset. In spite of the disappointing electrical output, the PV array is currently proving to be a sound investment and enabling the council to present itself as an investor in the environmental agenda.

Stuart Mitchenall,
Head of Business Support Services and
Stephen Weigel,
Chief Executive Tandridge District Council

Introduction

Every local authority that is serious about the green agenda needs a comprehensive climate change strategy. This is examined further below. The purpose of the strategy is to set out the position of the council and to detail its plan of action. It needs to cover a wide range of issues.

It is necessary to develop a strategy before the authority embarks on any type of renewable energy project, including a solar PV installation. However, if an authority has undertaken some disparate renewable energy projects already, it can still think about formalising a strategy before going further.

This strategy is a crucial document, because without it, any council's claims to be a 'green' authority are fairly worthless. The strength of the strategy will largely determine how much credence any green agenda claims really have. In other words, if the delivery plans are vague, not properly resourced and have no clear timelines and metrics associated with them, the council's statements will be dismissed as mere platitudes. On the other hand, if there are clear targets, a route map showing how to get there and projects to form the steps along the way, this will demonstrate that the council is serious about 'walking the walk' rather than just 'talking the talk.'

The importance of the climate change strategy cannot be overstated and this is a particular area of weakness in many authorities. To properly complete a strategy an authority needs:

- *Vision*
- *Commitment*
- *Resources*
- *Time*
- *Consensus*
- *Data*

Purpose and Contents of the Strategy

As stated above, every local authority should have a 'holistic' climate change strategy. This is not just a bit of PV here and a biomass boiler there – but a fully thought through view on how climate change will affect the area; and what the council is going to do about it. Areas covered should include: emissions reduction, renewable energy, behaviour change, the living environment, the economic angles, green jobs and so on. It does not matter that the aspirations are modest, as opposed to bold and ambitious. What matters is that the council has produced a strategy and is working towards it. That alone will mean that such an authority will stand out from the rest of local government.

The strategy should have a number of different strands and each should have its own delivery plan. The Green Cornwall Programme, developed by Cornwall Council in 2009, had a renewable energy strand as one of its seven limbs and then a Renewable Energy Strategy below it.

The three key elements in the whole package are:

- *Targets, aims or goals as to what the council wants to achieve*
- *A 'route map' of how it is going to get there*
- *Projects, to form the steps on that route*

This is illustrated in Figure 5.1 below.

- *Targets / aims / or goals as to what the council wants to achieve. An example is that the authority will produce 25% of the energy it uses from renewable sources by 2015*
- *A 'route map' of how to get there. In order to deliver that, for example, the council will install (X) MW of solar PV, (Y) MW of wind or install so many biomass boilers*
- *Identify projects that will deliver those goals. For example, the first projects will be solar PV on the council's depot and followed by (X, Y and Z)*

Figure 5.1 – Elements in a Strategy

It should be emphasised that this is more than mere neatness in approach. It goes to the heart of the legal powers relied upon and also assists greatly if there are objections to any project. This might be relevant, for example, to a wind energy or anaerobic digestion plant project, rather than solar PV.

Political Vision and Leadership

Having said what the structure of the strategy document should be, it should be emphasised that it is up to the members of the council to decide what targets should actually be chosen. This can be done based on its current performance, where it wants to get to and the internal and external resources available to help it get there.

Support from elected members is crucially important and as performance will need to be monitored and reported back; it is vital that councillors agree the degree of 'stretch' involved. The key players are the Leader, Cabinet and Portfolio Holder for climate change. They will need to drive the ambition and ensure that sufficient priority is given to it.

In order to determine what the targets should be, two influences will come to bear: the first is the council's actual performance to date, based on data; the second is the level of ambition its councillors want to achieve. This will be linked to other areas of governance, not least the priority given to the programme, the resources available, attitudes to borrowing and so on. Some authorities have included climate change within their small number of core priorities. But as seen in **Chapter 4**, it is much less of a priority in others.

A serious Renewable Energy Strategy should also be highly relevant to the short, medium and longer-term financial strategy of each council. This is because the elements of energy efficiency and renewable energy generation should both result in financial savings and / or income. As an example, one Council in the North of England intends to add the income from its wind energy project into its formal annual budgetary process, meaning that it will rely upon the income to meet the council's various financial liabilities. This obviously requires elected members' involvement at the highest level.

Data to Underpin Climate Change Strategies

It was mentioned above that one of the influences on members seeking to set new targets will be performance to date. This will require a careful analysis of data. Since the Performance Indicators for local government (National Indicator 185 and 186 and so on) were abolished, it has been up to each authority what data it keeps and uses. The development of a good strategy will undoubtedly expose flaws in poor data capture and storage processes.

Figure 5.2 considers some of the most basic data that needs to be available to inform this process. However, it is often the case that authorities do not have all of this data, or it is kept by different departments in different places and not stored centrally. This might be a good time, therefore, to examine this position and put together a 'dashboard' of key data on climate change and energy use for the Cabinet and / or Corporate Management Team in their overview of this function.

Energy Spend and Procurement

- *What is the authority's current spend on energy – including gas, electricity and oil?*
- *Does the authority have flexible procurement arrangements in place for the procurement of energy – or does it do it itself?*
- *How many MWh of energy does the council use per annum?*
- *Does the council consider itself to be "good" at energy management?*
- *Is it part of corporate arrangements or left to the energy manager?*

Carbon Footprint / CRC

- *What is the council's carbon footprint?*
- *What is the % represented by the council, compared to the regional / total footprint?*
- *How is the carbon footprint broken down in terms of transport, buildings etc?*

- Does the authority have an Automatic Meter Reading strategy, Carbon Trust Standard or the Carbon Trust's buildings programme Local Authority Carbon Management?
- Does the council have a specific energy efficiency strategy?

Data Certainty

- How robust is the data on which these answers are based. Is it NI 185/6 or better data?
- How much resource goes into data gathering in this area?

Strategies and Targets

- What targets does the authority have for reducing its carbon footprint?
- Does the authority have a climate change strategy?
- Does it have a renewable energy strategy?

Buildings

- How many buildings does the authority have and what is the profile, condition and data on them?
- What is the energy performance of the building stock – good or average?
- How much in resources has been used to upgrade the energy efficiency of buildings?
- Has the authority used consultants to advise on renewables?
- Has there been a survey with renewables in mind?
- How many council houses does the authority retain and what is the condition of them?

Current Renewables

- Does the council have any ground source or air source heat pumps in operation?
- Does it have any solar panels?
- Does it have any wind generation?
- Does it have any biomass boilers?

Income Generation and Borrowing

- What is the council's attitude to income generation?
- Does it have a history or record of charging and trading?
- What is the authority's attitude to borrowing?
- What is the authority's attitude to debt?
- Is the director of finance / portfolio holder for finance cautious or ambitious?

Budgets and Responsibility

- Does the authority have a "green" budget and if so how much is it?
- What is the process for accessing "green" monies?
- What is the authority's prudential limit and how close is the council to it?
- How regularly does the authority borrow money externally for projects?
- Is a single Cabinet Member responsible for the "green" agenda?
- Is a single officer responsible for drawing together all of the "green" issues?
- Is there competition between departments for "green" issues or harmony in working?
- How are these issues fed into the corporate management of the authority?

Figure 5.2 – Data to Inform a Strategy

Once all of these various strands of data are available, the task can begin of charting where the authority has reached and from there, how high to set the targets. There is an art to this, in that it would seem fruitless for an authority with no track record of serious greenhouse gas emissions reduction work to set huge reduction targets, such as being carbon neutral, as these are unlikely to be reached. Similarly, those authorities with no renewable energy are best not to aim for energy self-sufficiency, as this may well be unattainable within a reasonable time frame.

Instead, a cool look needs to be taken at the authority's performance to date, its culture, values, commitment in the past to the green agenda and work already completed in order to form a sensible view of how far it should now promise to go. This will naturally form a scale from 'modest' to 'ambitious' within reason. It is preferable if decisions on targets are taken with some consensus between the officers and members about the goals and level of effort necessary to reach them. For well-run authorities, this is common practice and would not differ from other areas of performance.

Once the targets have been set, the council can then consider the best way to meet them and develop its route map. This might involve both energy efficiency and renewable energy projects, as well as other areas relevant to any climate change strategy, such as green spaces, economic development and so on.

In the Green Cornwall Programme in 2009, the wider Programme contained sections on all of the main areas, including emissions, renewables, the living environment, economic development and behaviour change. Then beneath each main strand of the climate change strategy, there is a sub strategy for that area. This is how a renewable energy strategy differs from a climate change strategy, but is nonetheless closely linked. The latter strategy covers only renewables, but its wider aims are transposed into the climate change strategy, which oversees all areas. This is why the main climate change strategy is referred to as 'holistic' in nature.

In relation to solar power, it is the renewable energy strategy that is most relevant. Featured below are several examples of how such a strategy might be comprised.

Examples of Renewable Energy Strategies

These are two examples of renewable energy strategies that are worth consideration, the National Trust and Cornwall Council.

The National Trust

This is featured in the document Energy: Grow your Own, published in 2010. It is well written, clear and sets challenging but achievable goals for the organisation. It also makes clear the position of the National Trust on the issue of climate change.

The target for the National Trust is set out on page 1 and is:

"We intend to reduce our use of fossil fuels for heat and electricity by 50% by 2020."

This is a clear aim and easily understood. It is followed by details about the use of energy, stating that in 2008 the National Trust used 86,100 MWh of energy, emitting 32,000 tonnes of CO_2 in the process. From this, it is clear how far the organisation needs to go.

The Action Plan then follows. This has four strands:

- *Conserving energy*
- *Growing our own electricity and heat*
- *Getting off oil*
- *Energy inspiration*

Then follow two or three pages on each of the four sections, with examples, case studies and photographs. Conserving energy means using less power and better energy efficiency, with examples of where insulation has helped. Growing your own electricity refers to solar PV, wind power and hydropower, each with examples. Growing your own heat, talks about switching to solar thermal, wood burning boilers and heat pumps. The conclusion recognizes that, "there is still much work to be done ..." but the "next ten years will be exciting for us ..."

Whilst it may not be seen to be essential to have a glossy report that can be circulated via the website and handed out in hard copy, this is in fact hugely advantageous in PR terms as **Chapter 13** illustrates.

If it is necessary to go digging round in council reports to find out what the various elements are – or even worse forced out via Freedom of Information Act requests – then the council has erred in its judgement. It should use its renewable energy strategy as a way of advertising its position on this area, demonstrating community leadership and assisting its own position, both financially and non-financially. This point is developed further below, when those benefits are examined.

Cornwall Council

Cornwall Council developed a renewable energy strategy in 2009 as part of the Green Cornwall Programme. The council has developed these plans further since then and they may differ, but it still offers a useful illustration of the point of such strategies.

The aim of the strategy was given as energy self-sufficiency by 2025. This gave a 16-year window from when the authority had been created in 2009. At that stage, the council used approximately 140,000 MWh of gas, electricity and oil. However, rather than adopt this total as the renewable energy generation target, it was determined that the total energy use should reduce by at least 10% over the period, meaning that the council would be aiming for around 100,000 MWh pa of generating capacity. The reductions would be delivered by a behaviour change programme and improvements to energy efficiency. In this way, the council was respecting the hierarchy mentioned in **Chapter 6** ie: use less energy; improve energy efficiency; and generate new energy from renewable sources.

There then followed four phases – each of four years with an election at the end, allowing the Council to review its priorities – to deliver the required total of renewable energy.

Figure 5.3 illustrates the contents of the phases.

- Phase 1 – 2009-13 included 30 MW of solar PV
- Phase 2 – 2013 -17 included 30 MW of wind power
- Phase 3 – 2017-21 included heat networks and the replacement of gas use
- Phase 4 – 2021-25 swept up any remaining elements

Figure 5.3 – Phases in the Renewable Energy Strategy

The capital cost of the projects was estimated at (then) current prices, for example £60m for the solar PV, £40m for the wind and so on. In this way, the cost of reaching the target that the council had set could be estimated. It may well be that an authority looks again at its target, having done this calculation, or seeks to take on board some joint venture partners.

The strategy then went through methods of funding this work and the pros and cons of each potential avenue. These are considered in **Chapter 10**. If this plan were achieved, then the council would save £8m pa at 2009 prices on fuel (probably c£15m pa by 2025) and would have a revenue stream of tens of millions of pounds per annum.

Developing A Strategy

In developing a new Renewable Energy Strategy, it depends first on what has already been agreed by the authority. It may well be that there are already targets in place, albeit ones that have not been arrived at with the diligence of the process encouraged above. It goes without saying that no authority wants any hostages to fortune, namely targets that cannot be delivered.

So the place to start is - what targets has the council agreed already? Does the authority have goals that can be modified? Consideration also needs to be given to which technologies will work for that authority; as an example, wave / tidal is, of course, unlikely to be of use to an inland authority.

Next, the data is required. This was dealt with above and answers to all the questions that will arise, including energy use, the costs of energy and the carbon footprint created will be necessary.

The strategy could also refer to the creation of jobs and boost to the local economy. This is examined further below.

Developing a 'Ten Year Plan'

Another way of looking at it is to develop a wider plan for the authority. Most renewable energy solutions are not short-term and will need careful planning and execution. The more astute authorities will ensure they are making quick progress on easier areas, whilst putting in place preparatory work for the longer-term projects.

Solar PV is a good example of the former, with a district heating network, fuelled by renewable combined heat and power, is a good example of the latter.

So some authorities have chosen to incorporate all this in a ten-year plan. In many ways, this is just another strand of good corporate management, but this time exclusively focusing on the green agenda.

Creation of Jobs

Jobs are highly relevant to the green agenda and so need to be covered in the strategy. Types of jobs vary in accordance with technology – for example solar PV creates fitting jobs, whereas generally wind does not – and this issue can be worked into the mix. In the Cornwall example above, this would form part of the wider Green Cornwall Strategy and not necessarily be under the specific renewable energy section. This is because the economic development issues have a wider relevance to the overall Programme.

The essential elements of an economic section are:

What type of jobs?

An analysis of the different technologies needs to be undertaken. The type of work will vary from fitters of PV panels (electricians, roofers and builders) to white collar jobs created as well, for example in finance, business plans, and financial incentives administration. It would be usual to undertake a review of current types of employment in local government and how these might be adapted to meet the requirements of the new technologies.

What type of workforce is needed to fit those jobs?

This is followed by an analysis of what skills are available in the workforce and how these could be re-profiled to meet new requirements.

Training

It will be necessary to undertake an analysis of the training requirements for the new technologies. What sort of training is there to meet these requirements? The Government has recognised this for Green Deal and set up many new arrangements. It might be that recommendations need to be made for new, more focused training to be developed in the area.

Accreditation & Qualifications

Safety, standards, and Quality Assurance are all important to new job creation. What accreditation is there for these new jobs? The Microgeneration Certification Scheme is a good example of a new accreditation and certification scheme that has been introduced.

Training, qualifications, and accreditation all go hand in hand. This is a good opportunity for the local authority to engage with local universities and colleges about courses and qualifications needed to push this agenda forwards in the area.

Benefits to the Local Economy

This section should include material from national research, for example the paper *More Bang for the Public Buck* (APSE – February 2010). This concludes that for each £1 of public expenditure spent in an area, £1.64 is generated in the local economy through employment and supply chains.

Supply Chains

Capturing the supply chain is key to success in the economic arena. Solar PV is a good example here, with thousands of jobs being created fitting solar panels. Whilst the panels themselves may have come from China, the USA or Germany, many of the other components in the supply chain are locally sourced, creating further opportunities elsewhere in the local economy.

Benefits To The Local Authority Of A Renewable Energy Or Energy Efficiency Scheme

It was mentioned above that there are significant benefits to any local authority that engages in renewable energy generation. These have not been widely acknowledged but some councils have now started to appreciate them. The following is a brief summary of the main potential benefits of a project:

* ## Community Leadership

Local authorities are encouraged to 'lead from the front' and to provide an example to their local areas. The community leadership role is closely tied to the development and delivery of the sustainable community strategy under the Local Government Act 2000. This provides an excellent example of how community leadership can be seen in action.

Every local authority should be considering action on the PV front, not just for its own buildings, but also other buildings in its area. This offers the prospect of bringing together other parts of the public sector and potentially the third sector too, behind a common goal. The more organisations that follow this route, the greater the local benefits.

The Government's Localism Act 2011 also contains new powers of general competence for local authorities (see **Chapter 3**), which may well spur a renaissance in this type of activity.

• *Energy Security*

The Department of Energy and Climate Change has already confirmed that there will be power cuts in the next decade, due to the loss of current fossil fuel based power generation and inability to introduce further nuclear energy or sufficient amounts of renewable energy in time to take up the demand.

Any area that might be affected by such cuts will be in a stronger position if it has its own renewable energy sources. This is particularly important in more rural areas and remote parts of the UK, but is highly relevant everywhere. The only way that the risk can be reduced is to have some renewable energy generating capacity.

• *Carbon Benefits*

The Government is legislating to place ever more stringent targets in relation to greenhouse gases. The Climate Change Act 2008 targets will be very challenging and part of the burden of delivering them will fall on to local government.

Whilst energy generation does not count directly under the CRC Energy Efficiency Scheme, there will be carbon benefits from such generation, as authorities using energy directly generated themselves, will reduce their carbon footprint, and therefore the number of allowances under the regime that it has to purchase.

• *Effectiveness and Efficiency*

Local authorities are always under the microscope over their expenditure and whether it offers maximum value for money. The solar PV option gives the local authority the chance to save money, by using the energy that is generated from its solar arrays, thereby meaning that external energy costs do not have to be incurred.

It is also the case that energy efficiency goes hand in hand with renewables and if some of the income generated is recycled back into energy efficiency, then running costs of buildings will fall still further, offering another efficiency.

• *Economic Benefits*

Local authorities are also critically aware of the state of their local economies. Whilst all have been hit hard by the recession, some have suffered more than others, particularly those where public sector employment is a higher proportion of the local economy.

The green agenda offers the best potential for growth at the present time; indeed, some believe that this is the only likely source of growth for the next couple of years.

The aim is to stimulate the local supply chain positively. This might mean obtaining supplies locally, using local labour where possible and so on. It takes time and effort to develop a sound and lawful strategy to stimulate the local economy but this will pay dividends.

• *Other Green Benefits*

If a local authority developed a 'holistic' climate change plan, as has been suggested above, then it would take some funds to resource that programme. One way of 'locking in' the benefits to such a green programme is to use the surplus from any renewable energy projects to fund the wider green agenda work.

Income Generation

This has been an issue of some controversy for some time, as the Secretary of State, Eric Pickles, accused councils of simply hiking up fees for parking and other services in order to maximise its available income in difficult times. He referred to local authorities, "turning motorists into cash cows" and instead urged there to be innovation.

With renewable energy, income generation is possible with no such stigma. This is an activity heavily supported by the Government and which does not involve the public being charged. As such, it is an important way to generate further funds. Such funds can be recycled back into other green agenda activities, or simply used to supplement the General Fund.

It can be seen from the above that there are many benefits of engaging in renewable energy and often these will harmonize nicely with other elements of the policy agenda for a local authority, such as creating jobs and becoming more efficient. This surely is a 'win-win' situation.

Consulting on and Publicising the Strategy

It will be necessary to consult widely on the plan, whilst in draft form, both internally and externally. Internal deliberations should come first. These should include all of the relevant officers and elected members. This is actually a wide group of people, including sustainability officers, energy managers, policy personnel, service departments and so on. If proper consultation is not undertaken, then some of those internal departments may not 'own' the targets and demonstrate the necessary commitment once they are implemented.

After internal consultations have been undertaken, the council needs to undertake a through PR exercise on it, as this is useful for reinforcing a positive image of the council. These exercises are referred to as a communications plan, as detailed in **Chapter 13**.

A useful example here is Birmingham City Council. Its Birmingham Declaration makes perfectly clear what targets it has set itself as an authority, even though the detail is largely elsewhere. Figure 5.4 summarises its contents. Every council should aspire to a similar statement.

The Council believes that by 2015:

- *All vehicles procured by the Council should be electrically powered or run on Liquefied Petroleum Gas*
- *There will be at least 500 electric cars running on the streets of the city as we will develop the EV charging infrastructure*
- *50% of electricity used by the council should be generated from renewable sources*
- *The City Council's energy consumption will be reduced by 25%*
- *10% of Birmingham homes will be linked to district heating systems*
- *10% of Birmingham homes will have retrofit insulation*
- *There will be at least 10 'low carbon communities' similar to the successful example of Summerfield Eco- neighbourhood*

Figure 5.4 – The Birmingham Declaration

A Wider Approach

The previous discussion concerns the council itself and its projects and developments. A different approach, either alone or in conjunction with the above, would be to look outwards.

There are two relevant areas here:

- *The 'community'*
- *The wider local economy*

The Community

Here, the council can consider what steps it could take to assist local community groups to undertake their own projects and developments.

In a report, published by the Energy Saving Trust in 2009, entitled Power in Numbers – the Benefits and Potential of Distributed Energy at the Small Community Scale, this area was examined and the conclusion drawn that a relatively small amount of assistance can have a significant effect on ensuring that more community schemes come to fruition.

The question then becomes, what can a local authority do to help this along? An example might be to create a new post of 'community energy officer', which could be fixed term for, say, two years. This officer would then be available to assist any community group in the area that wants to pursue a renewable energy project to help it along. Obvious areas are developing business cases, helping to approach the bank to borrow money and completing the forms for planning permission. This is a sort of 'gearing' effect ie: a small amount of help has a much larger and more beneficial outcome.

The reason that more local authorities have not gone down this route is simply lack of funds. If a council can raise the funds (perhaps from income derived from renewable energy installations) that could make a big difference. The council could then appraise the performance of the officer and decide whether to continue funding for future years.

The Wider Economy

This builds on the last point. Whilst the council is looking outwards there, its gaze only goes so far as community groups. This proposal suggests something wider. The other part of the economy is the private sector and the council can also bring its influence to bear here too.

A simple example would be to publish planning guidance (such as a special planning document) that gives assistance on how to apply for planning consent for renewables and other green projects. Cornwall Council did this by publishing *Renewable And Low Carbon Energy – Supplementary Planning Document (June 2010)*. Its dual purpose was to specifically encourage applications for renewable energy, whilst improving their quality by imparting information as to what the Planning Authority was looking for in such applications.

Another possibility is the pursuit of a Community Infrastructure Levy scheme, making clear that some of the benefits will go towards energy infrastructure that will help green energy developers, as discussed in **Chapter 3**. A district heating network could be another example, whereby the council funds the pipework on the basis that private finance is raised for the Combined Heat and Power (CHP) or other heating infrastructure.

If there was motivation to engage in a wider plan, such as those indicated above, then these would also need to be part of the council's overall strategy. Deciding how wide, or narrow, to be in this exercise is one of the very first decisions that needs to be taken.

The Isle of Wight is a good example of this approach, with its Eco Island initiative. The work there includes helping Vestas establish a new base to research and develop wind turbines in Newport; a environmental flagship store for Waitrose in East Cowes; and giving land to GKN to develop environmentally friendly aircraft engines. The council describes this as, "the council creating the conditions in which business can flourish ..." (*David Pugh, Leader of the Council, Local Government News, May 2012*).

(David Pugh, Leader of the Council, Local Government News, May 2012).

Conclusions

All of this work is achievable in every local authority but will take some time and effort. Naturally, the more people that buy into the strategy before it is finalised, the better. It is important that the strategy is not seen as a 'top down' requirement, but more of an iterative process, leading to an organically developed and widely supported series of measures. That means meetings with lots of people internally, but these meetings should tease out if there are any problems with anything in the strategy. Externally, a concerted effort is required to get the message over to a potentially sceptical public – hence the need for a good quality communications plan.

The data will also take time and effort to collect and needs to be well presented, with metrics for gauging future progress. Again, this can be done in-house and new procedures developed.

There are numerous examples of Renewable Energy Strategies, but those that are well written, focused and value-adding documents are far less common. Every authority should strive for its strategy to be an exemplar and a credit to the authority.

Key Learning Points

- *Every authority needs a strategy*
- *The strategy needs to set out goals, a route map and projects as steps along the way*
- *The council's performance to date and level of ambition will help gauge what targets should be set*
- *Find good examples elsewhere to inspire*
- *Include non-financial benefits in the strategy as well as financial benefits*
- *Choose whether it is just for the authority concerned, the wider community or the local economy too*
- *Publicise the strategy to draw attention to the council's work and engage with the public*

Renewable energy or energy efficiency?

Introduction

When considering any form of renewable energy, there is a need to put it in perspective. What is the aim of the programme and why is it being done? It could be for financial, carbon related or other non-financial reasons, such as those considered in **Chapter 5**. However, the entire Government policy objective, as illustrated in **Chapter 3**, is to impact on the emissions of greenhouse gases and to meet the international and EU targets for emissions reductions.

If the objective is viewed from this prism, it becomes clear that there will be some routes to reducing emissions that are easier and more cost effective than others. It is common sense that these should be taken before the more difficult or expensive routes. This truism has been fudged by the application of the Government's financial incentives. Under those, someone could do something just to claim the money, rather than for the intended reasons. So Government policy has to be carefully weighted to ensure that this does not happen.

In order to reduce emissions most cost effectively, there is a hierarchy that applies, which is illustrated in Figure 6.1 below. The goal of any local authority or public body should be to find the right balance between the three parts of the hierarchy. To have only some elements is unbalanced, as is focusing far more heavily on renewables, at the expense of energy use and efficiency.

• *Use less energy – this is the easiest and cheapest solution of all, as it requires no work and no financial investment. An organisation turns down the thermostat a few degrees, turns off the lights when not in use or closes down PCs at the end of the day. It is ridiculously simple, so the question has to be asked as to why it is not being done more?*

• *Secondly, and after the former has been done, energy efficiency is considered. The carbon footprint is greater due to heating a leaky building and using more energy than is strictly required. Therefore the insulation of the building, the roof space, the cavity walls and so on needs to be reviewed. The boiler might need replacing, theheating controls improved or changed, double glazing fitted and so on. If these simple measures are undertaken, fuel bills go down and so does the carbon footprint of the building. But best of all, money is saved that would otherwise have been wasted.*

• *Finally, when the energy usage of the building has been reduced as much as possible, and all of the necessary insulation and other energy saving measures have been undertaken, renewable energy solutions should be considered, such as fitting solar panels to the roof of the building and using the electricity generated. This involves the creation of the energy required for the function, but from renewable sources.*

Figure 6.1 – The Hierarchy of Emissions

The difficulty is that energy efficiency has traditionally not been an area of local government that has gripped the attention of corporate management. It has largely been the preserve of the energy manager and his or her staff. Accordingly, it has been difficult to bring forward major programmes of this nature. This is now changing, however, as discussed below.

Saving Energy

This is the first stage on a journey to reduce emissions. As shown in Figure 6.1, it is ridiculously simple, yet there has been very poor performance in this area for some considerable time.

There have been over ambitious claims made in the past about energy and foolhardy decisions made on the back of them. Nuclear energy at one point, was predicted to be "too cheap to justify metering ..."; new office blocks were built with no light switches and the lights left on permanently, as this was deemed less expensive than the energy consumed. Of course, this was all a nonsense. Waste in any context is abhorrent but in energy terms is even worse, bearing in mind the finite supplies of fossil fuels mentioned in **Chapter 2**. Everyone has a duty to do all they can to reduce waste and preserve energy supplies.

Whilst there is an academic argument to be had over all of this, it has a far more important commercial and efficiency context in the public sector. Local authorities pay to heat their buildings and provide electricity. **Chapter 4** demonstrated that they are facing the worst austerity package since the Second World War. It does not take a high level of reasoning to see that one can help the other. This is also a very important link to the comment above about the attention of the corporate management of the organisation. If this has not really had any priority hitherto, then there may well be significant 'quick wins' to be had by making changes.

Climate change work relates closely to asset management. The council should decide what functions it will provide and how it will deliver them. Each authority should then decide what buildings and other assets it requires, in what places and in what form, to facilitate that. It may well be with constant re-organisation and changes in the public sector, that the asset bank has not had detailed consideration for some time. The place to start, then, is to dispose of unwanted assets, or to let them out to others, so that they are not on the council's carbon footprint. The next stage is to review the energy usage and efficiency of all operational buildings. There are usually gains to be made by doing this.

Derby City Council, for example, is merging the staff from a dozen buildings into a new headquarters and making substantial savings along the way. It is also supplying the newly refurbished building with renewable energy from a hydropower scheme. Other authorities have undertaken a similar process of buildings rationalisation. Buildings that are surplus to requirements can then be disposed of to raise further funds for the transition process.

Leaving aside asset rescheduling, though, the other main way of saving energy is a behaviour change programme for the personnel who use any council buildings. The likelihood is that further substantial savings can be made on heating and electricity costs, even if there is no change in the buildings being used. This is because there is, sadly, a culture of waste in energy across the country, afflicting both public and private sectors. This can be very simply explained: buildings are heated to a temperature to suit the coldest worker; heating controls cannot be changed quickly; the lights in the whole building are left on until the last person has left and perhaps beyond; photocopiers and computers whirr away all night, even though everyone has left the office. This is happening in buildings up and down the country and is raising costs of heating and electricity needlessly.

A full resume of how to do something about this is not necessary here. Local government is a 'people' business and they hold the key. Many are concerned about the waste and would like to do something about it; they just need to be empowered to do so. A good approach is to canvass staff as to how energy can be saved. Genuine suggestion trawls and prizes for innovation definitely work. But there has to be some investment available too. If three old, and exhausted photocopiers could be replaced by one much more efficient, new one, then the money for that needs to be found.

Some local authorities have introduced projects to cut down on waste, decrease the use of energy and reduce heating very successfully. So called 'staff awareness programmes' can be highly effective, if supported by the corporate and political leadership of an authority.

In Cornwall, the Green Cornwall Programme looked to reduce the energy consumed by the council's operations by at least 10%, by the introduction of a staff energy awareness programme. Birmingham City Council in its 'Birmingham Declaration' (repeated in Figure 5.4) includes a pledge to reduce the "City Council's energy consumption by at least 25%".

The only issue to emphasise in relation to such programmes is that they need to be seriously approached and properly implemented. A half hearted, 'tick box' type approach will be apparent to the staff very quickly and is unlikely to succeed. A related point is that the system, whilst seeking to canvass the opinions of staff and tap their knowledge on the ground, has to be enforced once agreed. Often some investment is required to make improvements and this needs to be forthcoming. Staff cynicism grows quickly when there are further burdens imposed upon them without any visible benefits.

In many ways, this is no different to the normal corporate management of an authority. The best run authorities have positive and hard working cultures that are fostered over many years and therefore ingrained into their normal working practices. The same is required in relation to energy.

Energy Efficiency

So the council has reviewed its assets and followed a rationalisation programme. Already its carbon footprint, and emissions under the CRC Energy Efficiency Scheme, will be falling. Next, it has introduced a staff energy awareness programme, appointed 'green champions' and spent some time focusing on what changes need to be made to business practices. It is to be noted that so far, this has cost the authority very little in way of investment. This means the cost effectiveness of the measures so far is very high.

Next, the council needs to review the energy efficiency of its operations. This process is linear and progressional ie: it is necessary to start at the beginning and then work from there. However, many authorities (perhaps those not motivated by carbon abatement) have launched straight into renewable energy solutions. This is not the best strategy, as explained below.

Improved energy efficiency can be implemented at any scale. A small gain might be made by purchasing and using a pool cover in a municipal leisure centre, thereby preserving the pool temperature overnight and when not in use. At the other end of the scale, the complete leisure centre heating system could be replaced to provide a more efficient operating system, that involves considerably lower fuel costs.

Salix funding will be familiar to many energy managers and sustainability officers. This is a source of low cost funding to loan money to public bodies to implement energy efficiency measures. There are some requirements attached, such as a fairly swift payback, but the terms are otherwise highly attractive. Whilst this route has been successful in moving forwards energy efficiency, there is much more to be done.

Again, in some authorities this is because this type of work has not had any real focus or priority in the past. It is often the case that the relevant officers have suggested programmes, but these have not managed to gain sufficient priority to feature in capital programmes. Rising fossil fuel energy costs have, perversely, helped in this, as inflation quickly reaches the radar of the finance decision makers.

The Green Deal looks set to change all of this. The Green Deal, mentioned in **Chapter 3,** is the Government's new policy to persuade owners of buildings to improve energy efficiency, essentially by removing the need to fund the works up front. If it achieves nothing else, the Green Deal has already shone a bright light on energy efficiency and illustrated the need for radical improvements to be made. The Government policy behind Green Deal is, again, emissions related; notwithstanding this, many deals may be entered purely on cost and financial grounds.

Putting this back in the context of cost effectiveness, it was mentioned above that saving energy is the least expensive route. Energy efficiency comes next. It is often relatively inexpensive to make changes to heating and electricity equipment that achieve excellent savings. Energy efficiency therefore usually offers a better return than renewables. Bearing in mind the fact that renewable energy schemes are the most expensive of the hierarchy and offer the lowest return on investment, it is perhaps surprising that there is so much interest in that area. The reason for this is not to be found in any financial statement – it is human nature. Psychology plays a definite role here and that is why behaviour change is so important, a theme that is returned to below.

Renewable Energy

So the third and final area to consider is renewable energy. There are many different types of technology and these are briefly considered below, in order to give an overview. Any local authority considering a project in any of these areas should take specific advice first.

Solar Energy

The next Chapter considers solar power in more detail, but for the purposes of this overview, solar energy is a key element of renewable energy for the UK and has come to the fore since the advent of the Government's financial incentives in 2010.

Solar energy comes from the sun and there are two types of solar energy – solar photovoltaic for electricity generation and solar thermal, for water heating. The value of the energy depends on where you are – light levels are higher in the South of the United Kingdom and lower in the North.

Solar PV has two main areas: stand alone or land based systems (commonly referred to as solar parks); or buildings mounted solar installations, which might be much more modest.

Developing a strategy will depend on where you are in the UK and how much priority your authority gives to renewable energy. Some sizeable projects have already come forward, such as the project by Wrexham County Borough Council in North Wales to install solar PV panels on nearly 3,000 of its council houses.

There are no real objections to solar PV projects, other than aesthetic effects IE: the look of a hillside or roof covered in solar panels. In technical terms, they are very straightforward, with no moving parts, and therefore this is easiest renewable technology to implement.

This is why solar power is booming – particularly in the South West where the light levels are excellent.

Wind Energy

Wind energy is more lucrative in financial terms than solar power, but is considerably more controversial as well. Wind turbines seem to provoke considerable opposition in some quarters, even if it is only in a small minority of the population. Obtaining planning consent for a wind energy project is therefore more challenging.

The availability of wind in the UK is the best in Europe and this country is therefore well suited to wind energy. The wind is variable and so turbines will not operate all of the time. This is really no different to solar panels being more effective on brighter days and delivering fairly low energy on dull and wet winter days.

Wind turbines have many more moving parts than solar panels. Usually they are formed of a turbine, which rests on a tower with a three bladed airfoil propeller. This is mounted on a horizontal axle, the wind shaft, which drives a gearbox coupled to an electricity generator. Minimum wind speeds of five metres per second are required for operation (normally over seven m/s) and there are maximum speeds when the turbine needs to be shut down to avoid damage.

Wind turbines have a similar business case to solar panels, either via the feed in tariffs or the Renewables Obligation (RO). However, the return from wind energy is normally higher.

There are many objections to wind farm developments, although no local authority has yet planned and built a wholly civic owned scheme. The objections include:

- *Noise*
- *Flicker*
- *Shadows*
- *Landscape degradation*
- *Effects on wildlife*
- *Tourism*
- *Property values*
- *Employment*

The wind industry has demonstrated that most of the potential problems can be overcome and potential objections removed. However, some will always be against wind energy, whatever the facts.

Wind is a good form of renewable energy and will work in most areas of the UK. It is therefore inevitable that the public sector will want to avail itself of wind energy in order to reduce its carbon footprint. Whether an authority will pursue a scheme directly or not will depend on potential objections or protracted planning applications. The rise in community wind schemes shows that views are changing.

Biomass Energy

The term 'biomass' applies to any recently living organic matter. Biomass fuels are those that can be converted to energy. There are two categories of biomass: dry biomass (eg: woodchip) and wet biomass (agricultural slurries). The best example of wet biomass is pig slurry being turned into gas, via anaerobic digestion process. The best example of dry biomass is sawdust being turned into wood pellets and burned in biomass boilers.

This is an area that is under considered in the public sector. Every council should consider changing oil or coal burning boilers to biomass boilers, as Rotherham MBC in Yorkshire has done for example. However, if the authority has a biomass boiler implementation policy, then it needs to have some assurance over a suitable and stable supply chain of biomass feedstock. This is another area in which the public sector can get involved, by use of its land and equipment.

Biomass is connected to both electricity generation and heating. Biomass can be used as a fuel for generating electricity in order to claim Renewable Obligation Certificates or feed in tariffs. It is often used in combined heat and power plants, IE: creating electricity but then using the waste heat in a heating network. Most usually, biomass purely supplies heat, in which case the Renewable Heat Incentive would apply.

Whatever its use, whether heat or electricity, whether renewables or energy efficiency, biomass should form part of any authority's climate change and renewable energy plans.

Anaerobic Digestion (AD)

AD is one of the least developed technologies in local government schemes. This is interesting, bearing in mind that certain aspects of local authority operation are well suited to such schemes, such as civic farms and also food waste collection.

The AD process is where biodegradable materials are treated so that micro organisms break down the material producing biogas. The biogas can then be burned to provide a renewable source of both heat and power.

This is not a new technology. It has, in fact, been around for centuries. There are examples in the modern era, such as the biogas from a sewage works being used to fuel streetlights in Exeter.

The process takes place in the absence of oxygen in large tanks (hence the term anaerobic) and produces a side product called digestate, which is a good fertiliser. This is the residue that is left at the end of the AD process.

In order to build and run an AD plant, the Council needs to have land and a product that will provide the fuel. There are various products that have been used and these include sewage sludge, agricultural or farming residues, such as pig slurry or crops such as maize. Food waste is also a good fuel for AD. It is clear, therefore, that local authority owned farms would be ideal for this purpose and also the waste collection function for food waste.

AD plants have their issues. They are expensive to build and therefore scale is an issue. Whilst smaller farm based facilities are coming forwards, it is the commercial size plants that offer the best return. The Severn Trent plant at Stoke Bardolph in Nottingham is a £15m development, but one that makes £1.5m of income per annum. This means that collaboration with other authorities (such as a county council and its constituent districts) might offer a good way forwards.

There are also technical and planning issues to consider. Such plants have issues with smell and transport to deliver the fuel and so need to be away from residential areas. However, none of these would provide a difficulty for a local authority with rural land that could be used for this purpose.

The Government produced an Anaerobic Digestion Strategy and Action Plan in June 2011 and this set out the proposals for reducing organic waste. In tandem with this, the Government included AD in the financial incentives available for renewable energy, both under FITs and ROCs and also the Renewable Heat Incentive.

It is likely that there will be less AD plants than other forms of renewable energy, but some areas – particularly food waste – offer excellent prospects for income generation, as well as reducing the liability under a legal obligation ie to collect and dispose of the waste.

Hydropower

Hydropower has existed for centuries and is one of the oldest forms of renewable energy. However, until recently it had largely been forgotten. Now it is coming back to the fore as a very established and useful way of generating energy from renewable sources. It is particularly relevant to local authorities as many own land adjoining rivers or streams, or own old mills and similar buildings.

The UK is well suited to hydropower, due to its rainfall patterns and topography. As a form of energy, hydropower has one of the highest efficiency ratings possible – over 90%. This is considerably more efficient than wind energy, which only works when the wind blows, or solar energy, which only works during the daytime. Water runs day and night and – droughts aside – therefore provides a much more frequent supply of energy that can be used for base load.

Hydropower works by the energy in water being captured by the movement of the water from a higher level to a lower level. The two key elements are the quantity of water, known as the flow and the vertical height through which the water can fall, known as the head. The process sees the energy in the water converted first into mechanical energy and then into electrical energy.

Every scheme requires planning permission in the UK and may also need an Environmental Impact Assessment. But hydropower schemes also have special requirements as follows:

- **Abstraction license** – *needed to take the water out of the river*
- **Impounding license** – *needed for any structure that obstructs or impedes the flow of water, such as dams, weirs or a millpond*
- **Flood defense consents** – *needed to ensure that flooding does not result from a scheme*
- **Fisheries consent** – *needed to ensure fish are not harmed, for example fish passes are fitted, migrating salmon catered for and so on*

Hydropower forms a good example of renewable energy that any local authority can undertake. All rivers in the UK have been mapped by the Environment Agency and its website shows the availability of hydropower potential across the UK.

One of the best examples from a local authority viewpoint is Derby City Council, which has a new hydropower project to supply energy to its headquarters. This has been combined with an office rationalisation programme, as discussed above.

Community schemes are also frequent. A good example is the Settle Hydro project, where a community group has taken over the Bridge End Weir site on the River Ribble in Yorkshire and has spent £450,000 revamping the system via an Archimedian Screw.

Hydropower should be in every local authority's renewable energy plan. The capital cost of a scheme is usually high and the payback modest, but the schemes have long life spans, often of 50 years. The main advantage of a hydropower scheme is that there are very few objections raised, provided that the scheme is blended in. It is for this reason that hydro schemes have been constructed even in National Parks and areas of outstanding natural beauty.

Geothermal Energy

There are two real types of geothermal energy worth mentioning: the first is deep geothermal energy and the second ground (or water) source heat pumps. In renewable energy terms, the focus is on the former; heat pumps are more relevant to the heat debate.

Deep geothermal energy works by capturing the heat from the earth's core, where it is over 6,000 degrees Celsius. Heat is lost at the surface but the temperature increases by 30 degrees per km in depth.

If that energy could be harnessed, most - if not all - of the UK's energy needs could be met. The benefit of geothermal energy is its efficiency and its longevity. It can therefore be used as base load. This is very important.

There is a map illustrating geothermal energy available in the UK and some areas benefit greatly from this (particularly the South West).

Most deep geothermal energy systems work on the basis of drilled bore holes which take water / steam up from the ground and put it through a steam turbine to make electricity, before returning the water to the ground. The steam turbine turns the heat energy from the water into mechanical and then electrical energy. The bore holes can be up to 5 km deep. However, certain ground conditions are necessary: a saucer shaped geological structure, with aquifers for water movement and an insulating layer above, with water transmitting fractures in between. This type of ground condition only exists in certain places in the UK.

The capital costs of deep geothermal energy are very high and external finance may be needed to fully fund a project. Obviously the local authority has to be in a region with the right characteristics in order to benefit from this type of energy. Geothermal energy does overcome many of the other objections or problems, such as the variable nature of wind energy.

Deep geothermal energy does feature in the Government's 2050 Pathways document, examined in **Chapter 3**, although a very small amount of investment from the Government has gone into this technology so far. This is a solution for the long term and will take vision to make it a reality.

Wave And Tidal Energy

This is included in the longer term potential for renewable energy in the UK. Whilst wave and tidal energy is not yet proven commercially, it holds great promise for the UK, which is ideally suited to this form of energy (being an island surrounded by sea and with excellent tidal ranges and wind speed). It is anticipated that the commercial basis for such developments will be proven as the costs of the technology fall.

There is also the potential here to be the world market leader in the development of the technology (which is not possible in either wind or solar, where market leaders have already emerged). This is particularly attractive to the Government, which is desperately seeking jobs and inward investment.

Wave energy captures the energy from waves. This often works via some form of floating device, positioned to capture the energy from the breaking waves. Tidal energy, on the other hand, is completely different, using the range of the tide to generate the energy. These systems often work via barrages or tidal lagoons, which have hydropower turbines fitted to them, not dissimilar to those in operation in hydropower schemes in inland waters, as described above.

All coastal areas in the UK could implement wave or tidal schemes in due course, although some areas will be more suited than others. There are some very ambitious schemes in production, for example the River Severn tidal scheme.

It is also worth mentioning the Wave Hub, a publicly funded project to site a platform, which can test new wave technology, 12 miles off the North Coast of Cornwall. This was completed in November 2010 and consists of a platform, a fixture on the sea bed, cables to the shore and a new substation at Hayle, where the cables come ashore. This is now hailed as the "world's largest" test site for wave energy technology, with wave power devices expected to be connected to the Hub and their performance evaluated. The former Regional Development Agency and Cornwall Council have been closely involved.

In early 2012, the South West was designated as the UK's first Marine Energy Park. This will stretch from Bristol through to Cornwall and as far as the Isles of Scilly. It is intended to be a collaborative partnership between national and local government, Local Enterprise Partnerships, local universities and industry. The aim of the partnership is to speed up marine power development and keep the United Kingdom in the lead for this technology.

On an individual level, Cornwall Council expressed interest in wave and tidal technology some time ago, having over 400 miles of coastline within its own boundaries. Other coastal areas and authorities will also watch developments with interest.

As with any form of renewable energy, the local authority or public body has to develop a strategy first, which sets out what it is trying to achieve. Different technologies have different characteristics and advantages and disadvantages. In developing a sophisticated renewable energy strategy, each council needs to analyse its position and work out which ones, in order of priority, can best deliver its energy needs. So inland authorities will not be concerned with wave or tidal energy; biomass boilers may not be permitted in areas with air quality issues, such as London; and generally wind energy will not be appropriate for urban settings

Links Between Energy Efficiency and Renewable Energy Projects

It has been explained above that there is a hierarchy in play and it is sensible to start with energy reduction, work through energy efficiency and then arrive at the creation of new energy from renewable sources. The reason for this is simply cost effectiveness of carbon saved from finance invested. Energy reduction schemes could save 10% of a large local authority's energy bill, without costing anything other than officer time internally. Energy efficiency in terms of loft insulation will make major savings from a very low financial cost. Renewable energy projects normally require a very high investment – and up front.

It is for this reason that financially challenged public bodies should not start at this end, if their true aim is carbon abatement. However, it is likely that there would be no renewable energy schemes at all, were it not for the Government's financial incentives. Since there is, effectively, 'free' money on offer, many have embarked on solar PV and other installations, without recognising the operation of the hierarchy.

This is not a bad thing in itself, but the development of solar PV or other forms of energy should be used as an opportunity to breathe new life into the concept of energy efficiency in that authority. This is because the whole landscape, ie: energy use, through energy efficiency, to renewable energy, needs to be considered as a single picture, as indicated when considering strategy in **Chapter 5**. In other words, it does not matter if an authority has renewables as its effective entry point into the carbon agenda, provided that the focus then moves to the other parts of the hierarchy. This often follows naturally anyway: as an example, a local authority seeking to fit solar PV to its leisure centres and other non-domestic buildings, will usually look at energy use, so that the most favourable business case can be arrived at. Looking at energy use almost always leads to consideration of energy efficiency too.

Before 2011, the Government did not have any formal links between its policies on carbon abatement and renewable energy. However, during the difficult period endured by all in the solar PV industry as the feed in tariffs were adjusted by DECC, it became clear that a link could be established. In simple terms, this means that for the first time, DECC would indicate that if a party wants to receive the feed in tariff payments from the Government, it should have to do something about saving energy and energy efficiency in the building concerned. It became clear that another major strand of energy policy could be promoted in this way, without any further cost to the Government.

So, in the feed in tariff consultation held in February 2012, DECC consulted on the principle that to claim the full feed in tariff for solar PV, an occupied building would have to achieve certain standard of energy efficiency. This is referred to in **Chapter 3** when considering policy and linked the Energy Performance of Buildings agenda to solar PV feed in tariffs. The rule is that to receive a full feed in tariff, a building would need to score at least a 'D' rating on the Energy Performance Certificate. If it did not, then a very low baseline tariff of 7.1 pence per kwh (akin to land based solar installations) would apply.

The rating of property is done via the Standard Assessment Procedure (SAP), with a new form (known as Reduced Data SAP) being introduced as part of the arrangements for Green Deal.

The way SAP normally works is as part of a domestic energy assessment of the whole property. Various elements of the property's energy efficiency are looked at as part of this assessment, including fabric of the building, insulation and windows. Each is allocated points and they add up to an overall score. Where the SAP procedure cannot determine the precise details, assumptions are made as part of the process.

Ironically enough, the presence of a solar PV system itself counts positively under the process. Accordingly, under the new RD SAP, one of the questions asked is whether there is solar PV – yes/no? There is nothing about the size or details of the installation, just whether there is one. If there is, points are allocated for this in the SAP rating. So having a PV installation actually counts towards the EPC itself and helps towards a D rating.

On a practical level when the documents are sent off to register for the feed in tariff, a valid Energy Performance Certificate (EPC) will need to be sent alongside the Microgeneration Certificate Scheme (MCS) certificate if applicable and other documentation, discussed in **Chapter 14**. This is how the measure will be enforced.

If the score necessary for level D is not achieved, then measures should be taken to improve the rating, otherwise a lower feed in tariff rate will apply. In colloquial terms, this rule was introduced to prevent 'eco bling on leaky boxes'. However, as a point of principle it is important that for the first time, energy efficiency and renewables have been linked in Government policy terms. This means that in conjunction with Green Deal, this measure will start getting people used to the notion that energy efficiency is equally important as new renewable energy.

The Future

In simple policy terms, it seems obvious to try and join up the different strands of Government policy on energy, so that one supports another. For this reason, further measures such as the feed in tariff link to energy efficiency explained above are very likely to come forward.

There are a number of reasons for this. Primarily, there is insufficient attention on the area of energy efficiency, as illustrated above. Secondly, it is essential that this work is undertaken to meet the Government's legally binding targets. Thirdly, to be successful the Government's own Green Deal policy needs to make inroads into this area. Why should the Government not use a distinct 'lever' at its disposal to help encourage action in this area?

The best organised local authorities, that have climate change as one of their core priorities, already understand the importance of this and will, more than likely, have plans already developed. These authorities will want to take action as it saves money and provides the balance required. Accordingly, such links should not be feared.

The Government is also contemplating other ways to push a recalcitrant public sector towards more energy efficiency work. The possibilities here are a new legal duty and local carbon budgets.

On 17 May 2012, the Committee on Climate Change published guidance to local authorities on climate change (How Local Authorities Can Reduce Emissions and Manage Climate Risk). The report had been commissioned by Greg Barker, Minister for Energy and Climate Change.

It was recognised in this report that local government's involvement in this agenda is crucial in meeting the Government's Carbon Budgets, requiring further emissions reductions of 36% by 2025. The main recommendation to the Government was that it should impose a new statutory duty on local authorities to prepare at local level a Carbon Plan, "which would include a high level of ambition for emissions reductions" and focusing on emissions drivers over which local authorities have influence. The Committee stopped short of recommending that there should be binding carbon budgets at local level, which was also a possibility, considered below.

The notion that a new public duty, enforceable by law, is the answer is an interesting one but raises questions about whether it will deliver the outcome that the Committee on Climate Change actually wants.

There are different advantages and disadvantages to a new statutory duty. On the positive side, a duty gives clarity on what should be done by whom and when. It will encourage investment by the private sector, who are desperate for some indication that Government policy will not suddenly change, leaving them high and dry after having made expensive investments, as happened with feed in tariff changes for solar. It is suggested that it will help local authorities to prioritise an area that they might not otherwise prioritise. And it is suggested that hand in hand with a new duty, comes a responsibility on the part of Central Government to fund it.

On the negative side, the DCLG has pointed out that the Government's local government policy is travelling in entirely the opposite direction ie: fewer statutory duties and more discretionary powers and flexibility at local level. This does not fit with the notion of Big Society and Localism (discussed in **Chapter 4**) that it is up to the local authority, as the democratically elected body at local level, to decide what gets done and in what priority. More importantly, there is deep cynicism that accompanying funding will miraculously fail to appear and that this will simply be added to a very large pile of other statutory duties that local authorities have to fund in a very difficult financial climate.

This demonstrates that there is a complex balance to be drawn between Governmental policy in the two separate areas of local government and climate change. To introduce a new duty risks the Government being criticised for undermining its localism agenda; to leave the response as a voluntary one, risks the green lobby criticising the Government for missing a golden opportunity to push forward the energy efficiency agenda.

The simple point is this – will making it a statutory duty actually work? It may be naïve to suggest that simply because the law lays down a requirement to prepare a carbon plan, that means that local authorities will throw themselves wholeheartedly into the abating of the 20m tonnes of carbon the Committee on Climate Change report identifies it as having influence over. It could result in minimum compliance, being nothing more than a 'tick box' exercise and endless excuses as to why something or other has not been done.

Local authorities up and down the country are coming round to the benefits to them of taking action on climate change. In relation to renewable energy, those projects are being driven by two clear issues: jobs and money. In other words, the economic card trumps the green card every time. Moreover, amongst Cabinet members and Corporate Management Teams there is considerably more understanding and enthusiasm for growth and jobs, than there is for saving carbon. This raises an interesting question of why is there such an inability to engage with the political and managerial leadership of the average council on the subject of carbon?

But, instead of pondering that too much, perhaps time and effort should be put into trying to persuade local authorities of the benefits of taking voluntary action in other ways. There is, of course, a careful balance to be drawn here. It is not so much a point of principle, as a matter of what will work in practice.

It is interesting that the other alternative – local carbon budgets – appears to have been dismissed. The Climate Change Act 2008, as seen in **Chapter 3**, sets down legally binding carbon budgets, which the Government has to meet. However, below the Secretary of State, there is no formal infrastructure to assist with delivery of those plans.

In some ways, if a national total on carbon is agreed, then it would be sensible to look at the composition of this total, in both type of activity and region, and seek to allocate responsibility for contributing towards the targets.

In policy terms, it appears that the Government looks at centrally imposed carbon budgets as against its work in the localist agenda. A good argument can be made to the contrary, though, that the allocation of carbon budgets to an area is actually empowering, and very fair in terms of transferring to the area the wherewithal for making the necessary changes that will deliver them.

For now, local carbon budgets do not seem to be on the agenda. However, they will have to come at some stage in order to implement the 2008 Act properly.

Conclusion

It was stated in **Chapter 5** that every local authority and public body should have a credible climate change strategy. This should include the extent and makeup of its carbon footprint and what action is being taken to reduce this.

If a local authority is to maximise the gains it achieves, in comparison to its financial and other investment, it is essential to achieve a good balance between the three key areas of energy saving, energy efficiency and renewable energy. This is not technically difficult, but to be fully effective it requires attention to behaviour change and changing the culture of the organisation.

Few authorities seem to have addressed behaviour change in this formal sense. The concept can be looked at crudely (for example 'carrots and sticks' to encourage simple behaviour changes) or in terms of more subtle forms of education that seek to challenge deeply held values and judgements. The latter has been championed by the Worldwide Fund for Nature and results are very promising. This is one of the key areas that the public sector has to focus more upon as the climate change agenda develops.

Key Learning Points

- *It is essential to understand the climate change hierarchy in* **Figure 6.1**
- *Every local authority needs to find a balance between the three areas*
- *Saving energy is easy and is far too overlooked at present*
- *Energy efficiency is also deliverable, but has to be prioritised, with the focus on carbon as well as money*
- *Renewable energy comes after that*
- *The key renewable energy sources that are commercially proven are solar PV and thermal, wind, biomass and hydropower*
- *Others, such as deep geothermal and wave and tidal are not yet proven commercially but will come to the fore over time*
- *If the Government introduces a duty to measure carbon on the part of local authorities, this type of work will become essential*
- *What is done now depends on the authority's strategy*

Solar power

7

Introduction

Having considered the situation concerning climate change in the United Kingdom, the Government's policies in relation to it and the specific situation within local government, a local authority should now have developed a strategy for climate change and renewable energy. Viewed against the hierarchy of energy (use less, improve energy efficiency and then create new energy from renewable sources), decisions have to be taken as to where the authority's time and efforts should be focused.

Assuming that a balanced position is adopted, some renewable energy projects will need to be considered. This is where solar power comes into its own. It is definitely the easiest of the renewable energy technologies and undertaking a scheme is well within the capability of the average council. But in order to determine that solar power is the chosen one, some research into this area is required. This Chapter looks at the power of the sun and explains how solar power actually works.

The Sun's Energy

The sun is a star in the solar system. It is immensely powerful and is the root of most of life. There can be no doubt that the sun has sufficient power to meet all the needs of mankind – globally – on an ongoing basis. The issue is whether, how, and at what cost this energy can be harnessed.

Jeremy Leggett notes in his book The Solar Century, that:

"the current global power requirement is 13 TW, growing to about 20 TW in 2020 unless we get serious about energy efficiency. The amount of sunlight falling on the planet at any one time is around 120,000 TW. In other words, the amount of solar irradiance available for capture is well

over 9,000 times the global power requirement. Stated another way, if we capture a tiny fraction of 1% of that solar irradiance we could provide more power than the world currently needs."
(see The Solar Century at p9).

This is illustrated in Figure 7.1.

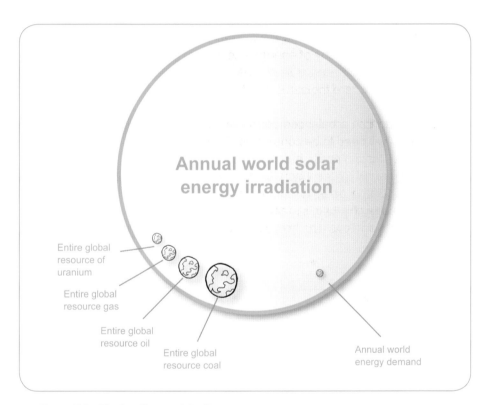

Figure 7.1 – The Irradiance of the Sun

Solar power is not, of course, new and has been used for thousands of years for a variety of purposes, including heating houses and water. The sun is also the source of many other forms of renewable energy, such as biomass, geothermal and wave and tidal energy. It also helped to create the fossil fuels that the world now relies upon so heavily.

For the modern world, there are four different types of solar energy that are relevant:

• *Passive solar – this refers to the design of buildings to make very well insulated buildings, with large, triple glazed windows that face South, together with some form of mechanical ventilation system that moves around the warm air created. It has been demonstrated that such systems can reduce the need for space heating by up to 80%.*

• *Solar thermal – this is the use of the sun to heat water and run heating systems. The solar panels contain a special fluid that absorbs the sun's heat and this is then passed through a heat exchanger to heat water. A normal domestic dwelling can obtain a high percentage of its water heating from this source*

• *Solar photovoltaic – the subject of this book. Here, as described below, the sun's rays are turned into electricity, which can then be used on site or transmitted to the electricity grid.*

• *Concentrated solar power – this might be either solar PV or solar thermal. Essentially, these systems work on the basis of concentrating the sun's rays by way of a mirror system focused on a small point, where the power is magnified many times. These systems work well in deserts and other areas nearer the Equator.*

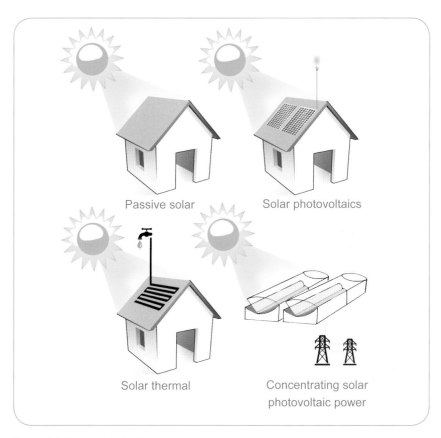

Figure 7.2 Types of Solar Power

The impact of the sun's rays on the earth is called irradiance. Levels of irradiance will differ, depending on where a person is in the world. Naturally, some parts of the world are warmer and more sunny than others. Even though solar power does not work directly from the sun – but from daylight – this will affect the level of energy that can be captured. Regard needs to be had, therefore, to the level of irradiance available for a solar project. It is often stated – erroneously – that the United Kingdom is "not sunny enough" to justify solar power. Whilst there is no doubt that European neighbours, such as Spain and Italy, do get higher levels of irradiance than the UK, the question is whether the levels are sufficient to make energy generation worthwhile.

Figure 7.3 reproduces the map of the UK with the irradiance levels illustrated. This shows that the South West and South of the country are the best places for solar power, hence the level of activity seen in Cornwall, Devon and the south coast areas from 2010 onwards. However, solar power works perfectly well in the Midlands and the North, albeit with lower levels of irradiance. The average irradiance in the UK is 800 kwh per annum of electricity, per kw of solar PV installed.

Figure 7.3 – UK irradiation and Solar Electricity Potential

United Kingdom

Yearly sum of global irradiation (kWh/m²)

<850	900	950	1000	1050	1100	1150	1200	1250	1300
<638	675	713	750	788	825	863	900	938	975

Yearly electricity generated by 1kW_peak system with performance ratio 0.75 (kWh/kW_peak)

The Science Behind Solar Photovoltaic Power

The solar photovoltaic effect was discovered in 1839 as a side effect of other photochemical experiments. The first silicon photovoltaic cell was created in the 1950's and this technology has been constantly refined since. Essentially, the process is founded on the ability of a semi-conductor to covert light into electrical energy.

The process works when the semi-conductor material absorbs light and positive and negative electrons are released. These are then extracted from the semi-conductor as electric current. Most PV cells are made from silicon, which is readily available, being able to be extracted from sand, one of the earth's most available commodities.

This effect takes place in a solar 'cell' that is usually very small and fragile. The electricity generated by a single cell is very small, but when connected together in the form of a solar panel, this output is greatly increased. The cells are also protected by being sealed in a weatherproof module consisting of a glass front, aluminium frame and protective cover.

The first uses of the more modern PV cells took place in the United States space programme, which required a lightweight and compact energy source for its satellites. This ensured that further research took place on the photovoltaic effect and how to produce more efficient solar panels.

There are different types of solar cell and these are formed into different types of solar panel. The first type is a crystalline silicon solar cell; the other type is amorphous. Crystalline cells are cut from a solid ingot of silicon whereas amorphous (also known as thin film) is made by depositing a silicon compound on to glass. Crystalline PV cells are more efficient in their translation of light into electricity, but are also more expensive. One of the main activities in the solar PV industry has been to try and increase the level of efficiency of cells, in relation to their cost.

There are two types of crystalline cell: monocrystalline and polycrystalline. Monocrystalline is the more efficient of the two, but is again more expensive. However, the price difference may mean that polychrystalline is the better choice.

Thin film does not have the same level of performance as crystalline PV cells and, despite being substantially less expensive, does not have the market penetration either. In fact, 95% of world production is currently crystalline. The development of thin film has been detrimentally affected by the constant reduction in the cost of crystalline panels. Given the choice, the latter would always be preferable. No further consideration is therefore given to thin film technology.

The final point to note is that the electrical current that is created in the photovoltaic cell and subsequently extracted as a current, is direct current (DC) not the alternating current (AC) on which the normal mains supply in the UK operates. It is therefore necessary to pass this current through an inverter, to convert it to AC supply.

A Solar PV System

Having explained that solar cells are made into solar panels to maximise the electricity generated, it is then necessary to look at solar power systems. There are two types of system: those connected to the national grid and those that are not (off grid systems). Obviously, those not connected to the grid have to use the power created on site, unless this can be stored in some form of battery arrangement. Such systems are only to be found in remote rural areas and abroad. In the UK, almost all systems will be grid connected and the comments below are predicated on that basis.

The next choice is whether the system is to be mounted on a building or free standing (also known as solar farms). This area is developed in **Chapter 12**. The majority of systems developed in the early period after Feed in Tariffs were introduced were small domestic installations fitted for householders. However, as the solar industry in the UK grew in confidence, more land-based solar farms started to be developed.

This part of the industry then mushroomed, so by 2014 it was the biggest slice of the solar market, with 46%, compared to 333% for domestic systems and 26% for other areas. This latter category contains the commercial roof market, where progress has been very slow and the Government wants to accelerate deployment. Accordingly, the focus of public policy moved towards commercial roofs in the latter part of 2014.

The following components form a buildings based solar PV system:

- *The solar panels – a combination of a number of solar cells in a weathertight package*
- *The racking – this is the equipment that attaches the solar panels to the roof of the building. Racking normally attaches to the roof structure, fitting under roof tiles in a way that does not impact on their weatherproofness*
- *Cabling – special cabling is required for solar PV systems as they work on a slightly higher current*
- *The Inverter – this converts the DC current from the panels to AC current that can be used in the building or transferred to the grid*
- *Junction box – the terminus of the wiring with a separate isolator switch*
- *The meters – a generation meter is a legal requirement, in order to measure the amount of electricity that is generated from the solar panels (and thereby claim the Feed in Tariff); an export meter may also be used (though this is not a requirement in some circumstances) to measure the electricity exported to the grid; there will also be the normal electricity meters to measure power taken out of the grid*

Figure 7.4 illustrates this in relation to a domestic PV system.

Figure 7.4 A Grid Connected Building Based PV System

It is necessary to ensure that the different components in a system actually work well together. Some inverters are preferable with some types of panel and others with others. For this reason, it is normal to contract for a 'system' and the installer will ensure that the different component parts will all work in harmony together. If separate components are purchased, there is a risk that they will not work well together.

The power ratios also need to be carefully considered. If too low a capacity inverter is linked to an array of panels, for example, maximum power output will never be achieved from those panels.

A land based solar PV system is comprised of largely the same components: panels, racking, cabling, inverters and metering. However, as **Chapter 12** illustrates, it is set out somewhat differently.

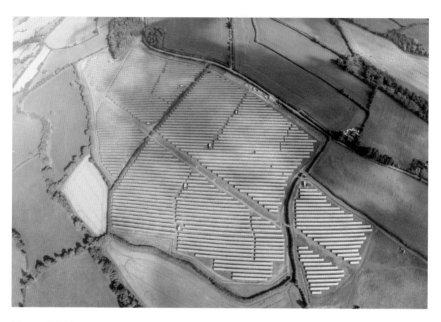

Figure 7.4 Photographs of large scale solar farms

Power and Energy

It is necessary to distinguish the two concepts of power and energy. PV systems are described using their maximum power, for example 4 kw (for a domestic system) or 5 MW (for a commercial sized solar farm). That is the maximum capacity at which the system can work and represents the rate at which energy is used. The more important element, therefore is energy, which is the actual output of the system.

So a 4 kw peak PV system in Leeds might deliver 3,200 kwh of energy per annum; a 5 MW solar farm in Cornwall might deliver 5,000 MWh of energy per annum. The reason that the energy is the key element, is that it is this number that feeds into the financial and business case calculations for the financial incentives.

Energy can be worked out and displayed in two ways

- *The first is kwh of electricity per kilowatt peak of capacity; under this method, the calculation is how many kwh of energy will be generated on average from a panel with a capacity of 1 kw peak; by using this method of measurement, it is possible to compare systems and outputs*

- *The second is kwh of electricity per square metre of panels; as the name suggests, this method uses the output from a certain area of coverage of panels*

The calculations below, when considering the business case for solar PV, use the former methodology.

Designing a Solar PV System

The purpose of a solar PV system is to translate as much daylight into electrical energy as possible. Naturally, there are a number of factors that will affect this purpose. The most commonly quoted is that a south-facing property is required. Whilst this is not actually true, it is correct to say that orientation of the property is one of the factors that will affect performance.

There are six main factors as follows:

- *Latitude*
- *Air mass*
- *Cloud cover*
- *Shading*
- *Tilt*
- *Orientation*

How well a system performs will be determined by these factors. What is more, they can all be predicted in advance as the position of the sun during its particular passage on any given day is set and does not change.

Latitude

There is not much a local authority or public body can do to change the geographical position of its land or buildings. However, if a solar investor is concerned, and there is a choice as to where to invest in a solar facility, then it is likely that the first choice would be a building or plot of land in the South. It is for this reason that there has been so much interest in solar power in the far South West of the UK. However, as suitable land for development in the South has become more scarce, the solar developers have moved further North, to such an extent that sites right up in Scotland are now being actively considered for development.

Air Mass

Air mass is the quality of the air that the daylight passes through to get to the solar panel. The air contains dust and gas particles and these will affect the solar energy as it passes through the atmosphere. Air mass increases with latitude ie: the further north a position is from the Equator; and is higher when the sun is lower in the sky.

Cloud Cover

The best weather is obviously a sunny day with clear skies. On such a day, the light passes directly through the atmosphere and into the solar panels. However, we all know the weather is often different from this ideal, particularly in the United Kingdom. So, for example, there could be clouds in the sky or it could be overcast. Here, the radiation will be less strong, although power will still be generated from the solar panels.
This point is illustrated in Figure 7.5.

It is for this reason that the European countries enjoy higher light levels than the UK.

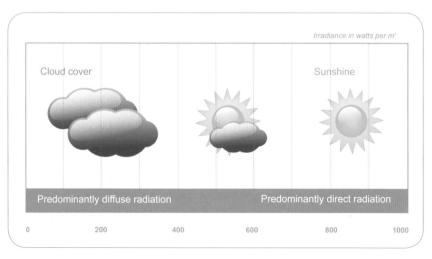

Figure 7.5 Levels of Irradiance

Shading

By definition, in order to work at maximum power, the light has to travel directly down to the solar panel. If there is an obstruction or other shading in the way, this will be a particular problem. This is the reason that solar PV panels must be sited with care.

Shading can come from anything from topography (IE: hills and valleys), trees, other buildings or features such as chimney breasts.

This may be more of a problem that is immediately apparent, due to the way that solar panels are wired up and work. Often, if one panel is shaded, it will affect the performance of all the other ones that are wired to it. This is because panels are wired together in 'strings', with the cabling joining the different panels and then feeding into the inverter. This means that if one panel is not creating a current, then there is no flow through the other panels and into the inverter and so the output from all of the affected panels will be lost. It is for this reason that systems have to be carefully designed.

The designer will usually use some form of software, such as PV Sol or PV-Syst, and this will determine where shaded areas on a roof will be an issue. As mentioned above, as the position of the sun at different parts of the day will always be known, the shading can be predicted and such areas avoided.

Tilt

The angle at which the panel faces the sun is also a key issue in relation to performance of panels. In the United Kingdom, the optimum tilt is between 30 degrees and 40 degrees, depending on latitude. This can be calculated precisely and this is one of the features of the software design systems mentioned above. The formula is latitude, minus 20 degrees. Cornwall has a latitude of 50 degrees and so the tilt should be 30 degrees. In Scotland, the latitude is nearer 60 degrees and so the tilt should be 40 degrees.

However, for a system that is being fitted to the roof of a building, it is not a simple choice of what tilt the designer wants in order to maximise performance; it is related to the pitch of the roof. A shallow roof might have a pitch of 10 degrees, whereas a steep roof might have a pitch of 50 degrees. However, the panels have to have a relationship to the pitch of the roof, both for aesthetic reasons and more generally. In other words, it would not be appropriate to put panels jutting out at a strange angle from a steep roof as this would not comply with planning or building regulation rules and would be inadvisable in any case.

Fortunately, the performance of a solar panel only reduces slightly when tilt is not maximized. If a solar panel is placed flat down on the ground, its performance will be over 80% of the maximum and so not much power is lost from a roof that is below the optimum tilt. Figure 7.6 illustrates this position.

This is another feature that is taken into account by professional design software systems for solar PV systems.

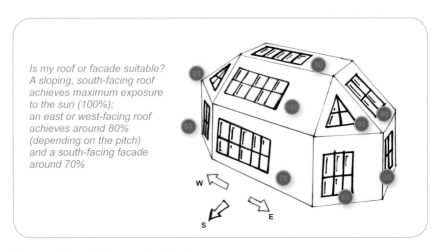

Is my roof or facade suitable? A sloping, south-facing roof achieves maximum exposure to the sun (100%); an east or west-facing roof achieves around 80% (depending on the pitch) and a south-facing facade around 70%

Figure 7.6 Orientation of Solar Panels

Orientation

The final factor is the orientation of the roof IE: which way it faces, North, South, East or West. This is referred to as the 'Azimuth' angle. As the sun rises in the East and sets in the West, a South facing orientation is preferable. The angle will change during the course of the day as the sun moves, and therefore so will the performance of the solar panel absorbing its energy. It is for this reason that free-standing solar farms, described below, often have tracking systems, where the panel actually moves with the sun to keep maximizing the orientation angle.

It is also clear from Figure 7.6 that the solar panel does not need to actually face South to attain a reasonable level of performance. This is another myth of the uninformed on solar energy, that "it doesn't work if you don't face South". In fact, roofs facing South West and South East perform to 95% of optimal output, with East or West facing roofs still offering acceptable levels of performance.

From this analysis, it can be concluded that the best solar PV system will be on a building in a southerly location, on a roof facing South, with the right degree of tilt and which is not shaded at any point. However, if some of these issues are not ideal, it may not be fatal to the design of a system. The most critical issues are shading (which can mean that the whole system is compromised) and facing North (where performance levels are lowest). But as stated above, all of this will be accommodated in a software based design system that will maximise efficiency.

Types of Solar PV System

There are two types of solar PV system: buildings based and land based. Each has different characteristics.

For buildings based systems, the key elements are the strength of the roof, orientation of the building, shading and other issues relating to performance, mentioned above. Figure 7.7 illustrates the different designs that can be accommodated on buildings. It can be seen from this that there are various options, depending on the nature of the roof.

If a flat roof is suitable, then any tilt or orientation may be possible, which would be an advantage. But the potential for penetrating the roof membrane might be problematic. Flat roofs are notorious for leaking and other problems and the buildings manager might be very unhappy at any thought of such a penetrating installation. Fortunately, this can be avoided by other means, such as a system held in place by ballast (normally rubber or concrete boots), rather than being formally fixed to the roof.

Roof lights offer a different path again and neatly illustrate the key design point, which is to design the system to fit the roof in both nature and style.

Most of the preceding comments relate to solar panels actually fitted to the roof structure. Of course, it should be borne in mind that there are also building integrated PV products (known as BIPV), such as solar PV roof tiles, where the roof is actually made from solar PV. Here, each tile plugs to the next like a giant Lego set and is then connected to the inverter. Figure 7.8 shows a photograph of a solar roof.

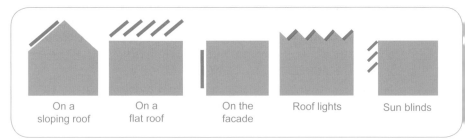

| On a sloping roof | On a flat roof | On the facade | Roof lights | Sun blinds |

Figure 7.7 Design of Solar Installations

In the future it is likely that many more integrated building products will come on to the market and become mainstream. The main reason why this has not happened yet is cost. Integrated building products cost significantly more than basic solar panels and so the business case is substantially different. However, just in the way that solar panel costs have fallen as the industry has taken off in the UK, so will new integrated products be designed and launched. This has to be a good thing and building products will also be promoted heavily through Green Deal, mentioned in **Chapter 3**.

Figure 7.8 – A Solar Roof in the UK

In the future it is likely that many more integrated building products will come on to the market and become mainstream. The main reason why this has not happened yet is cost. Integrated building products cost significantly more than basic solar panels and so the business case is substantially different. However, just in the way that solar panel costs have fallen as the industry has taken off in the UK, so will new integrated products be designed and launched. This has to be a good thing and building products will also be promoted heavily through Green Deal, mentioned in **Chapter 3**.

Turning to land based systems, in this context, there is not a great deal to say. As the panels are in a field, they can be faced any way that is appropriate and the racking designed to offer precisely the right degree of tilt. Fields well chosen will not suffer from shading and the main areas chosen to date for such solar farms have been in the South or South West of the country.

The main issue with solar farms is the size of the array and whether to choose static panels or tracking systems. Arrays can be any size within reason, for example, 100 standard sized panels on a platform to form an array; or racks that are only one panel high, in portrait formation, but extend for hundreds of metres in length. This is mainly a commercial and design decision.

The choice of fixed or tracking systems is more interesting. Tracker systems come in two varieties – East to West (or horizontal tracking systems) or up and down (vertical tracking systems) or both. The idea of the system is that it moves with the sun during the day and therefore maintains the absolute maximum orientation angle for as long as possible. This can increase the efficiency by up to 20%. As the position of the sun is always predictable in advance, such systems can be programmed very accurately.

However, tracking systems are considerably more expensive than fixed panels. One of the main advantages of solar PV is that there are no moving parts and there is therefore very little maintenance. Tracking systems, by definition, introduce moving parts and a level of maintenance complexity that would not otherwise exist. This is therefore an important decision. The general view of the solar industry in the UK is that tracker panels are not worth the extra cost, bearing in mind the additional efficiency that they deliver in this climate. Notwithstanding this, there are some examples of tracking panels in operation in the UK.

Other issues for solar farms, include security, metering and grid connection. On the security front, it is relatively difficult to steal a solar panel from a roof, but substantially easier from a ground mounted bracket. The value of panels is high, particularly when concentrated in such numbers as exist in a solar farm, which might also be in a remote, rural location. Theft is therefore a risk and security will have to be planned. This might be by fencing, CCTV or whatever means, but may also impact on other areas, such as planning permission. It is unlikely that a pretty site in an Area of Outstanding Natural Beauty would be permitted to have a 12-foot razor-wire fence around a solar farm. There is normally an alternative, though, and perhaps a natural thorn hedge might be acceptable to the planning authority and be equally effective.

Metering will also be a little different for solar farms, where the supply is all being transmitted into the national grid. Some form of inverter cabinets and meter housing will need to be added to the site for this purpose.

The grid connection will also be an issue for land based systems and this is considered in **Chapter 12.**

The Business Case for a Solar Installation

The main decision in relation to any installation is to determine whether it is economically viable. In order to determine this, it is necessary to gather the information assembled above in relation to capacity and efficiency of the installation and calculate the financial return.

However, before turning to this aspect, it should not be forgotten that there are numerous other, non-financial, benefits from a renewable energy installation. These should also be taken into account in deciding whether to proceed and are considered in **Chapter 5**.

The key areas to determine the business case are the cost of the panels and other equipment and the income from use or sale of the electricity and the Government's financial incentives.

The Cost of Systems

The cost of solar PV panels has been falling consistently for a number of years now. The market that was formerly dominated by the European manufacturers is now dominated by Chinese and US production. The Chinese have invested millions of pounds in state of the art new factories and have taken over the production of silicon, the main element on which the cells are based.

The solar panels are approximately 60% of the cost of a system and so the vast reductions in the cost of the panels means that the overall system prices have tumbled.

The usual method of comparing costs is on the basis of 'price per kw installed.' This means that if a 4 kw retrofit system costs £12,000, the cost is £4,000 per kw installed. Once in possession of this figure, it can be used to compare prices at any scale of installation.

Prices in 2010 could be as high as £4,000 per kw installed. During the early years of the Feed in Tariffs, the prices travelled down through £3,000 per kw installed to £2,000 and during 2014 fell to the £1,000 per kw installed mark.

This means that a 4 kw peak system costing £12,000 in 2010, would cost approximately half of that amount in 2012 and in 2014 might be as low as £5,000 (subject to precise details).

Following the completion of the Chinese anti dumping action (against which the European Union took action in 2014), prices are expected to reduce again by a significant margin.

Calculating the Return

This starts by working out the irradiance. The maximum irradiance available – at noon during good weather conditions – is 1,000 watts per square metre (1,000 W/m2). This is the benchmark against which performance is gauged. This means that a 250 W panel will only make 250 watts of power at 1,000 W/m2. As conditions are likely to be less than this, a different value will be achieved. These values can be predicted using design software for solar PV systems.

As mentioned above, there are two ways that the output of a solar panel can be reported: the first is kwh of energy produced per kw peak of capacity; and the second is kwh of energy produced per square metre of panels.

The example below uses the former of these methods. This is based on a 4 kw peak retrofit system, using 16 x 250 watt Sharp monocrystalline PV panels, fitted to a house in Leeds. The system cost £12,000 in 2011.

The estimated return is 800 kwh of electricity per kwp for this part of the country, which means that the total estimated output of the system per annum is just short of 3,200 kwh.

The Feed in Tariff at the time of fitting in 2011 was 43 pence per kwh of electricity generated (the generation tariff) and 3 pence per kwh of electricity put into the grid (the export tariff). The estimated business case is therefore calculated in Figure 7.9 opposite.

Under OFGEM rules, for domestic systems it was permitted to 'deem' that 50% of the electricity was passed into the grid, without having a dedicated export meter.

• **Expenditure**

£12,000 fitted

• **Income**

3,200 (kwh) x 43 p (FIT/generation) = £1376 pa
3,200 (kwh) x 50% (deemed export) x 3 p (FIT/export) = £48 pa
Use of electricity generated - 1000 kwh at 12 p per kwh, delivering a further saving of £120
Total income = £1, 544 per annum

Payback – 8 – 9 years
Return on capital – 14 %

Figure 7.9 – Business Case for a 4 kw PV system

This calculation is included here to illustrate how the power and other characteristics of a solar PV system will impact on the financial and business case. More detail is given in relation to the development of business cases, particularly in the commercial context, in **Chapter 9**.

Conclusion

The solar photovoltaic marketplace in the UK has boomed in the years 2010 to 2012, fuelled mainly by the Government's financial incentives.

Solar Power Portal has reported that over 1 GW of solar PV was installed in just over eighteen months after the introduction of the Feed in Tariff in April 2010. By 2014 this total had rapidly expanded to 5 GW IE 5,000 megawatts. Of this total, the vast majority of the early systems were small domestic systems, fitted by householders wishing to take advantage of the generous Feed in Tariff rates, with the second phase being large solar farms.

However, just as the introduction of generous Feed in Tariff rates fuelled the market, the reduction in those rates in 2012 undermined it. As **Chapter 8** reveals, installation plunged when the rates were slashed and this caused some concerns in the solar industry.

However, the financial elements are only one part of a solar PV scheme and the technology itself is sound, well tested, commercial proven and relatively straightforward to install. As such, any local authority that intends to pursue a renewable energy strategy should have solar PV in its portfolio.

Key Learning Points

- *Solar power is one of the oldest forms of renewable energy*
- *The irradiance of the sun is immense*
- *Solar PV cells turn daylight into electricity using a silicon semi-conductor*
- *There are different types of solar PV cell*
- *Different factors affect performance, including latitude, tilt and shading*
- *PV systems need to be professionally designed to maximise their output*

Introduction

"Wrexham Solar capital of the UK", "flagship solar panel scheme to power 3,000 houses" and "ambitious solar project, the first of its kind in the UK". These are just some of the headlines that have been used to describe Wrexham's solar scheme, which has seen Wrexham transform into a pioneering local authority area at the forefront of renewable energy deployment.

I was assigned project management responsibility for this ambitious scheme, and have led the project from its inception in the Winter of 2010, right the way through to the final solar panel being fitted in Spring 2012. From initial business case development, to tender evaluation, to the curious encounters in attempting to access 3,000 properties in only six months; this project can only be described as a turbulent journey.

The end result however is a flagship scheme which has delivered wide ranging benefits and one which is now looked upon enviably by other local authorities and housing associations up and down the UK. Having recently completed the project, now is a timely opportunity for me to reflect on the project as a whole, step back from the subsuming day to day project management activities, and evaluate what we have done, why we did it and what have been the key challenges along the way. Another relevant question I will also briefly consider is whether I would do it all again, at which point I will pick out a few hints and tips others may wish to consider if planning a similar scheme.

The starting point for this project and the bedrock on which it was founded was the development of a comprehensive business case and supporting economic appraisal. This identified the potential size and scope of the project, the key risks, the landscape within the solar industry, market research, technical appraisals and of course the anticipated costs and

FIT income over a 25 year period. Although this business case has continually evolved and contained an element of modelling/forecasting, it has proved to be the central reference point in guiding the delivery of the project.

The business case also proved to be pivotal in securing buy-in both politically and at strategic management level within the organisation. Many difficult decisions were made during the course of the project, most notably during the unexpected, premature review of FIT's. Adjusting the model and regularly presenting its contents to elected members ensured that commitment to the project was maintained despite the hype surrounding the FIT review.

Further reflection on the project supports and justifies the decision that the council took to engage professional technical and legal advice/ support. Limited internal capacity would have undermined the ability to undertake an expedient accelerated procurement process. In addition to this, the necessity to have sound legal advice underpinned with industry leading technical guidance required the council to look externally. This comprehensive and commercial approach leads me to think of the mantra "you only get out what you put in". This is relevant on two levels; in terms of effort and commitment and also in resourcing the project.

Why Wrexham? Why Solar?

This is a very interesting question and the answer may come as a surprise to some.

The initial driver behind this scheme was carbon reduction. In 2009 the council decided that reducing carbon was one of its top three priorities. This meant that specific focus and resource was to be directed to this area.

However, although such intentions are clearly commendable, as soon as the business case for this project was developed it quickly became apparent that cash (in the form of FIT income) as well as carbon was driving this project. Staying with the driving theme, it could be said that carbon reduction aspirations started the engine, whilst potential long term FIT income provided the fuel to drive the car.

Only as the project progressed and its actual size and scale became clearer, did the other benefits of the scheme become truly understood. Once understood however they provided the catalyst to continue with the project and ensure delivery in the face of a volatile and changeable FIT system. If carbon and cash were the only drivers, I sense that the project may have ended prematurely in the wake of changes to FIT in December 2011.

Project delivery achievements

In the most simple of terms, the project has delivered what it set out to achieve; to install up to 3,000 homes with solar PV panels within an ambitiously short time scale. However, when I consider the range of resultant benefits, it makes me wonder why many more local authorities have not done something very similar. As the project took shape it became apparent that it ticks all of the right boxes in relation to national policy and priority areas, including:

- *Carbon reduction (up to 3000 tonnes annually)*
- *Long term sustainable income generation (via FIT payments)*
- *Economic stimulation (job creation) and invigorating local supply chains*
- *Addressing social inequality issues / reducing fuel poverty*
- *Raising the profile and improving the reputation of the Council*
- *Improving the skills base of the local workforce (through training opportunities)*

The list could go on, yet each one of the above achievements would on their own constitute a solid platform and sound rationale for embarking on a multi-million pound capital expenditure scheme. The fact that Wrexham's scheme delivers on all of these levels is a testament to the potential of the renewable energy sector within the UK.

Challenges/Risks

In managing the delivery of this project I have encountered a series of different risks and challenges. Being prepared to tackle these risks head on and having the support to do so is essential when managing the impacts. Referral back to the business case and economic appraisal will inform how effectively the risks are being managed. Being open and transparent about the risks is something else I would advocate.

The unique nature of the scheme in Wrexham meant that the risks were often changing on a daily basis, thanks in no small part to the FIT review. Without wanting to deter any would be solar scheme I think it is important to highlight some of the other key risk areas. Rather than acting as a deterrent, I hope that sharing these risks will allow other organisations to learn from the experiences in Wrexham, and develop an informed approach to delivering a scheme. These risks include:

- *Un-established solar PV market within the uk*
- *Equipment specifications*
- *Equipment performance*
- *Unknown project mobilisation and delivery costs*
- *Suitability of property portfolio*
- *Adverse weather conditions*
- *Suitably qualified installers*
- *Accessing properties*
- *Accessing finance to deliver the scheme*

Engaging your residents

It is so important to effectively engage and communicate with tenants that I have decided to dedicate a short section to this aspect of project delivery.

What might be perceived as a "win, win, win" project from a local government officer perspective, may be seen as an inconvenience, waste of time, money and effort to a council tenant.

Raising awareness about solar PV, explaining its benefits, and why the council is investing in this technology was a key aspect of the comprehensive and proactive approach to resident engagement during Wrexham's solar scheme. A variety of different tools and techniques were used to secure this engagement, including open days, leaflets, production of an awareness raising DVD and the appointment of tenant liaison officers. Despite all of these good intentions some tenants still did not buy into the project. This is always to be expected and my expectation levels when engaging with certain tenants has certainly decreased over the past 18 months.

Equally important is the ability to engage with tenants and residents not within the scope of the project. Unfortunately, solar PV is not an all inclusive technology, and cannot simply be rolled out across an entire housing stock. In Wrexham we took a simple, yet relatively effective approach to managing the negative press that surfaced in relation to residents not receiving PV. We tried to cushion the blow by offering an alternative, low cost gesture to those residents that were not benefiting from the scheme.

Would I go through this again?

The project has been rewarding and pioneering on so many levels and I certainly see a bright future for renewable energy schemes.

The benefits are there for all to see, and in all honesty can no longer be regarded as an unwelcome distraction from the day job. Pressures for local authorities to innovate, generate their own income streams, manage their environmental responsibility and address social issues within their area will ensure that renewable energy schemes are forced higher up the agenda and given far more priority and consideration.

The key to turning these pressures into tangible, deliverable projects will of course vary amongst organisations. What I can confidently assert, is that for solar schemes to succeed, there needs to be top down commitment, a professional approach to business case development, robust communication channels, reputable contractors, high quality equipment and also.....a fair degree of good fortune.

Jonathan Edwards
Service Development Manager / Solar PV Project Manager
Wrexham County Borough Council

Financial incentives from the government

Introduction

The Government policy that is described in **Chapter 3** is dependent on a number of different drivers, often referred to as 'carrots' and 'sticks'. This obvious reference is to legal obligations and targets (the sticks) and incentives of some sort (carrots).

Financial incentives are the lynchpin of the positive side of these levers. They are the real driver of deployment in renewable energy technologies. The reason is finance: solar PV is still more expensive than brown energy from the electricity grid and the financial incentive makes up the gap. In other words it helps to remove the financial disincentive to pay extra for green energy.

The nature and extent of the financial incentive is therefore key to finding the balance between providing a reasonable return on investment – and therefore persuading people to do it – as opposed to being over generous and not offering value for money on the public purse. It is this balance that the Government struggled with in the early days of the Feed in Tariff regime.

The UK Government is not, however, alone in this. More than 70 'feed in tariff 'type schemes exist across the world and most were already in operation in 2010 when the UK scheme was launched. The precedents from those schemes were quite clear: fast deployment attracted by the financial incentives, often followed by a necessity to cut back on the tariff rates. So tariffs clearly worked in actually getting renewables deployed – see Spain, Germany and Italy as examples. But with some pain if the rates were not accurately determined and had to be curtailed at short notice – again, see Spain as an example. It is disappointing that the Government did not learn these lessons in advance from the pain of other countries, rather than learning the hard way, which is effectively what it did. Feed in Tariffs are examined in detail in this Chapter.

However, Feed in Tariffs (FITs) are not the only financial incentive in play in the UK. The idea of incentives for renewable energy generation have been in operation since the early 1990's, but the Renewable Obligation (RO) was intended for larger projects and its operation is more complex. With the Government's intention to move to a system of decentralised energy, often being produced at domestic scale, it was necessary to introduce a separate financial incentive for this.

The Renewable Obligation has its own system of reviews and has introduced 'banding' as a way of incentivising certain technologies above others. Until 2014, the RO was available for solar at any level above 50kw. However, from 2015, it will only be available from 50 kw to 5 MW and above that it will not apply.

The Renewables Obligation is due to be phased out from 2017 in any event and replaced by a new system of FITs with Contracts for Difference (CFD). This is intended to apply to all large-scale renewables from 2017, but its introduction has been expedited for large scale solar PV as the Renewables Obligation is being removed from 2015. Solar PV is the only technology where the RO will not apply in this way until 2017.

There is also a big push in relation to renewable heat, as part of the national policies outlined in **Chapter 3**. Here a third financial incentive has been introduced, namely the Renewable Heat Incentive, which operates as a sort of FIT for heat. This not dealt with in this book and both the RO and contracts for difference are only touched on briefly, as the majority of the projects that are the main subject of this book will be under the Feed In Tariffs regime.

Types of Financial Incentive

The purpose of the financial incentives is to encourage more organizations to generate energy from renewable sources and in so doing, the Government achieves its policy aims of greenhouse gas reductions and other matters. However, they are intended to support the widespread deployment of proven technologies, not to support research and development into new areas.

There are three financial incentives to choose from, two in relation to electricity and one in relation to renewable heat:

- *The Renewables Obligation (RO). The Government has described this as "a complex scheme intended for professionals in the energy sector"*
- *The feed in tariff contracts for difference regime (CFDs) for large scale renewable energy projects*
- *The Feed in Tariff (FIT). This is for smaller schemes (under 5 MW)*
- *The Renewable Heat Incentive (RHI). This is for heat from renewable sources*

The issue of choice needs to be understood, as there are legal rules applicable. In particular, it is not possible to choose ROs or FITs at every level.

The first point to note is that the FIT regime only applies up to a capacity of 5 MW. Over and above this, the RO will apply until the end of March 2015 and thereafter the CFD regime has to be used. This is because an installation over 5 MW is a large installation and would therefore normally be operated by a professional generator. However, for PV installations under 5MW, there is a choice between the RO or FITs (or CFDs for that matter) but only down to 50 kw.

The Renewables Obligation Order 2009 states that Renewables Obligation Certificates (ROCs) will not be issued to PV micro-generators, which is defined as stations with a declared net capacity of 50kW or less (article 17B). Accordingly, below 50kw the FIT regime alone has to apply. However, above 50kW, but below 5MW at which stage FITs cannot be claimed, the generator must choose between ROCs and FITs (article 17D). However, it should be noted that this is a one-time only choice and cannot be changed thereafter. **Chapter 9** looks at business cases for both FITs and ROCs. **Chapter 12** looks at the type of installations. When over 5 MW, only CFDs will apply from 2015, although the RO is available for a period before then.

Whilst the RO does exist in all parts of the UK, the scheme in England and Wales is different to that in Scotland and Northern Ireland. In England and Wales the Renewables Obligation Order 2009 (**SI 2009 No X**) applies.

The CFDs regime is very different to the Renewables Obligation and is a new move by the Government to balance what it pays out in financial incentives with the rewards being made by those who develop schemes. CFDs is a more subtle mechanism, as explained below, that should ensure that the Government does not pay too much.

The Renewables Obligation

This was one of the first financial incentives and has been in place since the early 1990's, having followed the Non Fossil Fuels Obligation (NFFO) and was introduced using powers in the Electricity Act 1989. The original impetus for this initiative came from the EU and its Renewable Energy Directive.

The RO is the Government's chief mechanism for incentivising renewable electricity generation in the UK. As illustrated by **Chapter 3**, it is also an important part of the Government's programme for securing reductions in carbon dioxide emissions, working in support of other policy measures such as the EU Emissions Trading System.

The RO basically requires electricity suppliers to source an increasing proportion of their electricity from renewable sources, or pay a buy-out price. The obligation rises each year, beginning at 3% in 2002/3 and rising to 15% in 2015.

Since introduction in 2002 it has led to more than a doubling of the proportion of electricity sales attributable to eligible renewables in the UK (from 1.8% in 2002 to 4.4% in 2006), and in its current form is expected to deliver the 15% renewable electricity target by 2015.

Many of the aspects that are familiar from the FITs will be the same here. OFGEM supervises the regime and 'grandfathering' principles will apply

IE: once a generator registers a system under the RO, cover will not change for the period of the arrangement, which is usually 20 years.

The RO requires electricity suppliers to match a percentage of their electricity supplies with ROCs. When the system started, it was 1 ROC certificate per 1 MW of electricity (it is MW and not kw as larger schemes are covered). However, this was subsequently changed with 'banding' being introduced, as discussed below. These ROC certificates can be obtained by a company undertaking its own generation from renewable sources; by buying ROC certificates from other generators; or by paying into a 'buyout fund' at a fixed price set in February each year that increases with inflation (in 2014 the buyout price was £45 per ROC); or a mixture of these routes.

If suppliers choose to pay the buyout price to fulfil part, or all, of their obligation this money goes into a 'buyout fund'. The money in the buyout fund is then redistributed back to suppliers by OFGEM, according to the number of ROCs a supplier has used towards its obligation. The price that a ROC will command will therefore be a combination of the expected buyout recycle value and the avoidance of the buyout price. ROCs have hovered about the £50 per MW area for some time, equating to approximately 5 pence per kwh.

A number of changes have been made to the Renewables Obligation over the years. Of particular importance is the new system of 'banding' introduced in 2009. This has the effect of promoting new technology areas and helps meet development costs, for example for wave and tidal technology, by providing a higher reward. Under the banding system, some technologies were given proportionately greater reward, for example, wave and tidal qualified for two ROCs per MWh, solar PV two ROCs per MWh and offshore wind 1.5 ROCs per MWh. This simply meant that whatever the value of a ROC certificate is at that time, it was multiplied by the appropriate value. This is illustrated in practical terms by **Figure 9.5**.

When banding was introduced into the Renewables Obligation in April 2009, the Department of Energy and Climate Change committed to review support levels every four years. The most recent consultation on the UK Renewables Banding Review proposals closed in 2012, with new bands proposed to take effect in law on 1 April 2013. Under these provisions, offshore wind gets 2 ROCs per MWh and onshore wind 0.9 ROCs per MWh.

However, when the banding exercise started in 2012, the Government made clear that solar PV was not included in the main exercise, as solar prices had continued to fall and the Government therefore wanted to undertake a specific exercise in relation to solar PV.

The Consultation was undertaken in the summer of 2012 and the announcements made in December 2012. The decision was taken to cut solar tariffs by 20%, with the former 2 ROCs being reduced to 1.6 ROCs on 1 April 2013. The level would then drop to 1.4 ROCs for 2014/15, 1.3 ROCs for 2015/16 and 1.2 ROCs in 2016/17.

The Government's specific solar PV review also recommended the introduction of a new ROC banding, specifically for buildings based solar PV. Hitherto, all solar PV had been in the same band. But from 2013, it was decided the buildings bandings under the RO should be: 1.7 ROCs from 2013/14; 1.6 ROCs from 2014/15; 1.5 ROCs from 2015/16; and 1.4 ROCs from 2016/17.

It is also noted in **Chapter 11** is that from April 2017, the Renewables Obligation is due to be closed to new projects due to the introduction of the Feed In Tariff with Contracts for Difference under the proposed Electricity Market Reform process. Existing projects already on the Renewables Obligation Certificates system will be unaffected by the closure of the scheme and will remain on this system until the closure of the scheme in 2037. The Government specifically wanted to confirm that the Renewables Obligation would last until 2037, in order to give certainty to the market.

So in 2013, the solar PV industry believed that the banding processes were complete and the Government confirmed that it did not intend to have any further banding reviews before the closure of the RO in 2017. It was therefore greeted with shock, when the Government announced in 2014 that it proposed closing the RO altogether for solar PV projects over 5 MW from 1 April 2015. A consultation paper was issued on 13 May 2014 and the Government blamed the run on the Levy Control Framework budget as the reason. It is true to say that in the intervening years, land based solar PV projects had really got going in the UK and many hundreds of MW of capacity was being fitted. This caused the Government alarm and it was felt that it had to put a brake on this market. The best way that it could come up with to do this was to take away the main financial incentive that such schemes relied upon.

The announcements were made on 2 October and the Government confirmed that it would proceed with its proposed action. It did make clear, however, that the changes would only take effect on 1 April 2015 and there would be a 'grace' period for projects that were planned to complete before the deadline, but were held up due to grid connection problems. Moreover, the Government stressed that these changes did not remove all support for solar PV projects, as the contracts for difference regime was available. However, as is explained below, this was very new and untested and it was far from clear whether any support would be forthcoming either, due to the way in which the CFDs regime works.

The uncertainty about financial incentives is not limited to the RO. In many ways, the developments under FITs, described below, illustrate even more graphically how the Government has grappled with the dilemma of encouraging more renewable energy development but trying not to pay too much for it. From the industry side, the uncertainty is difficult to deal with in business planning terms and it claims that this damages growth. The main issue is to keep financial incentives in place from the Government until grid parity can be reached in the UK, whereupon it will be no longer necessary.

Contracts for Difference

Contracts for Difference were only introduced in 2014. However, their introduction had been planned for some time before that. It was the enactment of the Energy Act 2013 that paved the way for the formal regime to come into being.

CFDs are complex instruments and the few comments below are nothing more than a basic introduction to the subject. This is because few if any local authorities will go down this route for solar PV installations and none had done so at the publication of the second edition of this work in 2015.

They were introduced to replace the Renewables Obligation, which closes to new entrants in the Spring of 2017. In the period between the RO ending and the CFD regime taking over, generators will have a 'once only' choice as to which regime they come under. Once chosen, this cannot be changed.

However, it is not really relevant to solar PV any more, as the Government changed the rules in 2014 to close the RO to large scale solar PV from April 2015. This means that a local authority that wants to build a solar farm in excess of 5 MW capacity from 1 April 2015, would have to use the CFD mechanism. Most have chosen to reduce the size of their installations to 5 MW instead.

The new scheme is different in operation to the Renewables Obligation and was introduced as part of the Electricity Market Reform process. Under that the Government expects CFDs to work in tandem with the Capacity Market and he Emissions Performance Standard to deliver its aims and objectives of decarbonisation.

The aim of the CFD mechanism is to work alongside the project chains of developers of renewable energy projects, incentivising without dictating how to run the project. However, there is a clever mechanism built into the DNA of the model that means that the Government will pay less subsidy as electricity prices rise.

This is because there is a 'strike price' and a 'reference price' laid down. Generators will still sell their electricity into the marketplace as normal, under a Power Purchase Agreement, and be paid for that power. However, the incentive will operate on where that price lays between the strike price and the reference price. Where the strike price is higher than the reference price, the generator will be paid the difference. Where the strike price is lower than the reference price, the generator will pay that excess back to the counterparty body.

The strike prices are set down by the Government, and announcements were made in 2014 with the early strike prices set down. Solar PV was given a strike price of £115 per MWh. These prices have been set by DECC to reflect the cost of investing in a particular low carbon technology. The reference price, on the other hand, is a measure of the average market price payable for electricity at a particular point in time. As mentioned above, this means that if electricity prices are high, the Government is not paying any subsidy as the generator is deemed to be getting its investment costs met from the sale of the electricity. However, if they are lower, then the financial incentives kick in.

In order to operate the system, the Government has set up the Low Carbon Contracts Company, which will be the counterparty body for the CFD contract. The LCCC has now been designated as the CFD counterparty by the regulations and is working closely with National Grid, chosen as the Delivery Body and OFGEM, the industry regulator.

The other notable element of the system is that it is competitive, if there are more applications than budget to meet them. The first auctions process was held in the Autumn of 2014 and did include solar PV. There was heavy criticism from the solar PV industry because solar PV was put into the same 'pot' as more established technologies, such as onshore wind. However, offshore wind and biomass were put in different pots, with better prospects of getting funding.

This CFD mechanism is contained in the Energy Act 2013 and a host of other regulations (secondary legislation) made beneath the primary statutory provisions. Any local authority that is contemplating using the CFD mechanism should take detailed legal advice.

Feed in Tariffs (FITs)

The Policy Behind Feed in Tariffs

The Government published a consultation paper in 2009 entitled Consultation on Renewable Electricity Financial Incentives 2009. It stated that:

"The Renewables Obligation has mostly succeeded in encouraging investment from professional energy companies in large-scale renewables projects. A new system of Feed in Tariffs will provide support aimed at small low-carbon generators. This will open up low-carbon electricity generation beyond the traditional energy companies, making it more cost effective for communities and householders to take part."

It makes clear that most investors are looking for a rate of return on their investments. The levels of FIT rates proposed in the paper were "calculated to ensure that the total benefits that an investor can be expected to achieve – from the generation tariff, the export tariff and /or the offsetting benefit – should compensate the investor for the costs of the installation as well as provide such a rate of return."

It was on that basis that the scheme was developed and eventually launched in April the following year.

The legal powers for all financial incentives are set down in legislation. The Energy Act 2008 contains the legal authority for the FIT regime. As normal, the primary legislation contains only the basic power to introduce a system; the remaining detail is provided by secondary legislation. Accordingly, the Feed in Tariffs (Specified Maximum Capacity and Functions) Order 2010 was the first Statutory Instrument containing the relevant provisions. This was amended by three more separate Statutory Instruments in 2012.

The Background

FITs came into force in April 2010. The Government had published a table, reproduced as **Figure 8.1** on the next page, showing the various tariff rates for the various technologies covered. The best rate for solar PV was a domestic sized 4kw system, retrofitted to a domestic property. There, 43.3 pence per kilowatt hour of energy was payable.

Figure 8.1 Table of generation tariffs to 2020

Technology	Scale Scheme Year	Tariff level for new installations in period (p/kWh) (NB tariffs will be inlated annually)										
		1 1/4/10-31/3/11	2 to 31/3/12	3 to 31/3/13	4 to 31/3/14	5 to 31/3/15	6 to 31/3/16	7 to 31/3/17	8 to 31/3/18	9 to 31/3/19	10 to 31/3/20	11 to 31/3/21	
Anaerobic digestion	<500kW	11.5	11.5	11.5	11.5	11.5	11.5	11.5	11.5	11.5	11.5	11.5	20
Anaerobic digestion	>500kW	9.0	9.0	9.0	9.0	9.0	9.0	9.0	9.0	9.0	9.0	9.0	20
Hydro	<15kW	19.9	19.9	19.9	19.9	19.9	19.9	19.9	19.9	19.9	19.9	19.9	20
Hydro	>15-100 kW	17.8	17.8	17.8	17.8	17.8	17.8	17.8	17.8	17.8	17.8	17.8	20
Hydro	100 kW>2 MW	11.0	11.0	11.0	11.0	11.0	11.0	11.0	11.0	11.0	11.0	11.0	20
Hydro	>2MW-5 MW	4.5	4.5	4.5	4.5	4.5	4.5	4.5	4.5	4.5	4.5	4.5	20
MicroCHP pilot	<2 kW*	10*	10*	10*	10*	10*	10*	10*	10*	10*	10*	10*	10
PV	<4 kW (new build**)	36.1	36.1	33.0	30.2	27.6	25.1	22.9	20.8	19.0	17.2	15.7	25
PV	<4 kW (retroit**)	41.3	41.3	37.8	34.6	31.6	28.8	26.2	23.8	21.7	19.7	18.0	25
PV	>4-10kW	36.1	36.1	33.0	30.2	27.6	25.1	22.9	20.8	19.0	17.2	15.7	25
PV	>10-100kW	31.4	31.4	28.7	26.3	24.0	21.9	19.9	18.1	16.5	15.0	13.6	25
PV	>100kW-5MW	29.3	29.3	26.8	24.5	22.4	20.4	18.6	16.9	15.4	14.0	12.7	25
PV	Stand alone system**	29.3	29.3	26.8	24.5	22.4	20.4	18.6	16.9	15.4	14.0	12.7	25
Wind	<1.5kW	34.5	34.5	32.6	30.8	29.1	27.5	26.0	24.6	23.2	21.9	20.7	20
Wind	>1.5-15kW	26.7	26.7	25.5	24.3	23.2	22.2	21.2	20.2	19.3	18.4	17.6	20
Wind	>15-100kW	24.1	24.1	23.0	21.9	20.9	20.0	19.1	18.2	17.4	16.6	15.9	20
Wind	>100-500kW	18.8	18.8	18.8	18.8	18.8	18.8	18.8	18.8	18.8	18.8	18.8	20
Wind	>500kW-1.5MW	9.4	9.4	9.4	9.4	9.4	9.4	9.4	9.4	9.4	9.4	9.4	20
Wind	>1.5MW-5kW	4.5	4.5	4.5	4.5	4.5	4.5	4.5	4.5	4.5	4.5	4.5	20
Existing microgenerators transferred from the RO		9.0	9.0	9.0	9.0	9.0	9.0	9.0	9.0	9.0	9.0	9.0	to 2027

* Note the microCHIP pilot will support up to 30,000 installations with a review to start when the 12,000th installation has occurred

** "Retrofit" means installed on a building which is already occupied; "New Build" means where installed on a new building before first occupation; "Stand-alone" means not attached to a building and not wired to provide electricity to an occupied building

Figure 8.2 Feed-in Tariff Payment Rate Table for Photovoltaic Eligible Installations for FIT (1 April 2014-31 March 2015)

Description	For Eligible Installations with an Eligibility Date on or After 1 April 2014 and before 1 July 2014 (p/kWh)			For Eligible Installations with an Eligibility Date on or After 1 July 2014 and before 1 October 2014 (p/kWh)			For Eligible Installations with an Eligibility Date on or After 1 October 2014 and before 31 December 2014 (p/kWh)			For Eligible Installations with an Eligibility Date on or After 1 January 2015 and before 31 March 2015 (p/kWh)		
Solar photovoltaic with Total Installed Capacity of 4kW or less, where attached to or wired to provide electricity to a new building before first occupation	Higher rate	Middle rate	Lower rate	Higher rate	Middle rate	Lower rate	Higher rate	Middle rate	Lower rate	Higher rate	Middle rate	Lower rate
	14.38	12.94	6.61	14.38	12.94	6.38	14.38	12.94	6.38	13.88	12.49	6.38
Solar photovoltaic with Total Installed Capacity of 4kW or less, where attached to or wired to provide electricity to a building which is already occupied	Higher rate	Middle rate	Lower rate	Higher rate	Middle rate	Lower rate	Higher rate	Middle rate	Lower rate	Higher rate	Middle rate	Lower rate
	14.38	12.94	6.61	14.38	12.94	6.38	14.38	12.94	6.38	13.88	12.49	6.38
Solar photovoltaic (other than stand-alone) with Total Installed Capacity greater than 4kW but not exceeding 10kW	Higher rate	Middle rate	Lower rate	Higher rate	Middle rate	Lower rate	Higher rate	Middle rate	Lower rate	Higher rate	Middle rate	Lower rate
	13.03	11.73	6.61	13.03	11.73	6.38	13.03	11.73	6.38	12.57	11.32	6.38
Solar photovoltaic (other than stand-alone) with Total Installed Capacity greater than 10kW but not exceeding 50kW	Higher rate	Middle rate	Lower rate	Higher rate	Middle rate	Lower rate	Higher rate	Middle rate	Lower rate	Higher rate	Middle rate	Lower rate
	12.13	10.92	6.61	12.13	10.92	6.38	12.13	10.92	6.38	11.71	10.54	6.38
Solar photovoltaic (other than stand-alone) with Total Installed Capacity greater than 50kW but not exceeding 100kW	Higher rate	Middle rate	Lower rate	Higher rate	Middle rate	Lower rate	Higher rate	Middle rate	Lower rate	Higher rate	Middle rate	Lower rate
	10.71	9.64	6.61	10.34	9.31	6.38	10.34	9.31	6.38	10.34	9.31	6.38
Solar photovoltaic (other than stand-alone) with Total Installed Capacity greater than 100kW but not exceeding 150kW	Higher rate	Middle rate	Lower rate	Higher rate	Middle rate	Lower rate	Higher rate	Middle rate	Lower rate	Higher rate	Middle rate	Lower rate
	10.71	9.64	6.61	10.34	9.31	6.38	10.34	9.31	6.38	10.34	9.31	6.38
Solar photovoltaic (other than stand-alone) with Total Installed Capacity greater than 150kW but not exceeding 250kW	Higher rate	Middle rate	Lower rate	Higher rate	Middle rate	Lower rate	Higher rate	Middle rate	Lower rate	Higher rate	Middle rate	Lower rate
	10.25	9.22	6.61	9.89	8.90	6.38	9.89	8.90	6.38	9.89	8.90	6.38
Solar photovoltaic (other than stand-alone) with Total Installed Capacity greater than 250kW		6.61			6.38			6.38			6.38	
Stand-alone (autonomous) solar photovoltaic (not wired to provide electricity to a building)		6.61			6.38			6.38			6.38	
EXPORT TARIFF		4.77			4.77			4.77			4.77	

Note: Fit payment rates for installations have been determined by the Gas and Electricity Markets Authority (Ofgem) under Article 13 of the Feed-in Tariffs (Specified Maximum Capacity and Functions) Order 2012, in accordance with Annexes 2-4 to the Standard Licence Conditions. All tariff rates are specified as pence per kilowatt hour at 2014/15 values. Date of publication: 31 October 2014

Most people in the solar PV industry are relatively happy with the system of feed in tariffs that is now in place. However, its early transition to the current system was not without pain. Following the introduction of FITs, the Government realised that they had been set a little high and set about reducing them. The way that it did this caused considerable consternation in the industry, until the current system of degression, which is widely accepted, was introduced.

Going back to 2010, solar PV really took off quickly after the introduction of FITs. Firms geared up, took on staff and accredited to MCS. Advertising campaigns encouraged householders to invest in systems. It became clear from the figures published by OFGEM that the PV element of renewables was going to be a great success.

However, what happened over the next two years is not such a great story. This is how the Government learnt the lessons about progressive deployment of solar PV and the creation of a stable and sustainable PV industry the hard way. The timeline of the comments that follow is illustrated in **Figure 8.3** below.

April 2010 – *FITs introduced and solar PV is surprisingly attractive to the public and streams ahead*

February 2011 – *Government announces its intention to carry out a comprehensive review of the FITs scheme*

March 2011 – *Government decides to act on PV urgently with publication of the first consultation on PV FIT deployment known as the 'fast track review' – only over 50 kw in capacity*

June 2011 - *Announcements made on the results of the fast track review, with rates being cut sharply*

August 2011 – *Changes take effect – preceded by a massive spike in deployment*

October 2011 – *Second consultation on FIT deployment – focus on solar PV under 50 kw, but with further reductions on above 50 kw too – Phase 1 – and all FIT rates and technologies – Phase 2*

10 December 2011 – *Proposed 'reference date' provides deadline for rate cuts*

December 2011 - *Judicial Review of Phase 1 of consultation – issued in December and heard by high Court in same month. Changes declared unlawful*

January 2012 - *Government appeals the Judicial Review case – Court of Appeal hears appeal and dismisses it; Government determines to fight on with a request to the Supreme Court to hear a further appeal, which was unsuccessful*

January 2012 – *Government lays new papers before Parliament to introduce a new reference date of 3 March, and rates paid on 1 April 2012, together with an energy efficiency requirement and a multi installations degression of rates*

February 2012 - *Response to Phase 1 review – energy efficiency level and multi installation rules relaxed slightly but remain*

February 2012 –*Government publishes Phase 2A consultation on cost control for solar PV work. This indicated rates for FITs that would apply post 1 July 2012 for solar PV and also the frequency and level of degression thereafter*

February 2012 – *Government publishes Phase 2B consultation on the remainder of the FIT technologies and, importantly, the definition of 'community project'*

April 2012 – *New rates kick in on a reference date of 3 March; deadline preceded by massive spike in deployment*

April 2012 – *some FIT rates go up by inflation. RPI index causes relevant rates to rise by 4.8 %*

May 2012 – *Response to Review Phase 2A – Solar PV Cost Control*

May 2012 – *Cuts to solar PV FIT rate intended for 1 July 2012, delayed for a month to 1 August 2012, followed a slump in deployment following the March deadline*

Figure 8.3 – Timeline for Feed in Tariff Development

The Government quickly became concerned about the speed of deployment in solar. This was for two reasons. Firstly, solar PV was greatly outperforming any other technology, creating an imbalance. Secondly, it started to look at the rapidly decreasing budget available to pay the FIT monies to generators. A spending envelope of £867m had been secured for the Spending Review period 2010–2014 and this was reducing alarmingly fast.

By 2011 the Government was concerned and determined to review FIT rates. However, it did not feel that solar PV could wait for a general review and so embarked on a 'fast track' review in March 2011. This only dealt with the so-called 'larger' installations, that the Government deemed to be over 50kw. The problem, in the Government's eyes, was the large commercial developers who threatened taking the lion's share of FIT monies. Accordingly the Government proposed steep cuts to the FIT levels over 50 kw, for example, a 150 kw installation moving from 29.3 pence per kwh to 15 pence. Land-based installations suffered even heavier cuts, with a 5 MW solar farm going from 29.3 pence to 8.5 pence in one move.

The changes came into effect on 1 August 2011 and for the first time the UK experienced the 'boom and bust' scenario for solar PV energy. Leading up to the deadline a massive number of solar installations had been installed, including eleven 5 MW solar farms in the South of the UK.

But the data showed that most of the installations that were eating up the budget were in fact below 50 kw; indeed, most were domestic sized, actually proving that the Government's intention to enthuse householders into renewable energy deployment was actually working. This meant that the problem had not gone away.

In October 2011 the Government released a further consultation paper, again suggesting solar PV tariffs be reduced. This was called the Phase 1 review. This time the focus was on solar PV below 50 kw, but for the sake of completeness, further reductions to the higher rates were also proposed. It was called Phase 1 because the wider, comprehensive review of FITs, covering all technologies, was also announced, under the name Phase 2 Review.

The rate reductions in the Phase 1 consultation were, again, sharp. The 43.3 pence rate for a sub-4 kw retrofitted system was proposed to be halved to 21 pence, causing outrage in the solar PV industry. Many thought that the industry would collapse, whilst still very much in its infancy. The way that the Government proposed to make the changes was to create an effective date for the cut-off (called the reference date) of 12 December. However, as the consultation did not end until 31 December, many thought that the Government had overstepped its powers by bringing in the new provisions before the Consultation was completed.

Friends of the Earth and some other parties challenged the Government by Judicial Review, claiming that it had acted unlawfully. The side effect of this was that the whole solar PV industry was thrown into confusion and uncertainty.

The Government ultimately lost the Judicial Review case with both the High Court and the Court of Appeal agreeing that it had acted unlawfully. Accordingly, the 12 December date was never enforced. Not knowing this, many had rushed to get their systems fitted before the rates could go down and so there was another huge spike in deployment. In fact over 30,000 PV systems were installed just in the week before the deadline and some 350 MW of capacity since October.

As the court case was not going well, the Government determined that it should have a 'Plan B' and decided to lay papers before Parliament to reduce the tariffs anyway, even if the previous attempt was held to be invalid. On 19 January 2012, it laid further draft regulations that would create a new reference date of 3 March 2012 for the reduction of FIT rates. As it turned out, the legal case was lost, and so the rates did not degress on 12 December, but were held until 3 March. As soon as this became clear, there was yet another rush of deployment, followed by a major slump in fitting thereafter.

The January announcements also contained further provisions by DECC to dampen down demand: a link for the first time ever to energy efficiency of buildings; and a lower FIT rate for generators with multiple installations. The former required a certain level of energy efficiency to justify the FIT rate or a much lower rate would apply. The latter reduced rates further for those with many solar sites, as economies of scale were considered to apply. When the Government's decisions on the consultation process were announced, these provisions were slightly relaxed but remained applicable.

The FIT budget was completely spent by now. This is due to the fact that under the grandfathering principles, once a scheme is registered, the FIT rates are guaranteed for the full period of the arrangement, which was 25 years. So the calls on the budget each year are cumulative, with all of the already approved schemes needing to continue to be funded. The position was soon reached that the entire £867m had been earmarked. The Government therefore had to transfer some funds from the Renewable Obligation budget, which fortunately was underspent, to the FIT budget. This highlighted the need, once again, to put in place a mechanism for long term cost control under FITs.

In February 2012, therefore, the Government published new proposals for cost control in solar PV (Review 2A). This proposed three new routes for degression and is the foundation of the current system explained below. For the first time, an evidence based trigger mechanism was to be used, to automatically introduce degression in rates, based upon deployment in the preceding period.

Finally, the Phase 2B consultation sought views on on the Government's plans for the comprehensive review of all FIT rates and technologies. Whilst this consultation did not concern solar PV, it introduced the notion of a 'community' project for the first time – with the implication that they should be treated differently in terms of FIT rates due to their wider importance to the policy agenda and local economy.

During the period from the introduction of FITs until the current system was introduced in 2012 (illustrated in the timeline in Figure 8.3), deployment suffered from a 'boom and bust' consequence. This is very clearly illustrated by **Figure 8.4**, which is the OFGEM record of registered FIT applications. Each of the DECC deadlines is marked on the chart by a huge spike in registrations. It is for this reason that the Government determined that a change in the system was necessary.

So the Government learnt the lessons derived from the application of FITs to solar PV schemes between 2010 and 2012, but has now put the regime on a far steadier footing. Whilst not everyone in the solar PV industry agreed with the cuts or the changes, it is generally regarded that the current system is preferable in giving certainty of rates and an objective methodology for degression. **Figure 8.5** summarises the problems with the early period of the Feed in Tariffs.

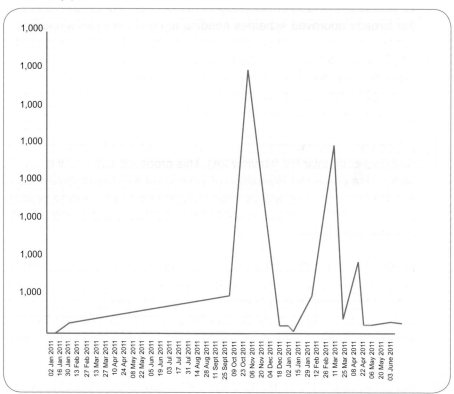

Figure 8.4 Number of PV installations per week, all tariff bands

- *The Government did not foresee the interest in solar PV in the UK, particularly in relation to solar farms*
- *The Government did not learn the lessons from abroad and from other similar schemes, where problems had been created by fast deployment, followed by cutting tariffs at short notice*
- *The Government did not have enough sufficiently accurate data on costs of solar panels and returns on investment*
- *The Government did not listen to the solar PV industry sufficiently well or deal with it effectively. Whilst the trade has a vested interest in all this, it does know how to build, maintain and grow a solar industry. When deployment was too high, the Government panicked that the FIT rates were too generous and the financial cap that had been placed on FITs would be broken and did not listen to the industry on how to deal with it*
- *The Government did not set up the FIT levels properly. The inclusion of the 5 MW limit also makes it hard for the Government to justify its subsequent claim that the FIT was only really intended to cover domestic installations and small community schemes*
- *The Government did not set the budgets up properly. There were no cost control mechanisms built in, the budget amount was insufficient and there was no ability to vire (legally transfer) money between different financial incentives*
- *The system lacked flexibility and was too rigid. The Government needs to be able to adjust rates as necessary; the industry needs certainty, in order to attract investment. The Government did not find the right balance in the early phase of the FIT*

Figure 8.5 – Problems with the Introduction of Feed in Tariffs

The key to all of this for local authorities is that the business case is all that matters. A rate of 43 pence per kwh for a 4 kw system costing £12,000 is the same as a rate of 21 pence on the same system costing £6,000. Fortunately, reductions in FITs have been mirrored by reductions in panel prices and so returns have not changed markedly over this period.

The Current Feed in Tariff Regime

As indicated above, the FIT regime changed in 2012. There is no purpose in explaining the regime prior to then, as any authority using this book to undertake a solar PV scheme will be doing so from late 2012 onwards. Featured below, therefore, are the current rules for the regime.

The basic system of the FIT is relatively straightforward. It is only when the degression rates and changes come into play that it becomes more complex.

The starting point is that Feed in Tariff is actually a misleading name, as the vast majority of the funds are actually for generation of electricity, not feeding it into the grid. The generation tariff is the first of the two parts to the FIT: the export tariff is the second. The third financial benefit, as explained in **Chapter 9**, is the value of the electricity that is both generated and used on site, and for which the authority does not therefore have to pay. As the name suggests, the generation tariff is paid for simply generating the energy, whatever happens to it. Once it has been generated, the power can be used by the authority or sold to a purchaser via a Power Purchase Agreement. However, if it decides to do neither of those and simply puts the excess power into the grid, it also qualifies for a further payment – the export tariff. This is the same for every technology and capacity of installation (4.5 pence per kwh originally, now 4.77 pence after inflation adjustments).

FIT rates depend on type of technology and capacity of system and are given in a chart published by DECC. **Figure 8.1** above reproduced the original FIT rate chart and **Figure 8.2** the one in force in December 2014. The rates were originally calculated on the basis of the cost of each technology and the return offered to investors, aimed at between 4% and 8%. However, solar PV has been particularly difficult to do this for, bearing in mind the constant improvement of manufacturing techniques and therefore reducing prices. Rates are increased each year by the Retail Prices Index and are then guaranteed for the full period of the agreement, which was formerly 25 years, but is now 20 years.

As indicated above, rates have changed radically since the first FIT chart was published, as illustrated in **Figure 8.2**, which reproduces the last OFGEM FIT table for 2014.

FITs are payable by the energy supplier after the system has been registered by OFGEM on its national Central FITs Register. The generator has to complete an application giving relevant details of the system and these are stored in the register. The generator is then given a tariff code that will identify the generation tariff that should be paid.

Larger electricity suppliers have to offer themselves as FIT licensees ie: offer to host renewable energy systems. But with smaller companies, this is optional. The costs of the FITs are distributed amongst all of the energy companies anyway, by a process known as 'levelisation'. The costs of the FITs regime are ultimately borne by public as costs are shared by all electricity consumers.

The basic components of the scheme are summarized in **Figure 8.6** below.

- *The FIT system is designed to promote renewable energy generation and intended to provide a return of 4% to 8% per annum*
- *The payments are for generation and export of electricity*
- *The amount of payment depends on the date the system is registered with OFGEM and the applicable DECC chart of tariffs*
- *The generation rate referable on the chart applies for that installation for a period of 20 years*
- *The export tariff is 4.5 pence per kwhs*
- *Each year the rates are increased by inflation, by reference the Retail Prices Index*
- *The generator has certain duties too, such as keeping the installation operating and in good order*
- *Agreements are grandfathered ie: the rate that was applicable at the time the system was registered will apply (subject to annual inflationary uplifts) for the full period of 20 years; despite the FIT rates being reduced subsequently – or abolished altogether*
- *FIT rates will degress ie: go down for new systems registered as time progresses. The amount of degression depends on a complex system of calculating deployment in a preceding period (as explained below)*
- *If it is a buildings based system, then the building has to have a Level D Energy Performance Certificate or above; if it does not, the lowest level FIT rate applies*

• Generators with multiple installations receive 90% of the relevant rate (where a generator has 25 installations or more)
• The full business case for any system can therefore be calculated – see Figures 9.2 and 9.3 in the next Chapter.

Figure 8.6 – The Feed in Tariff System

Specific Features of the FIT Regime

The Difference Between Stand Alone and Buildings Based Installations

This sounds a little fanciful as a statement – surely it is obvious that a stand-alone installation is in a field and a buildings based system is on the roof? Actually, it is not as clear cut as that.

It is possible, for example, that a large country house could have a roof structure that is not suitable for fixing solar panels. However, it has a large area of grounds and so could easily accommodate 4 – 10 kw of panels to the side of the property. Provided that the panels are wired into the house, this is counted as a buildings-based system. The National Trust has benefitted from this rule, for example with some of its ancient buildings, where fitting on the roof of, say, a castle was not possible but the in the grounds was possible. Another example might be a dairy farmer, who installs 150 kw of panels on his farm land but then links them into the milking shed to use the electricity there.

However, the Government realised that this was also a potential loophole. The simple reason is that in most cases, the FIT rate for a buildings-based system is higher than for a stand alone system. In the case of a leisure centre project that the author was involved in, the difference in rates was between 6.7 pence per kwh of electricity on the stand alone rate and 10.25 pence on the buildings rate. As this is payable for every unit of electricity, it can be seen that this rate could make quite a difference to a business case. So the Government became concerned that it was possible to link a very large solar PV system to a modest sized building and still come under the rule that it counts as a buildings based system.

Accordingly, in late 2014, the Government proposed a change to this rule. The consultation paper was published by DECC on 2 October 2014, with a view to the new rules coming into play in the summer of 2015. The new term 'other than stand alone' was forged to cover this change. Whilst this is not yet law at the time of writing, the proposal is to change the rule so that a minimum of 10% of the output of the installation has to be used in the building to which it is connected. This seems a reasonable amendment and it could be argued that even then this percentage is low.

Installations that cannot demonstrate this will be treated as stand alone, with the lower feed in tariff. These rules are only intended to cover schemes over 250kw in size and it is not proposed that they will apply to extensions to an existing facility either.

Splitting the Ground Based and Over 50 kw Buildings FIT Band

As mentioned above, the Government very much wanted to move the focus of solar PV in 2014 away from large ground mounted solar farms (which had provided it with some political problems) and on to the relatively untapped area of commercial roofs. There were, however, a number of barriers to the take off of the commercial roof sector.

One of those issues was the FIT rate for commercial roofs, which the solar industry had argued for some years, was too low to make such work economic. Even worse than that, was that the rates were constantly degressing too, as explained below, ie getting even lower as time goes on.

One issue that was seen to be of particular significance was that the three 'bands' that the Government had created for the degression system, included one for both stand alone systems and non stand alone systems over 50kw. Such was the success of ground mounted solar PV in the years to the end of 2014, with many hundreds of MW of capacity being fitted, that this was causing the FIT rates to degress steadily.

So the Government proposed that this band should be divided into two, thereby breaking the link between the success of land-based solar and the FIT rate payable to large roof based solar. It published a consultation paper on 13 May 2014, indicating that it proposed to split the FIT degression band for over 50kw capacity into two separate bands, one for stand alone facilities and one for large building based systems.

On 2 October 2014, the Government announced the results of the consultation and confirmed that it would implement the proposals. This would create two new bands for degression, one for over 50kw buildings and one for ground mounted. According to DECC, "this will protect building mounted installations from degression caused by stand alone deployment".

Most importantly, the funding for this former band would be divided to promote future buildings based schemes, by 65% of the budget being allocated to that side, with only 35% allocated to the stand-alone side. Put simply, this means that the FIT rates for stand alone solar farms will degress even faster, again putting a brake on this type of development. However, it should be noted that provided the stand-alone facility is below 5 MW, the Renewables Obligation is still available anyway, as explained above.

The Link to Energy Efficiency

Before 2012, there was no link between renewable energy and energy efficiency. This is curious, bearing in mind the hierarchy featured in **Figure 6.1** (use less energy, improve energy efficiency and then generate more energy from renewable sources). Purists would, of course, say that there is no point in putting any renewable energy technology on an old, leaky building that has no energy efficiency. This message was taken on board by the Government in 2012, when it recognised that this was a further level to help its energy efficiency policies. In 2012 a link made between solar PV and a building's energy efficiency rating under the Energy Performance Certificate (EPC). A level of D on an EPC now has to be achieved to qualify for the normal FIT rate; any building not qualifying will only be entitled to a much lower rate, based on the stand-alone installation rate, which is traditionally the lowest available rate.

Generators with Multiple Installations

For generators with multiple installations, different rates will apply. This is because economies of scale will apply to those generators. It was originally proposed that such generators should only receive 80% of the applicable rate, but this was subsequently changed to 90%. To qualify as a multiple installation operator, the generator has to have 25 or more different sites in its portfolio. There are various rules to prevent avoidance of this rule. Ironically, local authorities will be caught by this, simply because they have a large number of buildings, rather than because they are wealthy or commercial solar PV developers. Accordingly, there have been calls for this rule to be relaxed for the public sector; however, these have been unheeded to date.

Preliminary Accreditation of Schemes

Some schemes take considerable time to bring to fruition. A good example from the non-solar PV world would be hydropower schemes. These might take two years to build out from the time the planning is all complete. Accordingly, the issue arose as to whether some schemes could benefit from preliminary accreditation IE a lock in to a certain FIT tariff in advance, provided the scheme proceeds to completion.

A pre-accreditation system had already been in operation under the Renewables Obligation and pressure mounted for a similar system for FITs. The Government eventually consulted on this on 9 February 2012, as part of a wider review of FITs rates and administration (Consultation on Comprehensive Review Phase 2B:tariffs for non PV technologies and scheme administration issues). The proposal was to introduce a scheme for preliminary accreditation, but it was not at this stage seen to be necessary for solar PV to be included within it, bearing in mind the relatively swift development period involved with solar PV.

The results of that consultation exercise were published by DECC in July 2012 and they confirmed that a pre accreditation system would be introduced for FITs. As a result of industry pressure, solar PV over 50kw was also included in this new system. The reasons given were that three monthly degression of FIT rates for solar had been introduced and also that larger schemes had longer lead in times. In order to get preliminary accreditation, a scheme has to have planning consent and a grid connection in place, plus other conditions. The system then provides six months for a solar PV scheme to be completed after preliminary accreditation and then it will receive the FIT rate at the time preliminary accreditation was given.

The only downside of this new system is that preliminary accreditation figures count against degression triggers. This is not so much a problem in solar PV but has caused considerable difficulties for other sectors, particularly hydropower schemes.

Provisions for preliminary accreditation were also included for community schemes and schools and these are considered below.

Concessions for Community Schemes and Schools

It has been the case since the FIT regime was originally introduced that the public sector has clamoured for concessions. Schemes that are funded by public money and that are promoted for reasons far wider than just financial, have a greater benefit to society and the economy and should therefore be encouraged. The simplest way of doing this would be to pay higher tariffs for the power generated to guarantee a part of the LCF pot just for public sector projects. Sadly, such requests fell on deaf ears in DECC and no such provisions have been introduced. However, there are some concessions to report.

In the first FIT review in 2011, the Government had set out its ambition for some different rules to apply to community projects. It published a consultation paper on 9 February 2012 as part of the comprehensive review, which put forward proposals for special measures for community energy schemes and schools. The results of that consultation exercise were published in July 2012 and were, frankly, disappointing.

In short, a very narrow and unrealistic definition of 'community' was adopted, no extra tariffs were granted and only a small number of other benefits were given.

On the definition front, DECC decided to adopt the HM Revenue and Customs definition of community, which only covers community interest companies, cooperative societies or former Industrial and Provident Societies. Local authorities were not included, as discussed in **Chapter 13**.

One small benefit was in relation to energy efficiency. Usually, as indicated above, an EPC certificate demonstrating at least a level of D is required to claim a higher FIT. If this level is not achieved, then the project is only entitled to the lowest level of FIT (for stand alone projects). However, this rule has been relaxed for both community schemes and schools projects, for non-domestic properties.

Preliminary accreditation is discussed above and here, the Government decided to permit tariff guarantees for solar PV projects of over 50kw on non-domestic buildings for one year. This is a special concession for community energy projects, to reflect the fact that these projects often have longer lead in times than commercial projects.

Finally, it had been suggested that the public sector should benefit from not being subject to the multi-installation rules. If a local authority has a wide stock of buildings, then it could easily have a programme that results in more than 25 installations. This is not because it is a solar developer, but because it is a public authority with many assets. Despite calls for such bodies to be free of the multi installation tariff, the Government decided to take no action on this proposal.

As mentioned above, these provisions were disappointing and an opportunity lost to promote community energy in the wider sense. Interestingly enough, DECC published its Community Energy Strategy in 2014, as discussed in **Chapter 13** and then complained about the fact that there was not enough renewable energy deployment going on. It is hardly surprising that this should be the case, bearing in mind its own parsimonious approach to granting concessions to promote such activity. A wider discussion of community energy is featured in **Chapter 13**.

Transferring Systems Between Buildings

It was a feature of the early years of the Feed in Tariff that once a solar PV installation had been fitted, it could not be moved. This was particularly an issue for buildings, where an organisation might not be sure how long it would occupy the building in question and so would not proceed to fit solar. Landlords and tenants of commercial buildings were both affected.

This proved to be a large disincentive to fitting solar to commercial roofs. In 2014, it became a particular problem, because the Government wanted to move the emphasis away from large ground-based solar farms, to commercial roofs, which remained largely untouched. Consultations with the solar industry pointed to this issue as one of the barriers to the development of this market.

As a result of this, in late 2014, the Government embarked on a consultation exercise, proposing to change this rule and to allow transferability of systems between buildings, without penalty under the payment of FITs. DECC published a consultation paper on 25 November 2014, stating that its reasons for proposing the change were to increase the flexibility of the scheme, to decrease investment risk and increase investment attractiveness for investors.

Any transfer will be subject to a number of conditions set out by DECC. These include the installation staying the same size, continuing to be classified as 'other than stand alone' and planning permission and grid connection having been secured. The move will only apply to new installations and any move will not be permitted in the first five years of operation.

The proposals will not apply to installations below 50kw, where the economics of moving do not really make sense in any event and it would place a burden on the operation of the FIT system.

The proposals were not law at the time of writing but are likely to come into force in 2015 in similar form to the proposals.

Calculating the Rate of Degression

The final element to be considered is the system by which FIT rates actually degress. This is the cost control issue mentioned above, which has caused such a problem for the Government since the FITs were introduced in 2010. The Government's intention is that the FITs scheme remains within its budget (referred to as the Levy Control Framework) and offers value for money to consumers. However, it is the former of those issues that has proved problematic. The Government therefore consulted on proposals in February 2012 and announced its decisions in May 2012. Effectively, a new system came into operation on 1 August 2012.

The basics of this system are reproduced in **Figure 8.7**, which is taken from the consultation response – Feed in Tariffs Scheme: Government Response to Consultation on Comprehensive Review Phase 2A: Solar Cost Control (May 2012). Essentially, there will be a regular degression of rates, based on three bands and the deployment within them within a preceding period.

- A. Degression will take **place every three** months starting on 1 November 2012, with generation tariffs changing on the first day of the first month of the period for new installations eligible from that datem (i.e. 1 november, 1 February, 1 may, 1 August).

- B. Tariffs will be published **at least two months beore the degression date, and will be based on deployment in the three-month period before publication.**

- C. There will be **three bands with separate degression mechanisms:** (i) or installations in the 0-4 and >4-10kW tariff bands; (ii) for installations in the >10 50kW tariff band; and (iii) for installations tariff bands larger than 50kW and in the stand-alone tariff band.

- D. The degression mechanism will operate independently for each degression band, with separate deployment thresholds (but no larger tariff band will ever get a higher tariff than a smaller tariff band).

- E. The **baseline degression rate will be 3.5% every three months.**

- F. **Degression will be skipped if deployment is below a floor threshold** (for a maximum of two successive degressions- so there will be a minimum of 3.5% degression every 9 months).

- G. The baseline degression rate for a degression band will be doubled each time deployment within that band exceeds a threshold, up to a maximum of 28%.

- H. **Deployment statistics will be published on a monthly basis by DECC, and new tariffs will be published by the end of the first month of each three-month period by Ofgem,** based on the deployment statistics.

- i. Deployment will be assessed based on the **capacity of installations registered on the MCS database** (for installations up to 50kW) **or determined to meet the requirements for ROO-FIT accreditation** (for installations over 50kW) in the relevant period.

Figure 8.7 How the Degression Mechanism Will Operate

Box 1 from Feed in Tariffs Scheme: Government Response to Consultation on Comprehensive Review Phase 2A: Solar Cost Control (May 2012) at page 17.

Three separate bands have been chosen as the profile of deployment differs in these areas. A 5 MW solar farm in a rural area and on a commercial scale has little in common with a 2 kw, 8 panel domestic system in the suburbs. Accordingly, the Government has chosen three bands for degression purposes:

* A 'domestic' band, covering the 0 – 4 kw and 4 – 10 kw FIT bands
* A 'small commercial' band, covering installations in the 10 – 50 kw FIT band
* A 'large commercial' band, covering installations 50-100 kw/100 - 150 /150 -200 kw/250kw - 5 MW/ and stand alone FIT bands

(It should be noted that the Government proposed in 2014 to split the third band into two separate bands, as discussed above.)

The Government believes that these three bands represent the key market segments in solar PV. The flexibility offered by having separate bands is that the degression mechanism can operate independently in each band. This means that if domestic installations are very brisk and pushing against the cap but large commercial installations have stalled, then the FIT rate for one may go down, without the other changing.

The basic degression is 3.5% every three months, which is equivalent to 13.3 % on an annual basis. However, rates will go down if the deployment has reached defined levels, but will stay the same if it has not. The under-deployment mechanism will permit two degressions to be skipped in this way. However, the third will then apply automatically each time.

If deployment exceeds the threshold, then the degression increases, to a maximum of 28% in a single degression. These figures are based on DECC models and it is said that the projections are that no degression should exceed 3.5% before 2015 on these estimates. These figures proved to be sound, as no degression for solar PV had ever exceeded 3.5% by the start of January 2015. However, that statement is slightly misleading, as the overall rates were changed by DECC several times during this period in any event.

The precise figures are as follows:

- *For the 0 – 10 kw degression band, there will be no degression if the total deployment of 0 –10kw installations in the relevant 3 month period is less than 100 MW; generation tariffs for the 0 – 4kw and 4 -10kw tariff bands will be reduced by 3.5% if total deployment of 0-10kw installations is between 100 and 200 MW, and the degression amount will double for each additional 50 MW of deployment thereafter, up to a maximum of 28% degression if deployment in a three month period is over 300 MW.*

- *For the 10 – 50 kw and over 50kw and stand alone bands, there will be no degression if the total capacity installed in that degression band in the relevant three month period is less than 50 MW; generation tariffs will be reduced by 3.5% for all tariff bands within the degression band if total deployment in that degression band is between 50 and 100 MW, and the degression amount will double for every additional 50 MW of deployment up to a maximum degression if deployment in one three month period is over 200 MW.*

This is illustrated in **Figure 8. 8** on the following page, which is taken from the consultation response – *Feed in Tariffs Scheme: Government Response to Consultation on Comprehensive Review Phase 2A: Solar Cost Control* (May 2012).

Tariff point	Max deployment in 3-month period (MW)			
	0-10kW	10-50kW	50kW and stand-alone	
point 1	100	50	50	0%
point 2	200	100	50	3.5%
point 3	250	150	100	7%
point 4	300	200	200	14%
point 5	>300	>200	>200	28%

Figure 8.8 – Deployment Thresholds and Degression of Generation Tariffs

Table 3 from Feed in Tariffs Scheme: Government Response to Consultation on Comprehensive Review Phase 2A: Solar Cost Control (May 2012) at page 14.

The way that the system works is illustrated in **Figure 8.9** opposite. In simple terms, there is a three-month period where the level of deployment in the chosen bands is monitored. Then, one month after the end of that three month period, the the new tariff levels are announced. These then come into effect two months after the announcement and apply for a three-month period. The system then rolls on in a continuous fashion. This means that a three-month period for a new FIT rate to apply is also a three month period for the calculation of deployment to estimate the next degression. This system has added a certainty to the process and, as rates have only tended to degress by 3%, has ended the 'boom and bust' cycles of the past.

Figure 8.9 the system of degression in FIT rates

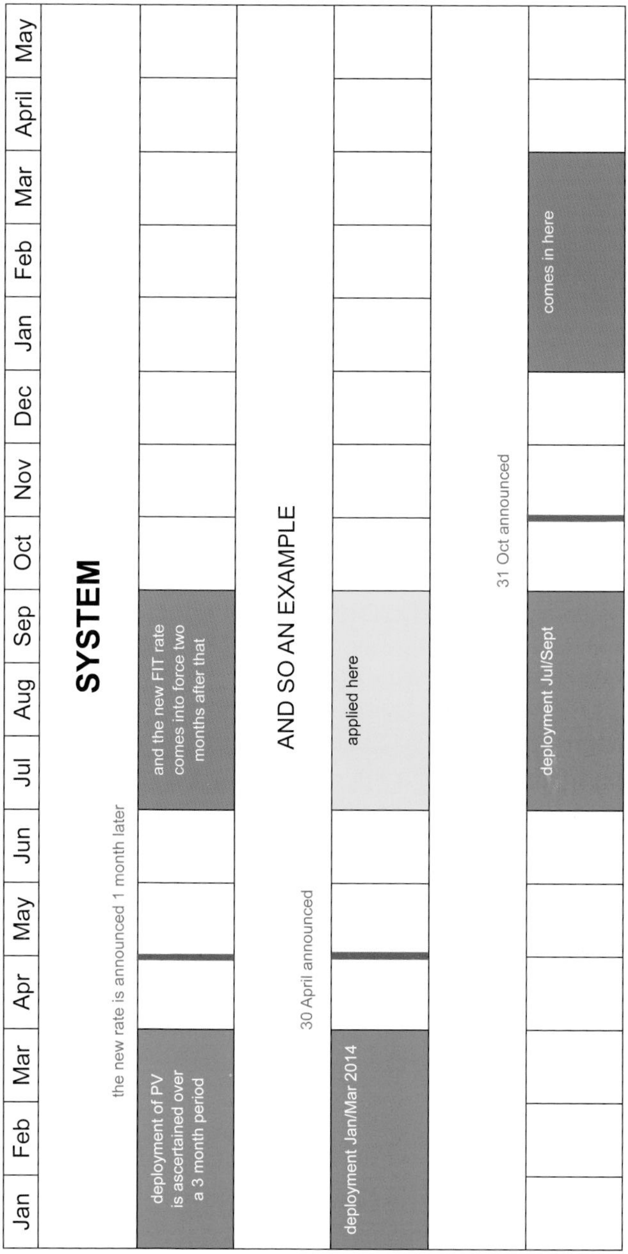

2014

| Jan | Feb | Mar | Apr | May | Jun | Jul | Aug | Sep | Oct | Nov | Dec | Jan | Feb | Mar | April | May |

2015

SYSTEM

the new rate is announced 1 month later

deployment of PV is ascertained over a 3 month period

and the new FIT rate comes into force two months after that

AND SO AN EXAMPLE

30 April announced

deployment Jan/Mar 2014

applied here

31 Oct announced

deployment Jul/Sept

comes in here

As one final point, it was also mentioned above that the data on which the FIT mechanism was introduced in the first place was suspect and DECC has learnt this lesson. This means that despite a solar PV installation being confirmed as accredited to receive the FIT once it is registered on to the OFGEM Central FITs Register, the Government will instead use more up to date data. It has indicated that it will use the MCS database and OFGEM's Renewables and Combined Heat and Power database instead. This is because this source provides a more "up to date measure of the level of deployment activity, and therefore how much capacity is likely to become eligible for FITs". Deployment statistics are published on a monthly basis on the DECC website (www.decc.gov.uk), with the new tariffs published by the end of the first month of each three month period by OFGEM, based on the deployment statistics published in that month for installations in the previous three months.

The FIT Review 2015

All of the foregoing comments in this Chapter have been applicable to the FIT system introduced in 2012 and which runs to the end of March 2016. However, in 2015, the whole Feed in Tariff system is to be reviewed. The proposal is that the current system (FIT 1) will be replaced by a successor system (FIT 2), which will run until 2020. The problem that DECC has is that grid parity, as explained in Chapter 16, is likely to have been reached before that date. This is expected around 2018 for large systems and 2020 for small systems. This means that the Government has a tricky balancing exercise to try and encourage solar PV deployment until then, without over paying subsidies.

The preliminary work on the exercise of determining FIT 2 was started by DECC towards the end of 2014 and it is said that the new system will be driven by EU state aid rules. It is also rumoured that FITs will only be available for much smaller capacity systems than is currently the case.

Conclusion

It can therefore be seen that financial incentives really are the key to opening up renewable energy in the UK. Whilst the Renewables Obligation was already working, it had limited application and it is the introduction of FITs that has really expanded the market. This is because FITs have introduced ordinary people to renewable energy at a domestic scale and made the system less complex and easier to use.

Despite the complexity of how the FIT degression system works, the overall FIT regime is relatively simple. In order to get over that particular hurdle, an interested party simply needs to check the DECC website for the relevant table of tariffs and the rest is fairly easy.

For a local authority considering a solar PV scheme, it still comes down to the basic tenet of the robustness of the business case. This is considered in the next Chapter.

Key Learning Points

- *The financial incentives are a mechanism to bridge the gap between more expensive renewable energy technologies and electricity from the grid*
- *There are four different incentives, three for electricity generation and one for heat*
- *The Renewables Obligation and Contracts for Difference are*
- *For large energy schemes; the FITs for smaller schemes and the RHI for heat schemes*
- *Feed in Tariffs are the most relevant for local authorities*
- *After some serious teething problems, the Government has now introduced a steadier path for FITs*
- *The rates will degress on a clear path, determined by the deployment of renewables in the preceding period*
- *For current FIT rates, the DECC website should be consulted*

Developing a business and financial case

Introduction

It has been commented on throughout this work that there are different drivers for a solar PV contract. Some will be motivated by pure environmental and sustainability reasons (such as to prevent climate change and save the world from global warming). Others will be less persuaded by such arguments, if not turned off completely. If local authority elected members and senior officers are in that latter camp, then it is likely to be the financial and other benefits that a project offers that will have a better chance of garnering their support. These are discussed in detail in **Chapter 3**. In reality, it is likely to be a mixture of the two camps and anyway, any major financial transaction will need to be properly planned and organised.

This is where the business case comes in. It has to be one of the most important documents in the whole process and a poor business case may result in a lack of support or support being undermined and waning as the proposal is examined. A strong business case has the opposite effect, winning over people to support the project.

The business case and the financial case are two separate documents, or at the very least two different parts of the same document. The business case is the rationale for undertaking the project and is akin to a document that would be presented to a bank in order to borrow money. It spells out what is to be done, why and what the various relevant factors are. Whilst it will cover the headline finances, it will not go into full detail on the costs or expenses. The financial case does just that: it sets out the full financial position in relation to income and expenditure and calculates a rate of return – sometimes referred to an 'ROI' or return on investment – and payback periods. Both need to be carefully prepared. This Chapter looks in detail at the business and financial cases, their purpose, format and contents and offers an example of how a return is calculated in relation to fitting solar panels..

The Nature of the Project

There are different ways in which a solar project can be undertaken. The first choice is whether the local authority undertakes fitting work itself or employs a private sector contractor to undertake the work on its behalf. This is a major decision, which impacts on every other part of the process, not least finance and risk, as mentioned in **Chapter 10**. The second choice, which is considered in **Chapter 12**, is whether to fit solar panels to the council's considerable buildings stock or to go for a land-based solar farm.

The essential point is that the business case will differ in each of these instances. If the council's direct labour organisation (DLO) is fitting panels, then the financial case will need to include considerable detail about the employment of people, grades of pay and the like. If it is a private sector contractor, then the tendered costs will be the major element, as there will have been a procurement exercise to appoint that contractor. Here the focus moves on to ensuring that the right information from the tenderers is requested in the tender documents. If it is a land-based system, planning consent might be a major cost that will need to be financed; if it is housing, it is covered by Permitted Development rights and therefore not an issue.

This illustrates that the business and financial cases are complex areas of work and will take some time to properly think through and finalise. The length and complexity of each business case will reflect the project that it underpins. It may be that external assistance will be required to ensure that the benefits from this exercise will be fully maximised, for larger projects.

The Role of the Business Case

Experience shows that it is usually the business case that allows officers to engage with councillors and the corporate management team of the authority on this area. If everyone is driven by a desire to improve the environment then all the better, but experience also shows that this is rarely the case in an authority. Usually, elected members want to consider income and jobs, growth and employment and their inevitable positive effect on the local economies that have been so bruised by the recession.

If this is to be the focus, then the most positive exposition needs to be forwarded. Income is backed by HM Treasury under the Feed in Tariffs and the Renewables Obligation and is therefore very secure. So-called 'grandfathering' principles apply. This means that if financial incentives are reduced in future years, this is only for new entrants to the scheme and not for original entrants. Solar technology is well tried and tested across the world and is known to be fully reliable.

The operation of the system leads to income, the income provides a return on the capital invested and once the costs have been met, a surplus. The surpluses can be re-invested in other projects, each having an impact on jobs and the economy as well as the environment. It is a powerful argument, when considered against alternatives to offer growth and income.

However, there will be doubters and some caution at play here and so the business case needs to ensure that it can assuage those challenging voices.

Format of the Business and Financial Cases

No specific format is required for either document and they should be written and presented in the normal style of the authority concerned.

Each authority has its own Standing Orders and Financial Regulations and a plethora of other procedures as to how the capital programme is developed and reported to members for decisions. There are different organisational and reporting arrangements and it is not possible to generalise.

Of more help, perhaps, is who should be involved in the production of the material. Obviously, technical financial assistance is required, in the form of the Finance Director and his or her staff, but also the sustainability officer, energy manager, project management personnel, policy officers and others should be on the team. The finance personnel usually appreciate the finer points of the council's financial systems, including its capacity for borrowing, but are not well versed in how to determine the return from a solar PV system. The energy manager will contribute to the element on whether the electricity is used on site or passed to the grid. The sustainability officer will know the carbon savings incurred. These are all parts of the documentation.

Essential Elements of the Business Case

It is therefore necessary to focus on what material comprises a business case. Figure 9.1 below, summarises the contents of both the business case and the financial case.

The Business Case

- *This is the rationale for the project*
- *It says how the project fits with the wider council strategy*
- *What the project will deliver in both financial and non-financial benefits*
- *What the risks are*
- *And provides an overview*

The Financial Case

- *This includes all of the relevant supporting figures*
- *The anticipated costs of the project*
- *The anticipated income from the project*
- *The return on the investment*
- *The payback period*
- *Presented in a profit and loss account and a balance sheet*

Figure 9.1 – The Business and Financial Cases for a Solar PV Project

The Business Case

This is the rationale for the project. In other words, it explains why the council is undertaking it. A simple example might be, the council is fitting solar PV installations to its major buildings, in order to reduce the running costs of those buildings, improve their CO_2 emissions and to provide local employment.

In order to put this in context, it needs to make reference to Government policy and the national targets for CO_2 emissions. It might confirm the council's views on its own carbon footprint and the plans in place to reduce that over time. It should refer to the wider climate change strategy the council has produced.

As noted in **Chapter 5**, whilst the preparation of a full climate change strategy, that is properly thought through and recorded, is an onerous task, it pays dividends later. This is one example of that, as the individual business cases of the projects themselves do not then need such a high level of detail and reference can be made to the overall plans. It should be made clear how this project fits into those plans (for example a housing project might refer to fuel poverty) and what contribution it will make to the overall targets.

The non-financial benefits also need to be examined, as no project is just about the money. These other areas might be equally – if not more – important. A simple example might be a project to fit solar PV to buildings using local installation companies, which will boost employment in the area. Energy security might be mentioned, and the other benefits outlined in **Chapter 4**.

The business case will be presented to the corporate management of the authority first and then the politicians. It needs to be persuasive to gather the necessary commitment to push forward a scheme. There is always a reason not to do something or a context in which action is inconvenient. All the successful schemes in the solar PV arena have been championed by the corporate management teams and cabinets of the authorities concerned.

The business case will also feed into the communications strategy, which is considered in detail in **Chapter 13**. It is important to be transparent about what the council is intending to do and why, in order to ensure that public support is maintained.

Sometimes the business case will have a section on the detailed financial arrangements; in others it is presented in a separate financial case, and that is the next area to consider.

The Financial Case

This is the nitty gritty of the finances underpinning the arrangements. How much will the scheme cost? How much will it make? There are many questions to be answered. The financial case is the blueprint for the operation of the facility or arrangements, and so needs to be both detailed and precise in its calculations. They are certain to scrutinised widely, both inside and outside the authority.

Some local authorities, such as Swindon Borough Council (via its company Swindon Commercial Services) have developed their own financial programmes for solar PV work. Others might need to engage external assistance to prepare a plan of this type.

The key areas to determine the financial case are the cost of the panels and other equipment and the income from use or sale of the electricity and the Government's financial incentives. This means that the two main areas that need to be covered in the financial case are:

- *Calculating the income*
- *Calculating the costs*

Calculating the Income

This starts by working out the irradiance. **Chapter 7** demonstrated that the maximum irradiance available – at noon during good weather conditions – is 1000 watts per square metre (1000 W/m2). This is the benchmark against which performance is gauged. This means that a 250 W panel will only make 250 watts of power at 1000 W/m2. As conditions are likely to be less than this, a different value will be achieved. These values can be predicted using design software for solar PV systems.

The example below uses the method of calculation of kwh of energy per kw peak of capacity. This is based on a 4 kw peak retrofit system, using 16 x 250 watt Sharp monocrystalline PV panels, fitted to a house in Leeds in 2011. The system cost £12,000.

The national solar map described in **Chapter 7** demonstrates that the estimated return for this part of the country is 800 kwh of electricity per kwp. This means that the total estimated output of this system per annum is just short of 3,200 kwh.

As this is a domestic sized system, FIT rates will apply. The FIT at the time of fitting the system was 43 pence per kwh of electricity generated and 3 pence per kwh of electricity put into the grid. The estimated business case is therefore calculated in **Figure 9.2** below.

Under OFGEM rules, for domestic systems it was permitted to 'deem' that 50% of the electricity was passed into the grid, without having a dedicated export meter.

Irradiance level – 850 kwh per kw peak
Price of solar PV - £3,000 per kw installed
FIT rate 43 pence per kwh
Export rate 3 pence per kwh

• **Expenditure**
£12,000 fitted

• **Income**
3,200 (kwh) x 43 p (FIT/generation) = £1376 pa
3,200 (kwh) x 50% (deemed export) x 3 p (FIT/export) = £48 pa
Use of electricity generated - 1000 kwh at 12 p per kwh, delivering a
further saving of £120
Total income = £1, 544 per annum

Payback – 8 – 9 years Return on capital – 14 %

Figure 9.2 – Financial Case for a 4 kw retrofitted domestic PV system in 2011

Irradiance level – 850 kwh per kw peak
Price of solar PV - £1,500 per kw installed
FIT rate 14.38 pence per kwh
Export rate 4.77 pence per kwh

• **Expenditure**
£6,000 fitted

• **Income**
3,200 (kwh) x 14.38 p (FIT/generation) = £460.16 pa
3,200 (kwh) x 50% (deemed export) x 4.77 p (FIT/export) = £152.64 pa
Use of electricity generated - 1000 kwh at 12 p per kwh, delivering a
further saving of £120
Total income = £732.80 per annum

Payback – 8 – 9 years Return on capital – 14%

Figure 9.3 – Financial Case for a 4 kw retrofitted domestic PV system in 2014

These calculations illustrate how the power and other characteristics of a solar PV system will impact on the financial and business cases. They also show how returns have stayed the same as both FIT rates and costs of solar PV have fallen over time. So the return on an investment of just £6,000 now is roughly the same as it was for a system costing double that in 2011.

Although these calculations are for a domestic sized system, the principles are the same for larger systems. As an example, a solar farm might be 5 MW in size, with an output of 5,000 MWh (or 5,000,000 kwh). Here, either FITs or the RO can be used.

If the FIT rate is 6.61 pence for land-based systems, then the income is £330,500 on the same basis. If the system is fitted after August 2012, then the export rate is 4.77 pence and the overall financial case is illustrated in Figure 9.4.

Irradiance level – 850 kwh per kw peak
Price of solar PV - £1,000 per kw installed
FIT rate 6.61 pence per kwh
Export rate 4.77 pence per kwh

- **Expenditure**
£5,000,000 fitted – turnkey cost

- **Income**
5,000,000 (kwh) x 6.61 p (FIT/generation) = £330,500 pa
5,000,000 (kwh) export x 4.77 p (FIT/export) = £238,500 pa
Total income = £569,000 per annum

Payback – 8 – 9 years
Return on capital – 11.4 %

Figure 9.4 – Financial Case for a 5 MW Installation Using Feed in Tariffs

If the FIT regime is not to be used, but the RO instead, then there are only two parts to the income calculation, namely the amount for the ROC payments and the sums from the Power Purchase Agreements for the sale of the electricity. This is illustrated in Figure 9. 5 below.

* *under the RO system, banding applies to the various technologies and for solar PV 1.4 ROC's were available in 2014*
* *If a ROC is worth roughly £50 per MWh of electricity-that would equate to 5 pence per kwh; 1.4 ROCs therefore means 7 pence per kwh for each unit of power;*
* *There is no export tariff under the RO and the generator has to enter into a power purchase agreement (PPA) with a user of the power; an average PPA might generate approximately 5-6 pence per kwh, assume 5 p for these purposes;*
* *this totals 15 pence per kwh under a RO scheme*

* **Expenditure**

£5,000,000 fitted – turnkey cost, based on a cost of solar of £1,000 per kw installed

* **Income**

5,000,000 (kwh) x 7p (1.4 ROCs) = £350,000 pa
5,000,000 (kwh) export x 5 p (PPA) = £250,000 pa
Total income = £600,000 per annum

Payback – 8 – 9 years
Return on capital – 12 %

Figure 9.5 – Financial Case for a 5 MW Installation Using the Renewables Obligation

The Cost of Systems

The second part of the calculation is the cost of solar PV panels and other equipment. This has been falling consistently for a number of years now. This is due to improved manufacturing processes, led by China.

The usual method of comparing costs is on the basis of 'price per kw installed.' This means that if a 4 kw retrofit system costs £12,000, the cost is £3,000 per kw installed. Once in possession of this figure, it can be used to compare prices at any scale of installation as any installation can be reduced to the number of its kw capacity.

Prices in 2010 could have been as high as £4,000 per kw installed. During the early years of FITs, the prices travelled down through £3,000 per kw installed to £2,000 per kw installed and in later years even through that barrier to nearer £1,000 per kw installed. For large-scale solar PV developments in the latter part of 2014, that commercial rate was between £800,000 and £900,000 per kw installed. This would mean that a 5 MW park would come in below £4.5m.

The calculation in Figure 9.4 above, for a commercially sized installation, has been prepared on a price per kw installed of £1,000, including grid connection and other costs.

An Example of a Housing Based Financial Model

Featured in this section are comments in relation to a financial model for a social housing project. This project involves the council undertaking the work itself, to create a revolving fund, as described in **Chapter 15**.

The normal starting point would be to prepare some preliminary figures (often described as 'back of an envelope') to see the sort of financial performance that can be expected. These calculations then go through a number of iterations to become a final, honed and detailed financial matrix, often presented in an Excel spreadsheet format. For land-based systems, this includes formal solar curve graphs, showing output across a defined period, prepared by technical solar consultants.

The Different Areas to be Covered

There should be a summary to cover the proposal overall. This should make clear the basic deal: the number of houses to be fitted, the number of panels to be fitted, the output from the panels and the so on. These are the so-called 'headline' figures.

Then each area of the summary needs to be expanded and broken down into its own section.

The Installation Costs

This would be one section, covering all of the issues relevant to installation matters. Obviously, the number of houses, the size of installation for each (kwp or average kwp) plus the number of panels, inverters and other equipment (meters if relevant, isolators and so on).

These figures should be broken down and the source of the figures disclosed.

After equipment come labour costs. The number of people in each team is relevant here, together with labour costs in the area. The different grades (electrician, tradesperson and scaffolder and so on) should be included. Notes should indicate how these have been arrived at.

The work undertaken by each person should also be identified, for example, one electrician to two tradespersons to undertake an installation.

If there are overhead or on-costs to be added, these need to be mentioned and broken down here.

The summary of the people costs and the equipment costs leads to a full cost per installation. This is a number that will be important.

In the document somewhere it is also necessary to say what assumptions have been used in the council's calculations. This will include light levels, performance of panels, speed of fitting teams, cost of borrowing and so on.

The maintenance figures need to be included in the installation figures. A failure rate needs to be included. There is no norm, as this depends on the make of the panels. A failure rate of 1 panel in 500 would be a reasonable figure. This section needs to include the costs for the re-scaffolding, the labour and materials (taking into account warranty issues).

Inverters will definitely not last the 25 years and so a sinking fund for replacement is necessary, or another system to accommodate this. The idea of a sinking fund is that an amount is paid into a separate account throughout the life of the arrangement and then used to replace inverters as and when – and if – necessary.

There is much debate in the market regarding the likelihood, frequency and timing of inverter replacement. It is prudent to allow for this and the model should allow for the movement of both percentage failures and timing of replacement. This also includes an inflationary element to make costs current at the time they affect the summary. The council needs to choose a figure and say why in its financial case. This should also include labour costs.

Performance Figures

This section includes the panel performance assumptions in terms of sunlight hours, the efficiency of the panels and the efficiency of the system (performance ratio). These are 'headline' figures too.

Roll Out

This section needs to translate the overall target number of installations across the year to the first degression point of the FIT against the labour team resource requirements. This will show a rising level of execution capacity needed to achieve a challenging target. This should include a reflection for holidays and the seasonal influences on installations.

How the installation resource would be created, trained and managed should be explicitly covered in the model, and could be explained through separate notes, including the costs associated with this.

Core Financial Figures

Next on to the finances. The cost of borrowing needs to be identified for now and estimated over the life of the project.

The speed of installation will dictate the speed of the borrowing – or in other words, how quickly the money is needed. If this is a programme where fitting takes more than a year, that will make a difference as all of the money will not be borrowed in year one.

Then the costings from above need to be included. This will include cash flow items, such as the fact that the FITs are paid quarterly in arrears. Also, the FITs are adjustable in accordance with the RPI and another estimation is required here.

The financial performance of the system depends on the actual performance of the panels, IE: did they produce the estimated kwh and efficiency included. This needs to be projected forwards in the sense of deterioration in the performance over time. In Year 20 the panels will only be operating at 80% of their full capacity and this needs to be factored in.

The speed with which the debt is repaid (payback) will be part of these calculations and forms another 'headline figure'. Again, this is dependent on a decision on the part of the council – does it want to apply all of the income to the debt (in which case the debt should be discharged in under 10 years) or finance the whole operation over, for example, 25 years? This would cost more (in terms of loan charges) and give a lower overall return, but would give income to be reinvested straight away. This is a matter for each council to decide.

A 'profit and loss' account should be prepared. This will indicate the income coming in (uplifted for RPI etc.) and also the costs going out and calculating an operating profit. Inflation is another variable in the calculation, where the council simply needs to decide on its estimate and include it.

This section shows the part of the model where the comparison of revenue and cost translates into profit and loss. This should include the depreciation treatment and the implications for the assumptions under bank lending. The interest rate assumption is likely to be based on an "all in" cost of capital, at whatever percentage is relevant. A view needs to be taken on what is a fair cost for debt in the current economic climate, using public sector borrowing sources.

The model may benefit from a cash flow sheet. This would allow the VAT treatment to be shown and the maximum cash exposure the roll out programme would experience. Advice should be sought on FIT VAT treatment and the recovery of VAT against capital (output) costs. This is by no means a settled position with HMRC and there are said to be differing views on the VAT position.

It should also include an annual return on investment figure (ROI). This will also be important as a 'headline' figure.

In terms of presentation, it would be worth a council preparing some simple to understand graphs, showing the profit line and performance, which can then be used to report to members and in the communications strategy.

The headline financial case for a social housing project is illustrated in Figure 9.6 below.

Project to install solar PV on a stock of 1,000 houses
Number of systems – 1,000
Capacity on average – 2 kw
Total capacity – 2 MW
Irradiance 850 kwh per kw peak

Costs
Tendered costs for the project, including client side costs, overheads and other add-ons - £2,000,000, based on a figure of £1,000 per kw installed on average.

Income
Feed in tariff rates – 14.38 pence per kwh
Total income, based on 1,700,000 kwh per annum = £244,460 per annum.

Payback - 8-9 years
Surplus over costs - £2.9 m, not including finance costs

Figure 9.6 - Headline Business Case for Large Social Housing Project

Shelf Life of Figures

When the first edition of this book was published, FIT rates below 20 pence were not in sight. Costs of solar were still well over £2,000 per kw installed. How times have changed.

This demonstrates that the figures reproduced on these pages will be accurate for a very short period of time. What is more important is that those who seek to embark on a scheme understand how to work out the figures for their own scheme. For this you need a number of factors:

- *On the income side, the current FIT rate for the capacity of installation that is to be fitted;*
- *And the current export tariff rate applicable;*
- *The irradiance level for the area of the UK where the installation will be;*
- *The proposed capacity of the scheme;*

The first two of these are available from OFGEM's website. The irradiance is obtainable from the MCS irradiance map.

- *On the expenditure side, the current cost of solar PV in the market is required.*

This is more difficult to come by but the renewable energy organisations such as the Solar Trade Association or Renewable Energy Association will be able to help, along with consultants and other advisers, such as the author via his website www.publicsectorenergy.co.uk.

Conclusion

The different stages of a solar PV project are described throughout the chapters of this book. Some are more important than others and some have deeper implications. The business and financial cases are amongst the most important in the whole process.

To start with, general figures or those from another council's project can be used for the purposes of a 'back of an envelope' illustration. However, as the project planning develops, a much more sophisticated and developed financial plan has to take shape. This can be an iterative process, as the project crystallises. At some stage, however, the business and financial case has to be sufficiently complete to be presented to members for the purposes of supporting a decision. Experience has shown that if the business and financial case is wanting at this stage, it can be damaging to the project. Confidence can be fragile at this stage, so the business and financial case has to be sufficiently robust to compensate for this.

It is a living document, of course, and so can and will be amended, refined and improved as the project develops. This is particularly so in projects involving an external contractor, as the tendered costs will only be known further into the project in any event.

The next issue is where the council finds the funds to undertake the project, and that is considered in the next Chapter.

Key Learning Points

- *Both a business and financial case will be required for a solar PV project*
- *The business case is the rationale for doing it; the financial case is the detailed figures*
- *Income and expenditure need to be carefully calculated and projected over the life of the project*
- *Different business cases will apply under the RO and FIT regimes*
- *This is the part that most authorities get wrong – by using erroneous figures, not including all of the relevant matters and being unaware of current panel prices*

Financing of renewable energy projects and options for delivery 10

Introduction

In this Chapter, the potential options for the delivery of green projects are considered and specifically how they might be funded. There are many comments around as to what is best and what provides the right solutions. Accordingly, this Chapter will attempt to clearly set out the options and look at the rationale for a local authority entering each different type of arrangement. The conclusion, inevitably, is that there is no 'one size fits all' solution and the best option will depend on the authority concerned, the circumstances and a host of other factors.

In this regard, it should be emphasised that it is up to the members of each council to decide what their targets should be and what schemes they want to invest in. The green agenda offers all sorts of different arrangements: not just between renewable technologies (wind or solar), but between electricity or heat, and renewables and energy efficiency (under Green Deal). The operational arrangements and the funding arrangements will differ in relation to each type of work. The material below should therefore be used as a guide to identify the right option for a particular authority's project.

Preliminary Work

Previous Chapters have outlined the situation in relation to the role of the local authority (**Chapter 4**) and the need to develop a comprehensive strategy for climate change (**Chapter 5**). Such a strategy should cover both emissions reductions and renewable energy and set down the goals for the authority, the route map to get there and identify projects that would form the steps along the way.

The financial incentives were explained in **Chapter 8** and the income streams that might be provided, for example from a FIT scheme. **Chapter 9** outlined the need for a business and financial case to underpin any particular project and to identify the level of investment required and the return on capital that will ensue.

It is assumed that these crucial steps have all been taken and the authority is therefore ready to embark on a project. At this time two key decisions arise. Where will the money for the project be found? And in what way should it be delivered? These are considered below.

The Options for Delivery

Any local authority considering a renewable energy project will consider a number of inter-related factors. One of the main ones will be whether to undertake a project alone or in conjunction with others.

As mentioned in **Chapter 4**, local government finds itself in austere times. Historically, less joint work and shared services between authorities has happened than the Government wanted; but this is changing, again stimulated by financial hardship. So the first point of call might be other local authorities or public bodies. But there are also partners external to the public sector that will be interested in joining up to develop projects. This has been so for decades and is no different in relation to green energy schemes.

Another strand of public policy already mentioned is the localism agenda and the desire to decentralise services, not just to the local authority level, but where appropriate, right down to community level. Again, a community enterprise or specific community project is a possibility.

A summary of the options for delivery is featured below.

• Acting alone

The 'do-it-yourself' model. The local authority determines that it does not need assistance from others in relation to a project and can handle the necessary work itself. This will include developing a strategy, raising the money, preparing a business case, undertaking procurement exercises, managing the project and dealing with risk.

Whether this model is appropriate or not will depend on a number of circumstances, including its size, the scale of the project, its previous experience and available expertise.

Examples of this choice are frequent in relation to solar photovoltaic projects.

• A public sector joint venture

As many local authorities are considering projects involving renewable energy and energy efficiency, there should be plenty of potential joint venture partners available. Obvious examples are in the two tier areas, where a County Council and all of the districts within its area can all work together.

Outside of local government, there are health bodies and a range of other public bodies that might also be interested. These include Registered Providers for housing as an obvious example.

Again, whether this is appropriate or not will depend on the circumstances. Scale will be key. If a regional biomass supply chain strategy is contemplated, one local authority would struggle to put all the necessary infrastructure together on its own. However, if all the authorities in an area agreed to introduce biomass strategies (whereby their boilers would be transferred to biomass fuels over time) and supplement them by pooling woodland supply, developing a processing plant and acquiring the necessary transport, then it becomes a different matter.

• A private sector joint venture

The other alternative is to join with a private sector partner or partners to undertake the work. The advantage with such an operation is that often financing can be woven into such a deal and the careful choice of partner can also introduce much needed expertise into the project. The private sector has a very well established renewable energy sector in most areas and technologies that would provide suitable partners. This is particularly so in relation to solar PV.

In this scenario, again, scale would be important and relevant to the partner concerned. Large-scale joint ventures, perhaps comparable to a PFI project, would need to be on a scale sufficient to attract larger players. However, there is no reason why a local authority could not enter into a very modestly sized arrangement with a small regional player; again, perhaps solar PV offers an example.

A community based model

Community energy projects are considered in more detail in **Chapter 13**. However, the material here is for the purposes of explaining funding arrangements. A community-based model may take more than one form. On the one hand, there are community initiative businesses springing up, which operate commercially but without profit, and on the other a small community group that just wants to do something.

The community initiative model is well illustrated by the national social enterprise Empower Community. Its purpose is to roll out solar PV to the public sector and it has secured substantial funds to back its operation. Empower Community is run commercially like any other company, with full time personnel from a commercial background. The only difference is that profits are ploughed back into the operation and the communities where projects are undertaken, rather than distributed to shareholders.

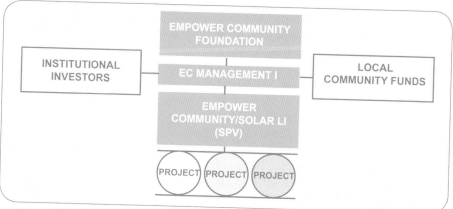

Figure 10.1 – Empower Community PV Offering (A national social enterprise)

Empower Community is a social enterprise focused on accelerating the transition to sustainable, low carbon local economies.

It has developed a solar PV programme over the last two years to offer a concept for a new way to undertake renewable energy and energy efficiency projects that benefits entire communities.

This includes attracting a major institutional pension scheme to invest up to £175m in solar PV projects with eight local authorities and housing associations across the UK. These involved gains being shared between the local authority or Registered Provider and the community, after costs have been deducted. The model works on the basis of profit distribution to all stakeholders. The principles inherent in the Empower Community model can be applied to other initiatives.

On the other hand, there is the first inner city solar power project in Brixton, South London. Solar panels have been fitted to an inner city urban housing block owned by Lambeth Council that will reduce the estate's carbon footprint, as well as earning income via the FITs for local investors. A community share issue offered 75,000 shares of £1 value each, which will result in a guaranteed return of 3% for investors, with remaining funds being invested in the carbon footprint of the Brixton area through a community energy efficiency fund, supporting energy saving improvements, education and re-skilling work. In the first five days of the offer being made, 14,000 shares had been allocated.

In contrast to Empower Community, this project seeks only to provide a single solar installation, though with plans to spend the surplus funds on other local community projects. Figure 10.2 contains details of this project, as an illustration of a small community offering.

This is a 100 % community owned solar project that started in April 2012.

A solar array with a capacity of 37kwp was fitted to the roof of a block on Loughborough Estate in Brixton, owned by Lambeth London Borough Council, and operated by an ALMO.

FITs will be claimed for the project, with a return of 5% planned, with 3% being returned to investors and the other 2% going towards a local community energy efficiency fund.

Source: Solar Power Portal

Figure 10.2 – Brixton Energy Solar 1 Project (A small community offering)

• A combination of the above

It would be possible to have a project with more than one partner, for example another public body and a community group. However, the more parties are involved, generally the more complex the arrangement will become.

There are a host of issues about governance of any joint arrangement, ranging from legal powers to engage in such a scheme, to the documenting of the agreement between the parties, its legal form and so on. Whilst it is unwise to generalise on such matters, as they very much depend on the circumstances, the following statements would represent a sensible guide:

- *Each authority has to decide what it wants to achieve first and then select the working arrangements that will deliver that model, not the other way round*
- *Scale will be key – there is no justification for creating expensive and complicated vehicles for a size of project that does not merit it*
- *It is generally true that the more partners there are, the more complex it becomes. Even a single joint venture arrangement is considerably more complex than an arrangement conducted entirely by the authority alone*

Deciding the right option for a project

The choice of option will obviously depend upon the circumstances of each authority at a particular time. The following are some factors that will be relevant in deciding which way to go:

- ## Risk

This is examined in detail in **Chapter 14**. Local authorities have become far more sophisticated in their knowledge of and treatment of risk in commercial transactions. Risk awareness was improved by new forms of procurement, such as PFI. It will now be possible to produce a good risk assessment, outlining what the risks are, what is the likelihood of them coming to pass, and who pays if they do. Whilst authorities may have limited experience of renewable energy projects, there is a mature industry in existence and so assistance can be procured.

- ## Reward

The business case for any project should not just deal with the finances. Just as the Government wants to put a price on carbon, so authorities should account for non-financial elements in a transaction. After all, as mentioned above, there are other tangible benefits from undertaking such a project and these need to be taken into account. If the electricity generated from the installation can be used by the council on the same site, it can defer commercial supply costing four times the value of the export tariff under FITs. Development of a comprehensive green strategy can bring different elements of the public sector together under a positive agenda and improve the wellbeing factor of an area. This has to be balanced against doing nothing and getting no such benefits.

- ## Accountability

Obviously, if the council undertakes a project itself, then the scheme will be covered by the normal operations of the council. However, if a joint venture is to be contemplated then governance arrangements will need to be considered. Other parties dilute democratic accountability in relation to a scheme.

• Ease and cost of implementation

Again, a distinction needs to be drawn between undertaking a single PV project, funded by the authority itself, and a major Green Deal arrangement which is multi party, worth tens of millions of pounds and complex.

Any addition of external parties to a project, increases the complexity. Any creation of new legal entities (special purpose vehicles, community interest companies etc) greatly increases the costs. Separate legal entities have all sorts of complications from legal powers, to tax, legal and financial advice requirements. It goes without saying that it will take much longer to put in place a complicated, multi party arrangement.

But authorities that have undertaken complex procurements in the past will understand these issues. They will have previous experience of comparable schemes to gauge any proposal by. Accordingly, it is up to each authority to decide what it is capable of and has the enthusiasm and drive to deliver.

If there are no such previous schemes to use as a benchmark, that says something about the capacity and experience of the authority for new ventures. In such circumstances, it is sensible to start modestly and build a green programme over, perhaps, ten years by a series of building blocks.

The Different Sources of Finance for a Project

There are a number of different ways that the council could finance a renewable energy project. These will need to be the subject of a detailed discussion within the authority. Different considerations will apply to different authorities and so it is for each authority to consider its position, what it is trying to do and then to identify the option best suited to that. A debt free district council would be in a very different position to a heavily indebted urban metropolitan authority.

Whilst all of the different sources are listed below, some will be more suitable than others and scale will again play an important part. As an example, pension funds will not be interested in any investment that is measured in less than tens of millions of pounds (usually at least £25m to £50m) and there will be a limit to the amount that any party can borrow on its own account.

Featured below are the relevant options for solar PV schemes. It should be noted that different, and more complex, funding models have been suggested for large housing retrofit work, such as Green Deal.

Reserves

Reserves are a curious concept in local authorities. This is simply money in the bank, kept as dictated by financial prudence for emergencies or when times are hard. Local authorities are subject to a fundamental duty in Section 151 of the Local Government Act 1972 to, "make arrangements for the proper administration of their financial affairs ..." This duty normally falls on the Director of Finance.

The money forming reserves might be on longer-term deposit, in bonds or gilts or simply on short-term deposit. The Icelandic banks problems of 2009, which are only now starting to be sorted, illustrated the different ways in which reserves can be held and the interest that can be earned and the problems that can arise.

On the political front, the Secretary of State for Local Government, Eric Pickles, has demonstrated his irritation at the level of local authority reserves in general. He points out that local government has squirrelled away over £10 billion and funds are desperately needed in the public sector economy. He wants some of this money spent to boost the local economies of the UK. Local authorities would refer him to the notion of prudence and point out that often despite there being big sums involved, it is only a small percentage of the annual operating costs of an authority.

Notwithstanding this, there is pressure on authorities to reduce reserves and a renewable energy project is an excellent example of a middle line.

If the authority has to spend some of its reserves, then it should spend them on something that delivers a gilt edged income, guaranteed by the Government, to continue with a position of financial prudence, as well as other policy benefits.

Slippage on other capital projects

A sizeable authority may well have a capital programme running into many millions of pounds over a number of years. Some projects will be on time and programme, others will be subject to a variety of delays or complications.

Depending on the size of the project, money earmarked for one project can often be used to fund another in the interim or where a funded project is removed from the capital programme.

Public Sector Borrowing

A local authority is able to borrow the money, using public sector channels, such as the Public Works Loans Board (PWLB). Whilst the interest rates under the PWLB went up as a result of the Comprehensive Spending Review 2010, the Budget of 2012 reduced rates slightly so that the rate is now just below 1% above gilts (80 basis points over Government gilts for loans). This means that it is still one of the best routes to inexpensive borrowing. This leads to an overall rate of around 5%, even now, and is less than any private sector company can borrow money in general.

There are other benefits from the PWLB too, which concern the conditions under which the money is loaned. Any commercial lender will normally place conditions on lending, and in the situation of renewable energy schemes, these can be onerous. For example, if a company seeks a loan for a wind energy project, the funder will want to ensure that the process has been properly followed and that industry standards have been adhered to. This might translate to the height of the wind test masts, the depth of boreholes or length for which data has been collected. This is because, if there is default, the lender might need to pass on the project to another developer to complete.

The PWLB will not impose any such conditions, as the loan is not just for one project, but is normally part of a package of borrowing arranged by the Director of Finance for a variety of projects and requirements for that year, as part of the authority's financial strategy. This is a significant commercial advantage in that it reduces the complexity and work otherwise associated with the loan.

Local authorities are well versed in lending from the PWLB and so such a proposal is unlikely to cause much concern in the council. It is simply a case of whether the money can be repaid, and that relates back to the legal duties of prudential borrowing and the business case, considered above.

Commercial lending

There are plenty of other offers of loans to a local authority, such as from the normal banks and commercial lenders. The reason that councils can normally arrange funding in this way is that the banks lend on the basis of the strength of the covenant of the customer. As local authorities cannot go into liquidation per se, they offer a much lower risk in relation to such borrowing under normal circumstances.

However, unless there are very competitive rates on offer, perhaps as part of some form of special arrangement, then the banks would struggle to match the rates offered by the PWLB, meaning that there is less of this type of borrowing in play.

Contribution by an Equity Partner

The next method of raising money is, effectively, to sell a stake in the system. In formal terms, this means offering an equity deal to a joint venture partner. The possible different parties in the deal were considered above, but assuming that an authority is not going to 'go it alone', then it will have one or more partners, whether public or private sector.

If a private sector party is chosen, this will often be because that party brings funding to the table. If there is a £10m investment to be made, then the council and its private sector partner can contribute £5m of investment each and take a 50% share in the venture. If this is the case, then the council would only need to find half of the money from its own sources or borrowing and will enjoy reduced risk.

However, there are other issues to consider here, as indicated above, and the main one is complexity from the number of partners and retaining control of the project.

Institutional Investors

Another way is to involve pension funds or other institutional investors to provide the capital for the deal. There is a difference between raising funds from a joint venture partner, which will be a hands-on contributor, involved in every stage, and an investor that is simply providing funds.

The major investors are looking for large-scale investments, often over £100m; if there are smaller projects, these are often packaged together to form a larger package that can be funded.

This includes the Green Investment Bank, which is only interested in funding at higher levels, with match funding from the private sector.

A Public Offering

This is perhaps the most interesting of the different options and something that has not yet been tried by any local authority in the country. Whilst there are examples of small community schemes seeking to raise money by public offerings, these are totally different.

The basic proposition here is to fund a commercial project to develop a renewable energy installation by selling a stake in the project to members of the public. There is a fundamental difference in a community project trying to raise money to build something that will be run on a 'not for profit' basis. As an example, the prospectus for the Saddleworth Community Hydro Ltd, which is a small scheme to raise money to put a water turbine on the reservoir in Saddleworth, states: "Investing in the Society should be seen as a social investment rather than a commercial investment." This means that the purpose of the company is to invest in other local projects and not to distribute money to the shareholders. By contrast, the local authority proposition here is to develop a commercial scheme and to pass on the commercial gains from that project to those that provide the finance (here, members of the public).

This perhaps raises a question as to why a local authority would want to engage in such a project? This is the link back to a comprehensive and sophisticated climate change strategy. An authority that has chosen high targets and that wants to create growth, has to invest time and energy in its creation. If a council pursues a renewable energy scheme, there are a variety of benefits that will arise. These have not been widely acknowledged, but were explained in **Chapter 5**. They are summarised in Figure 10.3 opposite.

These are some of the many benefits that will be realised by a local authority pursuing a renewable energy project. Often these will harmonise nicely with other elements of the policy agenda for a local authority, such as creating jobs and becoming more efficient. Hence, solar PV installations have been described as a 'win-win' situation.

In the public offering route of financing a major project, all of these benefits might still be captured by the local authority, save for the fact that it is passing on the surplus income to those who fund the project. In this way, it can still control the procurement, determine the size and position of any development and improve its energy security. And if the public likes the offering, and the offer is over-subscribed, then the council can bring forward the next major scheme in its green programme and have a public offering for that too. This would not just apply to solar PV schemes, of course, but to the whole green programme, featuring wind energy, biomass or heat networks.

If this were all to happen in accordance with the plan, then the area would get the economic boost by the supply chain being invigorated, jobs would be created and the financial returns, backed by the Government, would be reaped by the public investors.

- *Community Leadership*

Local authorities are encouraged to 'lead from the front' and to provide an example to their local areas.

- *Energy Security*

DECC has already confirmed that there are likely to be power cuts in the next decade, and any area that might be affected by such cuts will be in a stronger position if it has its own renewable energy sources.

- *Carbon Benefits*

The Government is legislating to place ever more stringent targets in relation to greenhouse gases. The CRC Energy Efficiency Scheme will require local authorities to purchase allowances in relation to their carbon emissions.

- *Effectiveness and Efficiency*

The renewables option gives the local authority the chance to save money, by using the energy that is generated from its own sources, thereby meaning that external energy costs do not have to be incurred.

- *Economic Benefits*

The green agenda offers the best potential for growth at the present time, by positively stimulating local supply chains.

- *Income Generation*

The green agenda is an important way to generate further funds, via the income streams from the financial incentives and the sale of excess electricity into the grid.

Figure 10.3 – Benefits of a Renewable Energy Scheme

There are a number of complications involved in such a proposal, such as the involvement of the Financial Conduct Authority and dealing with appropriate regulation, but these are capable of resolution. The local authority will need to seek advice on these points.

There are examples in Continental Europe of such developments, such as the Milagro Solar Park, developed in the Navarra region of Spain by the private company Acciona. Shares in this large 7.5 MW installation, illustrated in Figure 12.2, were sold to the public at the time of its construction. The offering was oversubscribed by members of the public who wanted to share in the benefits of the scheme and had calculated that a healthy surplus would result from the levels of Spanish FITs and the output of the installation.

There are a number of modern manifestations of the public offering concept. Two worth mentioning are the route of bonds/debentures and the other is crowd funding.

In 2014, a momentum had grown within local government circles to create a bond agency to raise finance for local authorities to rival the Public Works Loans Board. The Municipal Bonds Agency was proposed by the Local Government Association in 2013 and the idea is for the Agency to issue bonds and then lend the money to local authorities. The LGA said it expected councils to substantially reduce their borrowing costs through the creation of the agency. Bonds have, however, been considered for many years in local government circles, but nothing has come of this before.

In tandem with this, a number of independent proposals came forwards for bonds in relation to renewable energy schemes. Probably the best example of this the Big60Million bond from solar company Belectric. This bond for £4m was issued to raise the money to fund the Willsersey solar farm in Gloucester and was almost 20% over subscribed. The bonds were priced at £60 each, with a guaranteed fixed annual gross return on investment of 7 % and were sold in nine weeks. This was also the first bond to be officially certified as a 'climate bond' under the Climate Bond Standards and Certification Scheme.

Interestingly, there is an argument favoured by DECC that such schemes are not truly 'community', because they involve individuals getting the opportunity to invest, and not just the local community. However, a stronger view would seem to be that any type of individual investor is still a member of a community somewhere and so that is an advantage.

The individual investment idea has also been the subject of some success in a concept known as crowd funding. This is also sometimes referred to as 'democratic finance' based on the notion that an individual gets to invest in precisely what they choose to using this route. At the start this featured mainly small developers seeking to initiate   projects that would otherwise struggle to find investment. However, it has developed much more widely now and is seen as another mainstream way that funding can be raised.

The best-known proponent of crowd funding is Abundance, which was created in 2011 and was the first crowd funding platform to be approved by the Financial Conduct Authority. This raised more than £6m up to 2014 on renewable energy schemes. Investments are made in the form of a debenture, which entitles the investor to a proportion of the profits from the energy generated over the life of the debenture, which is usually 20 years.

Both of these forms of funding are of interest to local authorities. On the one hand, it could arrange for a bond to be issued to fund a development that it was in the process of procuring, but did not want to finance, and in the other it could seek assistance from a crowd funding organisation to raise some or all of the finance for one of its developments. Both would work well in the context of the local authority's covenant and financial standing in the community.

Advantages and Risk

Each of the ways described above is different. Some are very different, such as borrowing the money from the PWLB to fund a modestly sized solar PV installation and the entering of a complex joint venture with a partner or series of partners in the private sector, perhaps for a programme of work.

Again, there is no right or wrong and no 'one size fits all' solution. The following factors have been shown by experience to be relevant:

- *as ownership and control is divested, so the benefits dissipate. Obviously, if a local authority sells a half share in the facility, then it only benefits from a maximum of half of the income and surpluses*

- *scale will be important to the choice – some are for large scale investments only*

- *some are normal commercial transactions that are commonplace (such as bank borrowing); others are novel and have not yet been tried in this country*

- *some carry more risk than others and in each case a full risk assessment would need to be carried out*

Conclusion

This is a relatively new area, although the basic tenets of the commercial funding are the same as for other projects that have gone before. The essential difference between a renewable energy project and a Private Finance Initiative deal, one under the Building Schools for the Future arrangements or city centre regeneration project, is the availability of the financial incentives to provide a cast-iron income stream to service any loan requirements. This means that borrowing can be entered with significantly lower risk than would otherwise be the case; it also allows for projects and programmes to be 'ring fenced' in financial terms.

Local authorities are recommended to consider the various options when deciding on how to finance a project; look carefully at their own situation; appraise their knowledge, understanding, experience and expertise to date; keep an eye on the bigger picture (for example the link from renewables to Green Deal and energy efficiency) and to avoid acting in a fragmented way. There is no single correct way to do any of this. It is just a matter of deciding what is right for the authority.

Key Learning Points

- There are a number of different ways that a project can be financed
- There is no 'one size fits all' solution
- It depends on each authority, its appetite for risk and experience of commercial arrangements
- A key point will be its attitude to borrowing money to finance environmental projects
- It can be done alone, with other public sector bodes or the private sector
- It can be funded by reserves, borrowing, joint ventures, institutional investors or the public
- Care needs to be taken to choose the route that is right for the authority

11

Regulatory issues

Introduction

There are a number of regulatory issues that need to be considered when contemplating a solar PV project. Obviously, these will differ depending on the nature of the scheme. In Chapter 12, both land-based solar farms and buildings-based PV installations are considered, but have very different grid connection characteristics. The working of the national grid therefore needs some exploration. Naturally, a publication of this general nature can only give an overview.

Similarly, to connect to the grid, an interface with the Distribution Network Operator (DNO) will be required. These companies vary across the country, with some having better reputations in relation to the connection of renewable energy capacity than others. The system is overseen by the Office of Gas and Electricity Markets (OFGEM), which also has a role in the registration of renewable energy systems. Finally, in the electricity supply field, there are the big six energy companies, and a plethora of smaller electricity suppliers. Significant change is on the horizon for electricity, through a reform known as EMR (Electricity Market Reform) being promoted by the Government, but this is mentioned only in passing.

Also relevant to the regulatory mantle are the licensing requirements, for example to sell electricity to consumers and special requirements for those engaged in the fitting of renewable energy technologies, such as the Microgeneration Certification Scheme. All of these are considered below.

Finally, the issue of electricity storage is relevant to grid connections and the full impact of developments in this area will not be known for a while yet. However, it is already clear that storage technology is pressing ahead and has improved radically in the years to the end of 2014. Perhaps more importantly, the costs of storage have also fallen sharply and, in this regard, its progress is mirroring that of solar PV itself. This means that it is very likely that commercial storage solutions will be available in the next few years and this will further boost solar PV deployment.

However, it will have a different effect on grid connections, as if there is a solar farm with a large user needing constant power nearby, if a storage solution was available to provide power during the hours of darkness, only a lower capacity grid connection would be required.

The National Grid

What we know as the National Grid today has developed into its current form over many years. The basic system of AC supply using 230 volts was set at the beginning of the 20th Century. However, the system was never designed as a national system as such, which is one of its major problems. Another is that it is no longer fit for purpose, because it is designed and operated around fossil fuel supplies.

The grid grew organically over time, from being a small, decentralised system of generators at local level, to a connecting together of systems to make a larger and integrated system. It is ironic that the genesis of the system currently operated was distributed generation and that is precisely where the UK needs to return. The early part of the grid was accomplished by joining together 'regions' to provide back up for each other. All generators had to use AC supply at a common current, chosen as 50 Hz. Towards the end of the 1930's it was found to be safe to join all of the regional systems together to form a national network, controlled centrally. The system was nationalised in 1947 and privatised in 1989, but this did not affect its mode of operation.

The current system is for high voltage cables covering the UK and also linked to neighbouring countries. Energy is supplied from gigawatt sized, coal fired power stations, situated close to the source of the fuel (for example, Yorkshire or Wales); links have been added subsequently for nuclear power stations – again huge in size – that tend to be based on the coast in order to benefit from the water used for cooling purposes. The systems of England, Wales, Scotland and Northern Ireland are also linked together as part of this network.

These power stations are justified on economies of scale with distribution through a network of cables with reducing voltage, down ultimately to the consumer. So a high voltage system connects to the power station, then connects to the localised distribution networks, which deliver the electricity to the end user at a lower voltage.

The highest voltage is 400,000 volts (or 400 Kv) or 275 Kv run by the high voltage transmission companies, including National Grid. These are easily recognisable as the largest pylons, carrying power through the countryside.

Cables then reduce down through 132 Kv and 64 Kv, run by the Distribution Network Operators, down to the local distribution via 33Kv and 11 Kv substations. In order to use the power, consumers are able to link to cables supplying both 400 volt, 3 phase AC and 230 volt, single phase AC supply, supplied by a separate electricity supply company. The basic distribution is illustrated in **Figure 11.1** below.

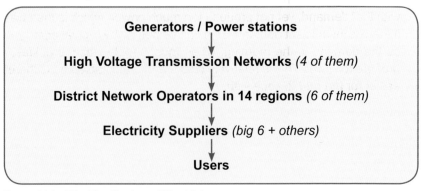

Generators / Power stations

↓

High Voltage Transmission Networks *(4 of them)*

↓

District Network Operators in 14 regions *(6 of them)*

↓

Electricity Suppliers *(big 6 + others)*

↓

Users

Figure 11.1 – The Distribution of Electricity

One of the key issues to understand about the operation of the National Grid is that, generally, no electricity is stored. The reason for this is quite simple: it is very difficult to store energy effectively. Accordingly, supply and demand are constantly matched and the overall system needs to have the capacity to achieve this.

Demand for electricity fluctuates during the day, depending on a number of factors, including weather, daylight conditions, time of day and what is on television. Matching supply and demand is becoming increasingly difficult, even before the advent of renewable energy. There are various reasons for this, including increased needs for energy, the way society works and the potential for losing major generating stations. This was demonstrated in 2014 when no less than eight of the major power stations were taken offline at the same time for one purpose or another. These included problems with nuclear stations and a major fire at one of the coal fired stations.

The need for more electricity stems from a society that has a voracious appetite for use of electrical equipment and, as **Chapter 2** notes, where use of energy is equated with badges of social success. This means that ever more generation of power is required.

The societal issue is best explained using the medium of television. When the 2012 European Championships Final (won by Spain) was being screened, it was watched by tens of millions of people. At half time it is fairly likely that most will have put the kettle on for a cup of tea, thereby placing huge demands on the electricity supply. It has to be able to cope with that demand, yet not produce too much power, which is then wasted if there is insufficient demand. This can be helped by regular activity, such as the demand in the morning, when most people wash, breakfast and prepare for work. This is relatively stable and predictable and is therefore easier for the grid to cope with.

Finally, having a large power station that produces GW of power break down is also a major problem, and cover has to be available. The problem is that power stations take a long time to get going from standstill. A nuclear power station will take 48 hours to reach full output from shutdown; a coal fired station 12 hours; oil fired will take eight hours. Whilst gas is better with combined cycle gas turbines (CCGT), these will still take six hours. So these power stations cannot simply be turned on and off. Running at reduced capacity also increases the levels of CO_2 per kilowatt of electricity produced, adversely affecting CO_2 targets. There is the ability to have some reserve capacity, which can be brought on line quickly. The balancing services to help with demand include 'spinning reserve' (conventional plant running at reduced capacity that can be upgraded); or demand management, provided by large industrial customers able to reduce demand on request.

So the national grid is already a complex and potentially fragile balance of supply and demand. Then renewable energy needs to be added to the mix. Firstly, it is all in the wrong places: out to sea (offshore wind), on the coast (wave and tidal), or in remote highland areas (onshore wind). Then there is the fact that it is variable (solar in the day only, wind only when the wind blows and so on). These added complications have caused significant concerns about the ability of the national grid to cope.

The mix of energy will also change radically from coal, gas and nuclear at present to nuclear, coal with carbon capture & storage and renewables at local level in the future. The capacity of the UK electricity system is currently around 75.5 GW – with a peak winter demand of 62.7 GW and a lowest summer demand of 20 GW. But the renewable energy national targets in the Climate Change Act 2008 will mean that hugely more energy from renewable sources will come on line, including wind, solar, wave and tidal and geothermal. All this has to be factored in.

The National Grid will therefore need to be reinforced and /or reconfigured, with substantial new cabling required to move power from the new sources of generation to the grid. This in itself is problematic, as such investment is massively expensive. A kilometre of 400 kv cable can cost around £300,000 if over ground or up to £5m if it is buried. A new process of electricity market reform has therefore been embarked upon by Government to pave the way for hugely more investment in renewable technologies and this is considered below. In the meantime, and for the purposes under discussion in this work, consideration will be given only to the key areas required.

High Voltage Transmission Networks

There are four high voltage transmission networks that act like a motorway system to take power directly from the large power stations and distribute it around the country.

These networks are owned by four companies:

- *National Grid*

- *Northern Ireland Electricity*

- *Scottish and Southern Energy*

- *Scottish Power*

Notwithstanding the separation of ownership, National Grid operates the electricity systems in England, Wales and Scotland as a single UK system.

The high voltage transmission network will cover the 400 kv cables mentioned above and illustrated in **Figure 11.2**.

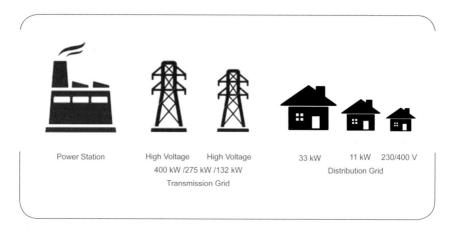

Figure 11.2 Transmission and Distribution of Electricity

The Role of the Distribution Network Operator

The Distribution Network Operator (DNO) is the level below high voltage transmission. There are fourteen licensed areas, geographically defined, within which area based distribution takes place. Each is operated by a DNO. The DNO's are companies licensed in the UK by OFGEM to distribute energy. There are six DNO's as indicated in **Figure 11.3** below.

The fourteen areas were based on the former Electricity Board boundaries. Aside from the six main DNO's, there are four independent DNO's operating smaller networks from within those areas.

The DNO distributes electricity from the national grid to homes and businesses. However, the Utilities Act 2000 prevents the distribution companies from supplying electricity. This is done by a range of electricity supply companies, chosen by the consumer, but dominated by the 'big six' outlined in **Figure 11.4**.

Scottish and Southern – *North Scotland & Southern England*

Scottish Power – *South Scotland/ North Wales, Merseyside and Cheshire*

Northern Powergrid – *North East England & Yorkshire*

Electricity North West Ltd – *North West*

Western Power Distribution – *East & West Midlands, South Wales and the South West*

UK Power Networks – *Eastern England, London & the South East*

Figure 11.3 – Distribution Network Operators

It can therefore be seen that the grid system is 'layered' with power generators at the top, moving through high voltage transmission networks, to local distribution networks, from which electricity suppliers supply customers and users.

- **British Gas**
- **EDF Energy**
- **E.On**
- **Npower**
- **Scottish Power**
- **Scottish and Southern Energy**

Figure 11.4 – Electricity Supply Companies - the 'Big Six'

The essential point of this analysis is that an agreement with the relevant network operator is necessary to connect a renewable energy system to the national grid or the local distribution system.

Connecting to the Grid

As mentioned above, this process will differ, depending on the nature of the installation.

Land Based Solar Farms

These are discussed in **Chapter 12** but for these purposes are large fields in which are placed thousands of solar panels, fixed on to racks and connected to the grid via inverters and metering equipment. As an example, a 5 MW solar farm would be expected to cover about 12 hectares of land and comprise over 25,000 panels.

The two main risks to any solar farm development are obtaining planning permission and organising a connection to the grid.

The grid connection is important, as there are normally no uses for that level of power on site. This is the essential difference between land based and buildings based systems. So if the power cannot be fed in to the grid, it is of no use, as it cannot generally be stored. It is also highly relevant that a large installation will produce a significant amount of electricity (for example a 5 MW solar farm in the South West might produce 5,000 MWh per annum) and that has to be safely incorporated into the national grid.

The ability to connect to the grid depends on there being a substation nearby. For a large installation, a 33 Kva substation will most probably be required or 11 Kva at the very least. Any less might be unable to cope with the generation capacity. Sometimes it will be possible to break into passing transmission lines across the land, depending on the circumstances.

The other issue is proximity. Solar farms tend to be in rural locations, but the substation needs to be fairly close, as it is expensive to cable high levels of power. Furthermore, other land may have to be crossed to reach a more distant substation, probably requiring wayleaves or other legal agreements.

The way that the system works essentially requires the generator to pay for any upgrade in the substation's equipment that is required in order to take the new source of power as well as paying for the costs of connecting the new source of power to that substation. The challenge from renewable energy is provided by connecting new sources of renewable energy to a distribution network that has traditionally carried power from large power stations in one direction only. This was a particular issue in Cornwall, where the peak winter load was around 550 MW, but the summer load was considerably less. In the summer with the influx of renewable energy projects such as solar farms, the generation could well exceed that level of capacity, thereby making the area a net exporter of electricity. Except that the grid was not designed to go the other way. This may therefore require upgrading of equipment and this can be expensive.

It is for this reason that the DNO is asked to provide an estimate of those costs at an early stage of the project, to see if it is affordable. Estimates can vary widely and so little guidance can be given on this. The author has had quotes of £80,000 for a 5 MW solar farm in the South West but is aware of similar quotes for over £1m for the same sized installation in another part of the country. Those costs might destroy the business case for the project. On average, for a land based solar farm, a developer will include around £75,000 per MW of capacity for a grid connection. So a 5 MW solar farm would be expected to be around £300k - £400k.

The DNO will not normally guarantee the connection either. It will give an estimate in terms of cost and time but will not offer a contract until the generator is ready to connect. There is a simple reason for this: if an agreement is reached and a formal offer made (which cannot be revoked) and accepted, if another generator comes along but the grid cannot take any more capacity, that latter generator would not be able to connect to the grid, despite having a working system. There is therefore a 'first come first served' basis in operation. The first generator that is ready to connect will enter into an agreement with the DNO. This can be problematic because if a generator did build a £10m facility but could not then connect to the grid, either at all or for a reasonable cost, this would be catastrophic. However, these matters can usually be managed. Once an offer is made by the DNO, it is open for a period of time to allow the necessary work to be completed.

With land based systems the generator also needs to consider whether to have a single circuit connection or two circuits. The latter will enable generation to continue if one of the circuits fails; the former will not. In a commercial system of say 5 MW, failure in the summer months for any length of time could be costly, as FITs or ROCs are based on amounts of energy generated. Again, this is a commercial decision, as two circuits come at a significantly higher cost.

Buildings Based Systems

Again, there is a difference, depending on the scale of the installation. A domestic system of, say 4 kw peak capacity, is a very different prospect to a large commercial building with a 300 kw peak system on the roof.

Domestic systems will invariably not be problematic. The wiring of the house will need to be checked but if it is in good order, then the installation should be possible, with the addition of a new fuse spur and isolation switch.

Social housing projects offer a different challenge, as these will involve hundreds of houses, potentially thousands, closely packed into a community. This will put the local grid under more pressure due to the electricity needing to be redistributed and the DNO will have to confirm that it can cope.

For a commercial sized installation, the nature of the building's electrical connection and system will be very relevant. Often buildings have one or three phase supply and more than one supply or meter point and this will need to be explored. It may be that work is necessary to the electrical system before an installation can proceed. This is one of the preliminary checks that should be carried out, as described in **Chapter 14**.

Tactics for Dealing with Grid Connections and DNOs

The grid is a real issue for local authorities seeking to develop larger solar parks. As time has gone on, the public sector has grown bolder in its aspirations and there are now plans afoot for local authorities that are large landowners to develop well in excess of 10MW of solar capacity. This will inevitably raise grid issues.

An example might be a County Council that wants to utilise its extensive land holdings for solar park development. It develops a programme, whereby up to 20 sites are identified as suitable for solar PV installations. The question then is how it gets grid connections for those sites.

The first point to make is that it is necessary to develop a relationship with the local DNO. The DNO is a body that will want to have a relationship with the local authority as there is mutual benefit from this. Accordingly, the approach should be made at the highest level, preferably by the Chief Executive of the authority to their counterpart at the DNO. The proposal is that the local authority wants to develop a programme of renewable energy that will require grid connections.

However, it is important at this very early stage to make it clear that the authority is not a commercial developer and should not be treated as such. This is not all about the money, but about improving the infrastructure of the area and ploughing the proceeds back into the local economy. In most circumstances, the DNO will treat the local authority differently from the many commercial developers that they normally deal with.

This may have a number of practical ramifications. The first is that, technically, any party that wants the DNO to look at a site and give an estimate of grid connection potential and costs will need to make an application. In the experience of the author this is rarely required for the local authority. Usually, a meeting can be arranged with the DNO representative to discuss local authority sites in an informal manner. This might be very helpful, for example if there are grid constraint problems and limited connectability. Here it has been known for the DNO to tell the local authority where there is capacity, so that the local authority can determine if it owns any land in that area that could be used for the purpose.

It should always be borne in mind that the grid is a problem in the UK and it is highly unlikely that any local authority would be able to obtain permission to connect a high number of sites to the local grid. One of the reasons for this is the extent of private sector development in land based solar PV that has gone on in the past four or five years.

Commercial Developer Solutions to the Grid Dilemma

This raises the question as to how such a large number of commercial solar farms have managed to connect to the grid over the past few years. The answer is that the larger developers have put in place provisions to build their own networks. Here, there is a rule similar to that which applies in local government for new roads. If a developer builds a road to proper standards, then the local authority will adopt it. Whilst the builder has suffered the costs of constructing the road, thereafter it is maintained at public expense.

This is largely the same for electricity grids. So developers have acquired large areas of land and have then put in their own grid to connect their solar sites to. Thereafter, the DNO has adopted the grid, being grateful that this new grid capacity that it did not have to fund itself. These networks are often referred to as local 'hubs'.

The relevance of this to local authorities might not be immediately apparent. However, it is very relevant for two reasons: firstly, with its developer hat on, a local authority might want to join with others to fund a grid extension, thereby facilitating a development on its land. But secondly, because it could use its economic development powers to undertake this work on behalf of many other developers in the community, whether commercial in nature, large or small, community or individual.

If a local authority cannot get a grid connection, then it is likely that other developers in its area will not be able to either. This means that projects are being held up - not a good situation for an area that wants to create new jobs and growth to continue the steady progress out of recession. But the Council can help with this, using its economic development powers.

good situation for an area that wants to create new jobs and growth to continue the steady progress out of recession. But the Council can help with this, using its economic development powers.

In an example with a County Council, the idea emerged that if someone could collect together all of the parties who seek a grid connection for a renewables project, then liaison with the DNO would be possible to create and cost up new capacity. This is not the DNO's responsibility, of course; even though they are statutory bodies, their formal duties are restricted to operation of the grid and related matters. Local authorities, by contrast, have economic development functions and a clearer form of economic development would be hard to identify.

This would be enhanced if the local authority also had a large project requiring grid connection that could act as the 'anchor tenant' in the negotiations. In the example here, the council would be developing a very large solar PV farm that would provide a sizeable amount of the fees needed to enhance the grid capacity. Other developers find grid issues hard to deal with (particularly community schemes) and would therefore welcome the operation of this facilitative role to help them get the connection they need to deliver their projects. The DNO's would not object to this intermediary role either, as it makes their statutory duties easier to comply with.

As has been seen elsewhere, projects create jobs and employment and the APSE research paper 'Powerful Impacts' (December 2011) demonstrated that for every pound spent on renewable energy in an area, there is £2.90 worth of benefit to the economy in cashable benefits – an almost threefold return on investment. On average, the schemes assessed by their researchers also created 12 jobs and saved 650 tonnes per annum in carbon emissions.

So by helping free up a grid logjam, the council would reap many benefits, not least the opportunity to develop its own scheme. It is this sort of progressive thinking that is necessary to free up grid problems.

G59 and G83 Applications

It is apparent from the examination of the electricity supply network above that a solar photovoltaic system is connected to the local distribution network. Whereas the traditional situation has been a small number of very large power stations being connected via the electricity network to a very large number of consumers, under renewable energy, it is more a case of a very large number of small generators connected to the local distribution network.

These generators are called small scale embedded generators (SSEG). As soon as a small system is connected up, the generator becomes an SSEG.

There are two sets of rules that govern small scale embedded generators and these are Engineering Recommendation G83 and Engineering Recommendation G59, published by the Energy Networks Association, which is a body representing all DNOs.

Domestic systems in excess of 3.68 kw, or 11.04 kw for large commercial buildings, have to comply with G59/1 which requires a written application to the DNO and various other procedural steps. Systems lower than 3.68 kw have to comply with G83/1, which is less onerous.

Engineering recommendation G83 sets out the standards required for the connection of small scale embedded generators of up to 16 amps per phase, single or multiple phases. Its main terms are that an inverter which is G83 type tested must be used; the system must be no more than 16 Amps per phase; there must be an isolating switch for the PV system near the point of connection; and the DNO must be sent all of the relevant documentation once the system has been commissioned.

Electricity Supply Licences

This book has been written on the basis that the electricity generated from a solar PV installation will either be:

- *Used on site (for buildings)*
- *Supplied to the grid (via a FIT licensee)*
- *Supplied to a private user via private wire*
- *Or sold wholesale (for solar farms)*
- *Sleeved to the local authority to use in its premises*

However, if a local authority wants to supply electricity directly to consumers, it needs a licence from OFGEM under the Electricity Act 1989. The problem is that an electricity supply licence is both complex and costly to procure, with the necessity to comply with complex industry codes. The big electricity suppliers are experienced in dealing with these codes and have the financial resources to develop new systems accordingly. Other generators, such as local authorities, would be at a significant disadvantage.

OFGEM therefore introduced a 'lite licence' for smaller generators, allowing them to supply electricity without the full burdens of obtaining a full supply licence. This junior supply licence requires a small energy generator to make arrangements with a larger energy supplier. However, the Local Government Association pointed out in its document Local Government's Offer on Climate Change (Local Government Group 2011), there is no requirement on the bigger suppliers to provide this service to small schemes and no incentive for them to do so. The licence lite concept is being promoted by the Greater London Authority on behalf of the public sector. In 2014 it submitted its formal application for a licence, but only for commercial not domestic premises. It is generally regarded that the licence lite format as it is currently in the rules will not work. However, OFGEM cannot recommend changes to the Government until it is clear that this is the case.

However, if a local authority wants to supply electricity directly to consumers, it needs a licence from OFGEM under the Electricity Act 1989. The problem is that an electricity supply licence is both complex and costly to procure, with the necessity to comply with complex industry codes. The big electricity suppliers are experienced in dealing with these codes and have the financial resources to develop new systems accordingly. Other generators, such as local authorities, would be at a significant disadvantage.

OFGEM therefore introduced a 'lite licence' for smaller generators, allowing them to supply electricity without the full burdens of obtaining a full supply licence. This junior supply licence requires a small energy generator to make arrangements with a larger energy supplier. However, the Local Government Association pointed out in its document Local Government's Offer on Climate Change (Local Government Group 2011), there is no requirement on the bigger suppliers to provide this service to small schemes and no incentive for them to do so. The licence lite concept is being promoted by the Greater London Authority on behalf of the public sector. In 2014 it submitted its formal application for a licence, but only for commercial not domestic premises. It is generally regarded that the licence lite format as it is currently in the rules will not work. However, OFGEM cannot recommend changes to the Government until it is clear that this is the case.

When the first edition of this book was published in 2012, the view of the author was that supplying electricity directly to consumers would probably not be an issue for many authorities. This was despite many having discussed the establishment of an Energy Services Company (ESCO). However, this view has changed in the intervening period. During 2014 it became clear that there were a number of local authorities and other bodies with aspirations to achieve full supply licences under the Electricity Act 1989. In particular Nottingham City Council has said that it will take this path and a group of Housing Associations in Scotland have set up a group called Our Power, which has also stated its intention in this regard.

The reason that an authority might aspire to this is very simple. In order to maximise the social value of the power generated by a local authority, it needs to supply directly to customers. Local government largely takes the view that the system in the UK is broken. It is a centralised system, dominated by six huge electricity suppliers. Prices continually rise and this has caused considerable concern amongst the public. High prices contribute to a range of social problems, including fuel poverty, health disorders and impacts on lifestyles. If a local authority could become a player in the local electricity market once again (this was the case 50 years ago) then this position could be positively influenced. However, to do this, there has to be direct supply.

The slow progress with licence lite – which has not seen a single licence granted after five years of work – has led to many authorities dismissing it as an option at all and aiming straight for direct licenced supply. In fact the best way to achieve this would be for all local authorities to collaborate on the establishment of a public sector licenced supplier, which could then front up all of their electricity generation across the country. However, this may not be practicable and so it is more likely that groupings will form, perhaps on a regional basis, for this purpose.

In the interim, 2014 also saw a new development where one of the non-big six electricity suppliers offered joint venture arrangements with local authorities and public bodies, whereby its supply network could be accessed by authorities and a local tariff determined for new customers of the joint venture arrangements. This is likely to be a popular half way house, although in these circumstances, the authority will not control the venture in quite the same way.

One of the other main advantages of being a direct supplier is that the prices for retail supply of electricity are higher than for wholesale supply. This means that there is a band of profit that is currently with the electricity supply companies that could be captured and used to either reduce prices or invest further in the local network.

Electricity Market Reform (EMR)

The Government has realised that the electricity system needs to be reformed in order to accommodate the move from largely fossil fuel based generation to renewable energy and distributed generation.

In December 2011 it released a consultation paper Electricity Market Reform, which set out the challenge as follows:

- *Demand for electricity may double by 2050; this is largely due to other developments in the climate change agenda, not least the move to electric transport and heating*
- *A quarter of the UK's existing electricity supply infrastructure will need to be replaced by 2020; old, polluting coal fired power stations are coming off line as they do not meet stringent new emissions controls; but the decision on new nuclear was delayed and it may not be possible to install enough renewable energy to meet the need by that date*
- *The power sector needs to lead the charge towards decarbonisation of the economy and needs to achieve the goal of decarbonisation by 2030; however, it is currently dominated by fossil fuels and there are cost barriers of entry to new technologies*
- *By 2030, 30% of electricity needs to come from renewable sources to meet the legally binding EU target under the Renewable Energy Directive*
- *Currently gas fired generation offers the lowest price and risk investment and will continue to play an important role in the market*

The goal is to enable more new technologies to get a foothold in the market and enjoy equal access. These include low carbon technologies, such as solar PV and wind, fossil fuel stations with Carbon Capture and Storage and technologies to better balance supply and demand.

OFGEM estimates that at least £200bn of investment will be required to achieve this goal. Of this, at least £100bn would be for new generation and transmission assets in electricity. As the Consultation Paper puts it:

"Without reform, the existing market will not deliver the scale of long term investment, at the pace we need, in particular in renewables, new nuclear and CCS, nor will it give consumers the best deal. However, if we are to meet our long term carbon targets, we need to reform the market now, to make low carbon investment more attractive."

The Government therefore proposed a series of reforms that will make low carbon technologies a more attractive option, whilst still maintaining a balance between the need to keep costs down for consumers and giving certainty to attract new investment. The proposals are fourfold and are set out in **Figure 11.5**.

1. *Carbon Price Support – supporting the carbon price will lead to further long term investment in low carbon technologies, by making fossil fuel generation more expensive*
2. *FITs – long term financial incentives provide more certainty for revenues from low carbon generation. A new FIT system is proposed, called the 'contract for difference', which will replace the current RO scheme*
3. *Capacity Payments – targeted payments to encourage security of supply through the construction of flexible reserve plants or demand reduction measures*
4. *An Emissions Performance Standard - a limit to how much CO2 the most carbon intensive power stations (coal) can emit. This effectively means no new coal fired power stations would be possible without CCS technology fitted*

Figure 11.5 – Proposals for Electricity Market Reform

The EMR process was taken a step further by the White Paper issued in July 2011 Planning Our Electric Future: A White Paper for Secure, Affordable and Low Carbon Electricity and the measures were included in the Energy Bill announced in the Queen's Speech in March 2011.

When the Energy Act 2013 was finally passed, the Government reiterated the need for its provisions. It said, the UK is at a critical juncture in the way it generates electricity, with around a fifth of capacity available in 2011 is set to close over the coming decade. At the same time, demand for electricity is expected to double from its current level by 2050, particularly with the expected electrification of heating and transport.

Set against this backdrop, it is imperative that the right mechanisms are in place to attract the £110 billion investment that is needed to ensure that the UK can meet its requirements for secure and flexible supplies of electricity at affordable prices. The reforms will ensure that low-carbon generation is sufficiently incentivised to ensure new plants are built, which will be crucial if the UK is to meet its obligations to reduce carbon emissions and increase the use of renewables.

With such large-scale changes to the electricity market, the key measures in the Energy Act focus on EMR, which consist of provisions for:

- *Contracts for Difference – long-term contracts between a CFD counter-party and eligible generators, funded by contributions from licensed electricity suppliers to provide stable and predictable incentives for companies to invest in low-carbon electricity generation*
- *Capacity Market – to ensure the security of electricity supply, including provisions to allow Electricity Demand Reduction to be delivered*
- *Investment contracts – long-term contracts broadly similar to CFDs to enable early investment in advance of the CFD regime coming into force*
- *Conflicts of Interest and Contingency Arrangements – to ensure the institution which will deliver these schemes is fit for purpose*
- *Liquidity and Power Purchase Agreements – to ensure a competitive wholesale market and help independent renewable electricity generators access the market to sell their power*
- *Renewables Transitional – transition arrangements for investments under the Renewables Obligation scheme and*
- *Emissions Performance Standard – to limit carbon dioxide emissions from new fossil fuel power stations*

Other Specific Regulatory Provisions

There are also other specific regulatory provisions, chiefly the Microgeneration Certification Scheme (MCS). This was introduced by the Government at the same time as the new FITs.

The MCS is an internationally recognised quality assurance scheme that demonstrates to customers that companies engaged in installation work on solar PV schemes are committed to meeting rigorous and tested standards. It has been designed with input from installer and product representatives. Similar to the Gas Safe Register, the MCS gives a mark of competency and demonstrates to customers that installations are to the highest quality every time.

Installer certification entails assessing the supply, design, installation, set-to-work and commissioning of renewable microgeneration technologies.

The MCS also provides an internationally recognised quality assurance scheme that demonstrates the quality and reliability of approved products by satisfying rigorous and tested standards. Product certification involves type testing of products and an assessment of the manufacturing processes, materials, procedures and staff training.

Under the FITs, where there is an MCS standard, both the technology and the installer must be MCS certificated to be eligible for FIT payments.

Those wishing to become a MCS certificated installer, or to have their products certificated under the MCS, must do so by applying to a Certification Body. All accredited Certification Bodies will have been accredited by UKAS under EN45011 to undertake certification assessments under the MCS. Installers and product manufacturers may select which Certification Body they apply to become certificated.

Lastly, to become an MCS Installation Company, a company needs to be a member of the REAL Assurance Scheme or an equivalent Office of Fair Trading approved consumer code scheme.

The MCS requirement is a response to the requirements placed on member states by the Renewable Energy Directive to ensure that the certification schemes are available for installers of renewable technologies. MCS and equivalent schemes under the European Standard EN 45011 provide consistent standards.

It should be noted that the MCS is a measure to protect consumers and only applies to systems with a capacity up to 50 kw. Thereafter, a system qualifies as a large system and the Government's view is that anyone procuring such a system must either understand what they are doing or be able to arrange appropriate advice.

Conclusion

The elements under the regulatory banner are quite complex and will not be of major concern to most local authorities approaching a scheme. It is the basic elements, like the grid connection and the G83 and G59 forms that will be most in issue, rather than the wider proposals for changing the whole system in operation in the UK.

The main advice to an authority is to consult the DNO early and develop a relationship with the company. The necessity for a regular and in-depth dialogue, between the council and the DNO, has been confirmed by most authorities that have already fitted solar PV systems. It is also necessary to ensure that sufficient time is allocated in timetables to accommodate this part of the exercise. Again, experience shows that it usually takes longer than predicted to get through this stage of the process, as mentioned in **Chapter 14**.

Key Learning Points

- *The electricity system in the UK is complex and difficult to understand*
- *It is also subject to a major reform programme that will change it fundamentally over the next decade*
- *But a basic understanding of the national grid is necessary, including high voltage networks, distribution network operators and the process of connecting to the grid*

Installing Solar PV on Commercial Buildings by Lancaster City Council

Background

Lancaster City Council has long demonstrated its commitment to tackling the challenges of climate change by focusing on reducing the council's energy costs and investigating ways to generate income. To achieve this, in 2008, the council commenced a programme to reduce its energy consumption with the aim of reducing the amount of carbon dioxide resulting from its activities and the associated costs. The target of this project has been to achieve an annual 3.4% reduction of carbon dioxide (CO_2) emissions with a view to achieving a 34% reduction by 2020.

Although the programme has targeted all council operations, in early 2011 a project was commenced which aimed to investigate the possibility of installing solar PV on one municipal building within the council building stock. However, following preliminary investigations, it became apparent that there existed the possibility to expand the project into one which could involve the installation of solar PV on to multiple municipal buildings.

To that end, on 4 October 2011, Cabinet approved the allocation of up to £750,000 from the General Fund's Invest to Save Reserve to install solar PV panels on the council's municipal buildings. In addition, Cabinet approved the allocation of up to £1m from the Housing Revenue Account's Major Repairs Reserve to install solar PV panels on council housing communal buildings. This decision was based on council priorities to reduce energy costs and increase income whilst also taking action to tackle the challenges of climate change.

Implementation

Once political support was secured, the project began in earnest and steps were made to start a tendering exercise to appoint a number of contractors to a framework contract. The installations would then be undertaken by the contractors on that framework with the initial order to be awarded to the tenderer who in the opinion of the council offered the best value for money option against the schedules provided.

To help inform the contractors, an initial exercise was undertaken to identify all of the buildings within the council's control and estimating the size of schemes which could be installed. However, the installation of solar PV is a new area of activity for the council and as such there existed no expertise in solar technology within the council. The use of independent expert advice therefore became a key element of the success of the project and, to maximise the expertise of the contractors, it was decided to run the project as a design and build, with the focus being on the contractor to identify the best schemes using the finance and the timescales available.

The business case behind the decision to approve the allocation of council funds was based on a model which maximised the financial gains available through the government's FIT scheme. However, during the implementation of the project the UK government announced a series of changes to the FIT scheme which meant that installations completed after 3 March 2012 would benefit from a lower financial incentive. In the light of these changes, the council revisited the financial model but found that it was still able to benefit from the higher FIT rates for most of the installations provided they could be delivered by the March deadline.

The change in deadline affected the scope of the project and limited the buildings chosen for installations to those where all works could be completed by the March deadline. All of the All of the additional works required to install panels, e.g. works required by the DNO and planning requirements, then became critical in determining which projects were viable in the given timescales.

However, with the revised deadline, the council worked with the principal contractor to complete installations at six properties comprising a mixture of municipal buildings and sheltered housing schemes. The total size of the systems installed at the six sites amounts to 212 kWp which will provide an annual output for the council of approximately 160,000 kWh and enable annual CO_2 savings of approximately 128,000 kg/annum.

Conclusion

In delivering this project, it provided a good opportunity to work in partnership with colleagues from across the public sector and beyond. Although the time scales for delivery were considered to be tight, the project appeared to run extremely well. The appointment of an external CDM Co-ordinator proved to be a success on the basis that having an external provider ensured a completely impartial approach; something which became a very valuable asset to the team and brought a tremendous amount of knowledge and experience from which all the parties have benefitted from.

There is no doubting that the change in FITs affected a large number of proposed solar PV installations throughout the UK and Lancaster City Council was no exception. However, whilst the changes added an extra dimension of complexity, it served to focus the attentions of those involved in the implementation of the project.

This success would not have been possible without the project team, consisting of officers from across Lancaster City Council, Lancashire County Council, the contractor Forrest and external consultants, all of whom have worked exceptionally well pulling all this together in such a short space of time. In doing so, Lancaster City Council has delivered a series of schemes with some providing estimated paybacks of approximately seven years.

Mark Davies
Head of environmental services
Lancaster City Council

Choosing land based or building systems

12

Introduction

Solar photovoltaic systems can be deployed in two main ways. The first is based on buildings, usually roofs and linked to the electricity supply of the building. The second is free standing, land-based systems, often referred to as solar farms.

The two methods differ considerably, despite both being effectively the fitting of solar panels. They may also have different motivations on the part of the local authority involved. Buildings based systems are often part of a larger asset management strategy, which may also include energy efficiency works, Green Deal or the like. The council might benefit from solar as part of a wider programme or fit solar PV as part of a retrofit contract for green improvements. By definition, such work can be at any scale and many small installations have been completed of this type.

Land-based systems are normally part of a different strategy. This time, it is more income generation and low carbon energy that is the motivation. This is often linked to an economic development strategy, with the energy being provided to the council itself, or to promote economic growth in the area via an Energy Services Company (ESCO). A good example of this might be a facility near an industrial or commercial park, where jobs can be created and businesses attracted to relocate. By definition, free-standing solar PV installations tend to be large, possibly very large, and therefore are quite different in nature.

The Choice of Development

Which type of development is right for which authority depends entirely on the nature and position of the council and its strategy. The wider strategic issues are considered in **Chapter 5** and it is emphasised there that the council has to be clear what it wants to achieve from any investment.

On the one hand, there might be a northern, urban local authority that wants to upgrade its buildings and facilitate the growth of new local employment. For it, a buildings-based programme, with many different buildings being fitted over a period of years, will create the local jobs desired and deliver a number of different outcomes for a relatively modest investment.

Another authority, though, might be a geographically large county council, with significant land assets that are not being exploited effectively and the potential to raise funds via borrowing or reserves. For such an authority, a land-based system might well present a better opportunity.

Both of the different approaches are explored below and **Figure 12.1** summarises the key points.

Land based

Pro's
- If the council has the land, it can be used effectively
- If the council has the land, there is no cost
- Large energy generation available in one go
- Local authorities capable of large commercial projects
- Land based projects do not rely on buildings, roof strength, stability or orientation

Con's
- It is a large project to deliver
- It requires substantial capital funding
- It is less linked to the climate change strategy than buildings based schemes
- There is more commercial risk
- There is more complexity eg Power Purchase Agreements
- Grid connection can be an issue, given the size of these projects

Building based

Pro's
- More local jobs are created
- Fewer objections from the public
- Better use of assets
- Clearer link to energy efficiency and Green Deal

Con's
- Smaller capacity so more projects required
- Many need planning consent anyway
- The DNO could be a problem
- The Buildings might not be suited to solar
- Specific problems such as wiring, meters and supply points

Figure 12.1. – Pro's and Con's of a Solar Scheme

Land Based Systems

Land-based systems are prevalent on the Continent, but did not reach the UK mainland until 2010. Before the advent of FITs, explained in Chapter 8, no solar farms had been built in this country. But the economic case for them improved to such an extent when the financial incentives came in, that plans to create installations mirroring those in Spain, Germany and Italy were drawn up.

When the feed in tariff was in its first phase, the FIT rate for a 5 MW solar farm was in the region of 29 pence per kwh. It did not take long for the commercial sector to realise that returns on investment exceeding 20% could be achieved in the far South and South West of England. Fortunately, there was extensive experience of solar farm developments already available in those European countries and so it was a natural extension of the market to introduce solar farms to the UK.

For reasons explained in **Chapter 8**, it was this factor that caused the Government to panic over the level of FITs, and started a review process that led to the rates for land based systems to be slashed. However, for reasons mentioned below, solar farms have now come full circle and are back on the agenda. This has largely been due to the significant reductions in their cost.

What is a Solar Farm?

The best way of explaining a land-based solar PV installation is to use an example. The one featured in **Figure 12.2** is the Milagro Solar Farm in the Navarra region of Spain, completed in 2007. This is a 9.5 MW solar PV installation built by international company Acciona. The photograph illustrates the size and nature of the arrays that comprise the overall installation. This is one of the hundreds of arrays on the site and the size can be determined by the visiting party from Cornwall Council (including the author) standing in front of it.

Figure 12.2 – An Array in the Milagro Solar Farm, Navarra, Spain

Normally, solar farms are comprised of a large, rural tract of land (at least 10 hectares), on which are fitted lines and lines of solar panels. As this is not a buildings based system, the panels sit on racks or arrays on the ground and are either fixed systems (very much like a solar panel on a roof) or 'tracker' systems. The latter work by moving, either side to side (horizontal tracking systems) or up and down (vertical tracking systems) - or both - in order to maximise the impact of the sun's rays throughout the day. The arrays are connected together via wiring, fed through inverters, and via a generation meter into the national grid.

A solar farm is quite a spectacle and they create wonder over their size and format. However, they are quite straightforward in construction terms and their working.

The purpose of a solar farm is quite simply the generation of power on a larger scale, as the electricity all goes to the national grid, rather than being used on site. One of the largest solar farms in the world was completed in Gujarat in India in 2012. Solar Power Portal reported that this was 600 MW capacity, covering 2,000 hectares of land. Before that, another farm over 600 MW had been completed in the United States. In Europe there are large installations too, such as the one in Moura, Portugal which is 45 MW capacity with 262,000 modules. It takes some thought to appreciate just how big these installations actually are.

In the UK are installations of 5 MW or below were common, using feed in tariffs; however, since the costs of land based solar starting consistently falling, so have installations grown in size. During 2014 a large number of sites around the 40 MW capacity were constructed using the Renewables Obligation. Due to changes in the rules regarding the availability of the Renewables Obligation, explained in **Chapter 8**, it is unlikely that this level of development will be maintained after 2015.

A 5 MW land based solar PV facility is well within the capability of a local authority to procure and it is those types of installations that are described below.

Requirements for a Solar Farm

The following are required to bring a solar farm project to fruition:

* *Land*
* *A strong business case*
* *Available finance*

* *Planning permission*
* *A viable grid connection*

(a) Choosing the Site

As mentioned above, local authorities own large tracts of land in different types of usage. The Government has made it clear that it does not want to see agricultural land of a good quality that is currently used for food production being lost to renewable energy (solar farms, biomass growing and so on). Fortunately, much of the land that local authorities own and control is not agricultural in nature; indeed, much of it is brown-field, contaminated or of little use for anything else. Good examples are former landfill sites and car parks. This means that there is much scope for using such land for solar installations.

In choosing a site, the first issue is ownership. If the land is in the ownership of another party, then it has to be secured by some form of legal agreement (lease, licence etc.) and this will add a cost to the business case and may take some time to arrange. Since the introduction of financial incentives, it has also become more common knowledge what land capable of hosting renewable facilities is worth, making the purchase or leasing of such land much more difficult. Accordingly, the material below is written on the basis that the land is already owned by the local authority and has no legal restrictions, for example restrictive covenants, preventing its use for this purpose.

It is also assumed that the sites are 'oven ready' IE there is nothing specifically that needs to be done to the site in preparation for the construction of a facility. It may be that a council owns land that requires treatment, decontamination or the like, before it will be possible to develop it. Again, this will delay matters and whilst this does not mean that such land cannot be used (for example decommissioned landfill sites), it is assumed any preliminary work has already been undertaken.

Evaluating what sites the council has available is something that needs to be done methodically, and as part of the wider climate change work of that authority. Sites will not only be required for solar PV, but may also be needed for wind installations, biomass production or whatever. The council therefore needs to evaluate its sites quickly and set up a process for this work.

To do this, an internal team needs to be set up. This should have representation from the corporate centre, the energy and sustainability areas, estates or asset management and planning. The group of officers need to draw up a clear methodology of appraising sites for development.

Internal Team:

- **Corporate centre – Chief Executive's Department**
- **Environment**
- **Energy management**
- **Sustainability**
- **Planning**

This work should start with a map indicating all of the agricultural and other land holdings within the ownership or control of the authority. Each site should be properly referenced. In support of the map, it is necessary to create a database of the sites, including all of the relevant details.

The database should have a section for each of the sites. This would include the reference mentioned above, a grid reference, site name and area. The relevant page for each site should also include a detailed map of each site and an aerial photograph to the same scale.

The other data that needs to be added will differ slightly in relation to the different technologies to be evaluated but will come from the following list:

• Connectivity to the electricity network

Is the site near an existing electricity substation? The grid connection is likely to need to be at least 11 KVA (see **Chapter 11**), preferably 33 KVA or above for a larger installation. If not, how far is the nearest substation?

There also needs to be sufficient capacity in the electricity network beyond the substation. If there is not, then reinforcement (at the cost of the council) will be required.

• Land area and Type

At least 10 ha is required for a solar or wind site, although different requirements may apply for biomass. What is the site area in total?

Is the land flat (required for solar) or on a hill (better for wind) etc?

• Landscape/Visual Assessment

Is the site located within, or adjacent to, a designated landscape, such as an Area of Outstanding Natural Beauty? (AONB) Is the site visible from any public vantage points or other sensitive receptors, such as nearby properties? What would be the impact of the proposed development within the local landscape and would the development be visually intrusive? Could any impact be mitigated by landscaping?

• Agricultural Land Quality

What is the quality of the agricultural land? Best and most versatile quality agricultural land (grades a, b and c1) should be avoided.

• Ecology

Are there any recognised ecological interests/designations on/adjoining the proposed site. The issues will be different for each technology, for example a proposed wind farm would need a careful consideration on both birds and bats.

• Archaeology

A desk-based assessment would need to be undertaken to ascertain the presence of any recorded features of archaeological interest.

• Road Access

An assessment would need to be made of the local highway network in order to ensure that it is able to accommodate the type and number of vehicle movements likely to be generated by the proposed development. Although the suitability of the highway network is not a critical factor for large-scale solar PV proposals (individual solar panels could be off-loaded from HGV's some distance from the site and imported using smaller vehicles) it is an important factor for wind turbines when importing turbine towers and rotor blades.

• Capacity

Sites for large scale solar PV facilities should have minimal constraints caused by shadowing from nearby features, including trees, buried/ overhead services or topography. North facing slopes should be avoided.

Each of these factors is then weighted 1 – 5 in order to ensure that the most important are given the right level of priority. As an example, no grid connection would be a serious impediment and therefore warrants a high weighting. Other factors might be less critical.

Each site can be surveyed and the checklist completed for that site. This will then lead to each site being given a score and this will inform the process of choosing sites appropriate for the facilities.

If this work can be commenced expeditiously and methodically worked through, it will put the council in an excellent position to identify the land required for the delivery of its Renewable Energy Strategy (as described in **Chapter 5**). It will also permit early preparatory work, such as Environmental Impact Assessments or applications for planning permission, as discussed below, to be addressed.

There will also be a number of different legal issues to consider in relation to non-buildings related sites. These include:

- *Checking the title to the land. Is it leasehold or freehold? What conditions are there, if any, upon it*
- *Have any village green applications been made and registered? Are any pending?*
- *Restrictive covenants – are there any? B1 / B2 / B8 uses do not include renewable energy. What is the purpose of any restrictive covenant*
- *what was it aimed at?*
- *Is the land mortgaged? If there is a mortgage in existence what is its terms?*
- *Will there be any Stamp Duty Land Tax implications?*
- *Will vacant possession be available? Check that there are no agricultural tenancies or the like on the land.*
- *What is the position regarding ownership of the surrounding land? A check needs to be made to ensure that no one can have ransom rights over the council's project, for example, control over a strip of land needed to run a cable to a substation.*
- *What about the mines and minerals rights? Who owns them?*
- *Finally, rights of access to the sites? Are there any legal restrictions on access to the sites? If a solar park is contemplated, then access will be necessary for all of the construction work.*

The above are simply examples of areas that could prove problematic. In each case, a proper legal review will be required.

It can be seen that approaching site identification as part of the wider green strategy is a time consuming process. However, undertaken in this way, the council will have all of the data it needs on its land-based assets, to consider any renewable energy applications that might be relevant for the future.

(b) The Business Case

The importance of the business case and its essential components is explained in **Chapter 9**. In order for a solar farm development to be viable, it has to be underpinned by a solid financial and business case. This is one of the areas where it is different to buildings based systems, where there are other benefits to be had, such a using the electricity or improving the building. Here it is mainly about generating the power and selling it to the grid or another party.

One factor that will have an impact on the business case is the use of tracker systems or fixed panel systems. Tracker systems are noted to be more efficient that fixed panels (certainly in sunnier European countries) but are also more expensive. There is a calculation to be made here but the general view of the solar industry is that tracker panels are not worth the extra cost in the UK, bearing in mind the limited additional capacity that they provide. Nonetheless, there are some tracker panels in operation in the UK, although not in the larger, commercial solar farms.

The other main element of the business case will be whether to use FITS, ROCs or CFDs. If the facility is over 5 MW, then it has to be CFDs from April 2015. If the facility is under 50kw, then it can only be FITs (See the Renewables Obligation Order 2009, article 17 B). Between 50 kw and 5 MW, it is a straight choice on the part of the developer. The issues between the various financial incentives are discussed in **Chapter 8**.

(c) The Finance

The next requirement is the capital expenditure that will be needed to fund the project. Decent sized solar farms are measured in millions of pounds of investment, rather than lesser sums. A 5 MW farm would cost between £6m and £10m of capital expenditure on a turnkey basis.

Chapter 10 discussed financing solar PV schemes and it is assumed that the money has been found from reserves or borrowed from the Public Works Loans Board, for this purpose.

(d) Planning Permission

Planning is completely different for a free standing solar farm, compared to buildings based systems, where specific consent may not even be required (for example under Permitted Development rights). This form of solar farm is a major development of land, just like any other, and therefore a formal planning process will need to be followed.

There will be a variety of different aspects to this, including the following:

- *The grade and use of the land. As mentioned above, the Government is very aware of the need not to worsen the food supply chain in the UK and does not, therefore, want good quality agricultural land to be used for renewable energy generation. This is particularly grade A and B land but also the higher elements of grade C too;*
- *The topography of the land will be relevant, its position and characteristics. Is it on a slope, hillside or flat?*
- *The landscape and visual assessment of the site. Will it be visible for many miles or is it hidden behind hedgerows on flat land?*
- *Archaeology – are there records of archaeological interest in the land?*
- *Ecology – this one is more likely. Ecology means the interface between living organisms and their environment; here this means birds, bats, newts and other wildlife in watercourses, nests, trees and hedgerows*
- *Drainage or flooding risk; is there water on the land; does it have a risk of flooding? Electrical equipment and flooding do not match well*
- *Access to the land. A 5 MW solar farm is likely to have over 25,000 individual solar panels included in it. All need to be delivered to the site; the impact on transport and road use is relevant.*

In large developments of other types, particularly wind energy, an Environmental Impact Assessment would definitely be required. However, such is the unobtrusive nature of solar PV that it is not normally required, save for the largest of installations. A screening application needs to be submitted to the local planning authority in order for a definitive determination of whether an EIA will be required. This is only a short document outlining the proposals and the planning authority has to respond within statutory time scales.

(e) Grid Connection

Again, there is a difference to a buildings based system. If a building has lights and electricity, then it has a grid connection. A field out in the countryside is a different proposition altogether and the amount of electricity generated will be significant. A 5 MW solar farm in the deep South West, could produce 5,000 MWh of energy each year and that has to be fed into the national grid via a 33 KVA substation. The availability of if a substation or other possible grid connection (such as a passing pylon) is therefore essential.

The grid map can be found on the National Grid website. From that, the various categories of cable explained in **Chapter 11** can be plotted, from 400 KVA through to 11 KVA substations and then the micro grid beyond.

Here, it is not just the availability of a substation that is relevant. How far away it is may be crucial too. Cabling of the size and scale needed here is very expensive indeed and may undermine an otherwise sound business case. Moreover, if the land between the substation and the site is in different ownership, then wayleaves or other legal agreements will have to be negotiated and may be used as ransom strips. Those who own or control such land are not normally afraid of extracting maximum value from that ownership or control, if the other party is in a position of needing to make an arrangement.

(f) Miscellaneous Issues

There are a wide variety of other issues that will be relevant to the project, such as security of the site. If the site is very rural, what provisions can be put in place to protect the installation? This might also have an impact on planning permission, as the local planning authority is unlikely to agree to a 12-foot razor-wire fence being constructed in an Area of Outstanding Natural Beauty. However, a natural thorn hedge could well meet both goals.

A risk analysis will need to be undertaken as part of the preparatory work on the project. The two biggest risks in any solar farm development are the planning consent and grid connection. The reason is simple: the impact of these risks is catastrophic and will mean that, without them, there is no project. Other risks, such as construction, performance and so on can be managed more easily and are discussed in **Chapter 14**.

Power Purchase Agreements

It is stated above that solar farms are about the generation of large amounts of power and supplying that power to the national grid. Under the FIT, there is a power to sell the electricity to the grid for a fixed fee of 3 - 5 pence per kwh (subject to when the agreement was entered and the uplift for RPI). There is no corresponding power in relation to ROCs. This is because the RO is for professional energy generators, and not the individual home-owners and others for whom the FIT regime was established. This means that a ROC based scheme has to rely on Power Purchase Agreements (PPAs), entered with organisations that want to purchase and use the power generated and so do contracts for difference (CFD).

So schemes between 50 kw and 5 MW have a choice as to whether to follow the RO, CFD or FIT regime. Even if it is a scheme governed by the FIT regime, it may still enter into power purchase agreements, instead of using the export tariff. The issue will be economic ie: can a greater return than 3 -5 pence per kwh be secured? There are some other issues, such as the complexity of the RO and the need to understand the basis on which it works, or buy in that expertise.

By their nature, solar farms almost always involve energy being fed to the grid, rather than used on site. It would need a very large user of energy near by for this not to be the case. Whilst this is not impossible, it is unlikely. A scheme proposed by Cornwall Council in 2009 and built in 2012 supplies the power from a 5 MW solar farm in council ownership to the nearby airport, also in council ownership. This is an excellent arrangement, as the power is mainly used locally, thereby avoiding transmission losses through the grid.

A power purchase agreement is simply a contract between a supplier and a customer. The council has the electricity that it has generated from its facility, the customer needs electricity and may well prefer 'green' power as opposed to brown electricity from the grid. The bargain that they enter is called a PPA and will define the terms of the deal, including the price. It would normally be possible to secure a better price than 3 - 5 pence per kwh under a PPA.

There are also other complex issues to be determined, such as whether to install a 'private wire' system or use the national grid to transfer the power to the customer. A private wire system is simply a direct cable that connects the generator to the user; however, there are complexities in relation to the legal status of private wire systems. These will need to be the subject of detailed technical and legal advice. Balanced against that is the fact that such an arrangement is unregulated and the local authority can charge whatever it feels is appropriate for the power. Moreover, there are no distribution charges, as there are with sleeving arrangements.

On a strategic point, the issue for a local authority undertaking a solar farm project is who to enter into PPAs with. Firstly, the authority itself might use considerably in excess of the electricity generated, and so ensure that it uses the total generated capacity. In this way, it makes a considerable saving on its current energy costs. The other way, perhaps if there is more power than is needed by the council, is to see what other bodies are around who might want to enter such an arrangement. Those with large energy requirements are preferable, for example a hospital or NHS facility, housing estates, or industrial / commercial users (factories, laundries, process plants). The local authority might well have connections here that will ensure it's securing the right customers for its power.

The electricity from such a facility can also be sold wholesale. The Office for Government Commerce (OGC) buys energy for the public sector and wouldB be interested in purchasing substantial blocks of energy of this nature.

Power purchase agreements are contracts for supply of power over a period of time. That period will also need to be carefully determined. Best prices on selling power are to be obtained by annual contracting; however, that might not suit the local authority, with its limited expertise in this area. Longer-term arrangements (say up to 10 years) may be accompanied by a lower price, but give the certainty of income and lower complexity that suits a public sector project. It is for each authority to decide the best option, with specific reference to its business case.

Construction and Commissioning

The most difficult work, requiring the most detailed planning and effort, comes early on in a solar farm project. By the time the contractors are ready to start construction, the hardest part is already over. By this time the council has:

- *A suitable site identified*
- *Planning permission granted*
- *A grid connection offer that is suitable and affordable*
- *A detailed business case developed*
- *Funding in place*

The procurement of the contractor to design, build and operate the plant is considered in **Chapter 14**.

The construction element can be concluded fairly quickly. Before 2011, a general rule of building one megawatt of PV capacity a month might be reasonable. However, due to the FIT issues and the deadlines set as a result of the Government continuing to cut the incentives, the industry learned to undertake construction much more efficiently. By 2014, this meant it was possible to build a megawatt a day! This demonstrates that once the other building blocks are in place, the actual construction can be undertaken fairly quickly.

It is an interesting point that the companies involved in solar farms and buildings based solar tend to differ. Those building the solar farms tend to be large, experienced solar PV companies, that have often operated across Europe. On the other hand, those engaged with the buildings based solar – particularly in housing work – tend to be established building maintenance companies. This is because those contracts require substantial experience in the area of dealing with tenants and the complex scheduling that housing contracts of this nature require in order to be successful.

Once the site is commissioned and operational, the registration with OFGEM needs to be completed and PPAs finalised. It is then simply a matter of operating the facility in accordance with the plans.

Specific Types of Land Based Solar Installation

The comments above relate largely to a standard form of solar farm, built on either low-grade agricultural land or a brownfield site that has been previously developed.

However, there are more specialist varieties of development and two that are worthy of further comment are former landfill sites and car parks.

Former Landfill Sites

Many local authorities will be waste management authorities and therefore may have ownership of old, capped landfill sites. Such sites are usually a liability that provides a headache for the authority: the site is no longer operational but still has to be maintained and therefore costs money. Legal liabilities can last for decades and so it is often difficult to know how to deal with such sites.

Notwithstanding a modern trend of companies offering to buy old landfill sites, so that they can be 'mined' IE re-opened so that the plastics and other recyclables that were deposited in them (and which continue to have value) can be extracted, there is another option – solar PV.

It is difficult to be generic here, as all sites differ and have their own complications, depending on what was deposited on the site, in what quantities, how long ago and what has happened since. However, these sites should always be considered.

This is because they are ideal in both planning policy terms and from the point of view of members. On the member front, such sites cost money to maintain in a time of austerity. Fitting solar PV cannot only turn a liability into an asset, but it can also raise money for use elsewhere. There are some interesting political decisions necessary as a result of such work, such as whether to ring fence money like this to the waste management function or apply it more broadly to the council's activities.

On the planning front, the DCLG has said that it wants formerly-used land to be considered for development and it would be difficult to find a better example.

On a technical level, it will be necessary to carry out a number of checks. These include subsidence, the issues with methane flaring, leachate collection and so on. Sometimes, these issues will mean the site is not suitable, in others they will not impact greatly on it. In most cases it is likely that the panels will need to be installed via concrete boots, instead of the normal aluminium racking which is piled below the surface. This is because capped sites cannot normally allow surface penetration.

There are other advantages from former landfill sites, including the fact that they are normally large tracts of land; are normally a blight on the landscape and detested by local residents; and invariably have a grid connection. This means that the public can be kept happy by the site being used for solar PV (and therefore properly covered and maintained), sufficient land being available for development and the problem of the grid being removed.

Car Parks

Car parks are another interesting example and one that really only started to come to the fore in 2014. Before that, they had been prevalent on the Continent, but not really in the UK.

Car parks offer an excellent site for solar PV. They provide a ready made source of space, it is pre-used land and a further income stream can be added without the loss of a single parking space. Looked at in this way, car parks are starting to be very popular.

The solar is normally fitted on canopies, similar to a bus shelter over the parking spaces, or can be a complete solar roof, with lighting beneath for the evening.

If the council owns a building nearby (which it normally does), the power can be piped directly into the building, thereby achieving a higher Feed in Tariff and ensuring that the business case is maximised, as described in **Chapter 9**.

Conclusion on land-based installations

As mentioned above, local authorities own a considerable amount of land that would be suitable for land based solar PV installations. They also have considerable energy requirements to perform all of their various statutory functions. Solar farms do, therefore, fit the profile of activities that local authorities should be considering.

In the past, these have been seen as developments that are the exclusive domain of the private sector. However, local government enters into major commercial contracts of a different nature (PFI, Building Schools for the Future, city centre regeneration contracts etc.) on a regular basis and so should not fear a contract of this size and scale. From 2012 onwards, there will be a resurgence of solar farm developments and some local authorities are likely to be included in that number.

What is required in order for a local authority to determine what assets it owns that are capable of development is a full asset review. This can look at all land (whether agricultural, farms, smallholdings, landfill sites or whatever) and all buildings (offices, depots, workshops, leisure centres, schools etc) to see what can be done. This is an essential part of developing a good solar strategy.

Building Based Systems

The second main area to consider is the buildings based system. As mentioned above, this does differ from a land based system in a number of important regards, not least the experience of the contractors necessary to do the fitting work.

Here, the decision to fit solar likely is to be linked to the extent and condition of the asset base of the council The following are likely to be relevant factors:

- *What buildings does the council have? This will itself depend on the nature of the authority ie: an urban metropolitan authority or a rural county council*

- *What is the profile of those buildings? Do they face South or in a different direction?*

- *What roof profile do they have? Are the roofs strong enough to take solar panels? Do they have suitable areas away from skylights, chimneys and shading?*

- *Are the buildings listed or in a Conservation Area?*
  What is the energy profile of the buildings? Are there buildings that have heavy use on a regular basis, for example leisure centres, depots, and offices?

- *What other plans does the council have to work on its asset base, for example energy efficiency works, office rationalisation, creation of open plan working, transfer to 'one stop shops' and so on?*

- *What relationships are in place that can be enhanced by solar PV works? A good example is schools, where the school governors usually welcome both the free electricity that results from a PV scheme and also the addition of a useful tool to the curriculum on environmental and energy subjects*

In many authorities a land-based system would be neither appropriate nor easily possible. However, all local authorities should have a solar PV strategy in relation to its buildings, as they are straightforward and add considerable value in both financial and non-financial terms.

The issues in relation to a buildings based project are considered below under the same headings as those used above in relation to land based systems. In this way the differences can easily be charted.

(a) Land / Buildings

The first requirement is to have some suitable buildings and / or land to found a project. The mention of land is worth emphasising here, as a buildings based project can also incorporate land-based panels. An example might be a council office in spacious grounds, where the roof is not that suitable for PV panels. Here, 20 kw of panels might be fitted in the grounds and connected to the office, in which case it is treated as a buildings based system under the regime. New provisions have been proposed in 2014 to require at least 10% of the energy to be used on site, if such a system is to be deemed a building – rather than a land-based – facility.

Those factors mentioned above in relation to roof space and nature will be highly relevant here. Of the five elements explained in **Chapter 7**, a number relate to the roof itself – orientation, tilt and shading and all of these will need careful consideration. Added to those issues are access, roof strength, suitability of electrical wiring and so on.

The best way to do this is to undertake a detailed survey of all of the council's buildings and to form a register, in exactly the same way as is mentioned above in relation to land for renewable energy projects. Here the database will contain essential details such as: address, type of building, occupation of building, energy use and type, roof orientation, roof strength and access and so on. If all of these details are available on the asset register, it becomes very easy to determine which buildings should be used for the installation work.

(b) Business Case

The business case is developed in a very similar way to a land-based system. The size of the facility and its capacity gives a total of estimated energy generated and this can be multiplied by the relevant Feed in Tariff band. This is on the income side; on the cost side, estimates will be received via tenders on the likely costs of the installation.

More important here will be the decision as to whether to use the energy or supply it to the grid. Almost all buildings systems will be FIT based and therefore the rate of 3 – 5 pence per kwh for supplying energy to the grid will be the relevant one. It is likely that an authority is paying at least 10 – 12 pence per kwh for its energy and so it becomes clear that substantial savings can be made by actually using the power generated, rather than putting this into the grid. A leisure centre in a Northern metropolitan authority provides an excellent example here. The centre was large enough to host 250 kw of solar PV. As all the power could be used on site, the authority benefitted not just from the FITs payable on the installation, but a huge saving on its electricity bill (as it was saving 10 pence for every unit used). This resulted in a return of around 17% on the system.

Chapter 9 considers the detail of preparing a financial and business case.

(c) Finance

A buildings-based system can be undertaken at virtually any scale. A small building, such as a public lavatory or park shelter can have a domestic sized installation fitted, right through to a 500 kw installation on a warehouse type structure.

The finance needs to be structured accordingly, but this is a scenario where simple borrowing from the Public Works Loans Board will usually suffice to fund such works.

(d) Planning Permission

Housing schemes are able to rely on Permitted Development rights, that have been given for domestic installations. The intention behind this move is to ensure that small, unobtrusive developments can be undertaken without the need for formal planning permission from the council. This is in line with the Government's overall policy aim of achieving both decentralised energy and microgeneration at local level. The rules are summarised in **Figure 12.3** below.

The permitted development rules will apply provided:

- *The equipment does not protrude more than 200 mm beyond the plane of the roof or wall that it is installed on*
- *It must not exceed the highest part of the roof*
- *In a Conservation Area or World Heritage Site, the equipment is not installed on a wall forming a principal or side elevation of the dwelling and is not visible from a highway; or is not installed on a wall of a building within the curtilage that is visible from a highway*
- *It is not installed on building within the curtilage of the dwelling, if the building is listed*

In addition to this, the siting of the equipment must be able to minimise the impact upon the appearance of the building and amenity of the area and the equipment must be removed once it is no longer needed.

See the Town and Country Planning (General Permitted Development) Order 1995 (SI 1995 No 418) as amended.

See the Town and Country Planning (General Permitted Development) Order 1995 (SI 1995 No 418) as amended.

If the installation is on non-domestic buildings, then planning consent is more likely to be necessary. In that instance a determination will need to be made by the authority's planning officer as to whether the circumstances for planning consent are met. Planning officers will often take a pragmatic view of this and if the solar panels are unlikely to have a material impact upon the appearance of the building and would not fall foul of any other Permitted Development rights that apply to non-residential buildings, it may well be that a formal application will not be required.

However, Government policy has intervened here to help with commercial PV installations. This is all part of the initiative to move solar PV away from land based solar farms on agricultural land, to commercial sized roofs. As a result of considerable opposition from the large solar developers to such a move, the Government agreed to slacken off the Permitted Development rights rules and allow solar PV installations up to a very sizeable limit of 1 MW without planning permission. This was also brought forward due to the fact that very few commercial roofs were actually being developed due to barriers such as this.

The proposals, published in a Technical Consultation on Planning by DCLG in July 2014 are reproduced in **Figure 12.3** below.

Renewable Obligation Certificates

- *under the RO system, banding applies to the various technologies and for solar PV, double ROC's are available*
- *if a ROC is worth roughly £50 per MWh, that is 5 pence per kwh equivalent; double ROCs means 10 pence per kwh*
- *there is no export tariff under the RO and the generator has to enter into a power purchase agreement (PPA) with a user of the power; an average PPA might generate approximately 5 pence per kwh*
- *this totals approximately 15 pence per kwh under a RO scheme*

Figure 12.3 – FITs or ROCs?

Proposal J: Solar PV panels for commercial properties

2.86 The aim of this proposal is to expand on the existing permitted development rights for the installation of solar panels on the roofs of non-domestic buildings to allow commercial properties to make greater use of their roof space to provide renewable energy.

2.87 In April 2014 the Department for Energy and Climate Change published the UK Solar PV Strategy Part 2: Delivering a Brighter Future. The strategy explores ways to help encourage the UK's performance in solar PV for commercial and industrial buildings. The strategy identified the planning system as one of the barriers to the installation of solar panels in the mid-size commercial market.

2.88 Permitted development rights for the installation of micro-generation solar equipment on non-domestic buildings up to a capacity of 50kW were introduced in 2012. This permitted development right has helped support the provision of small-scale solar power generation in the commercial sector. The installation of solar panels above 50kW currently requires a full planning application to the local planning authority. There is an opportunity to make more efficient use of our existing buildings and support the take up of much larger scale solar power generation across England. The use of roof space has the potential to reduce the demand on agricultural land to provide renewable energy: the roof of a large industrial unit could provide the same output as five acres of agricultural land as there is no need to leave a space between the panels.

2.89 The Government therefore proposes to introduce a new permitted development right to support the installation of photovoltaic panels (solar PV) on non-domestic buildings with a capacity up to one megawatt (20 times the current capacity) without a planning application to to the local authority. This right would:

- *Apply to all non-domestic buildings, as with the existing permitted development rights for installation of solar PV;*
- *Have a prior approval to consider the siting and design, in order to minimise the impact of glare on neighbouring or overlooking properties from the larger array of solar PV;*
- *Apply only to the roof of non-domestic buildings. As with the existing right, there will be restrictions on the protrusion of the panel beyond the roof slope and the height of solar PV equipment;*

> • *Not be permitted (as with the existing permitted development right) on a roof slope which fronts a highway in Article 1(5) land (i.e. land within a National Park, the Broads, an Area of Outstanding Natural Beauty, an area designated as a conservation area, and land within World Heritage Sites);*
> • *Exclude development on or in the following types of structures or areas as they raise issues requiring further consideration:*
>   • *listed buildings and buildings within the curtilage;*
>   • *scheduled monuments and land within the curtilage*

Figure 12.6 Technical Consultation on Planning (DCLG July 2014)

Where planning permission is required, the authority will need to submit an application in the normal way. Solar PV applications are a good deal less controversial than other technologies, such as wind and biomass, and should not raise many problems.

(e) Grid Connection

It is self evident that if a building has lights and an electricity supply, then it will have a connection to the national grid. However, that does not necessarily mean that the electricity supply of the building will be sufficient to take solar power.

On domestic schemes, it is necessary to undertake an electrical survey, to determine the age and condition of the wiring in the properties. If this is old and tired, it may be that a re-wiring exercise needs to be done before the installation can go ahead.

A similar situation exists with non-domestic buildings. The electricity supply may be new or old; there may be more than one meter; it might be single or three phase supply. It is therefore essential that a full electrical survey is carried out. In addition, the network operator should be consulted at an early stage.

(f) Scale

Whilst a land-based system can be constructed at almost any scale, buildings based systems tend to have an unofficial upper limit. There are roofs in existence that can take a full 5 MW of solar power, such as the Bentley Factory in Crewe. Bearing in mind that this is likely to be over 25,000 panels, an indication is gained of just how large that roof needs to be. The examples are aircraft hangers, railway sheds, massive goods warehouses and the like. Normally, though, buildings would not take more than 500 kw as an upper limit, with 250 – 300 kw being a relatively large scheme.

However, the buildings survey carried out by the authority will determine what assets it does have and if there is a roof that is capable of taking more solar PV than that, it becomes a simple matter of economics and the business case as to whether the council wants to fit a larger installation.

(g) Types of Building

Whilst each council is different, there are some buildings that every local authority owns and occupies, such as civic buildings (town halls, civic halls, offices and so on). There will also be more specialist buildings, such as the following:

- **Social housing** - mentioned above. Not every local authority has the housing function, which is the preserve of the district and unitary authority. Where there is, there are three types of social housing: traditional council housing in the ownership and control of the local authority; houses owned by the council but operated at arm's length (ALMOs); and housing that has been transferred by a Large Scale Voluntary Transfer process to a Registered Provider. Houses in the first two categories may be available for a solar PV installation.

- **Schools** - have particular issues associated with them, which are considered below.

- **Leisure centres** - again a district and unitary function, most local authorities have leisure centres, although some have outsourced them or transferred them to a trust of some sort. Leisure centres are ideal, as they perform an important function for health and wellbeing, but invariably make a loss and are a drain on a Council's finances. Where the buildings are still under council control, a PV scheme can help with this, by providing free electricity.

- **Council offices** - these come in all shapes and sizes and every authority has some at least. These buildings are usually occupied at least five days a week, ten hours a day, and have a reasonably high-energy requirement. Some, such as 'one stop shops' and advice centres, may be open even longer days and hours.

- **Miscellaneous buildings** - These could be anything from a council depot (for example for grounds maintenance, roads maintenance, buildings maintenance, refuse collection) to a garage/workshop, farm or warehouse. There will be opportunities on these buildings, perhaps to install a larger system, over 100 kw. Again, these buildings tend to have large energy usages.

Schools probably deserve a closer look, as they have particular issues associated with them. Of course, not every authority is an education authority, which is the preserve of county councils and unitary authorities. Where a council is an education authority it will mean that there is a stock of buildings, governed by education law, that will need to be maintained and energy supplied to them. This is ideal for a solar PV scheme. Schools usually welcome the free electricity and have no problem with the council fitting panels to the school roof as the council is the owner of the building anyway, despite its operation being subject to the detailed legislative education regime. Obviously, those schools outside council control, latterly Academies, will not fall in this group.

The Government published the UK Solar PV Strategy: Part 2 in April 2014. This document sets out how DECC sees the solar PV market in the UK developing over coming years and gave a clear indication that the Government wants the focus to shift from ground based solar PV to commercial roofs.

Greg Barker says in the Foreword that the Government will play its part in developing solar PV, by using the public estate: "such as MOD buildings, schools and hospitals to make sure that not one inch of suitable Government roof space is wasted ..." The aspiration was stated as 1 GW of solar PV from its own buildings, with the country's 24,000 schools at the heart of this.

But, unfortunately, it will be very difficult for the Government to deliver on this aim without the support of local government. There are various reasons for this.

Education is a service that is delivered by local, as opposed to central, government. However, it has been something of a battleground between central and local government. A succession of Education Acts have therefore brought in a plethora of provisions, including separate legal status for boards of governors and the ability to opt out of local government control entirely. The latter notion is framed in the form of free schools and academies, which receive their funding directly from the Government and not through the local education authority. This tangle of over regulation is crucial to the potential for solar PV on schools in the UK.

For local authority controlled schools, the assets are owned by the local authority itself and so nothing can be done with those buildings without its consent. The school is merely an occupier for this purpose. As the asset owners, any work on the buildings is relevant and local authorities normally have comprehensive programmes of building maintenance, both on a periodic and fault fixing basis. Installing PV could lead to damage to a roof for which it is responsible or interfere with planned refurbishment or maintenance programmes.

Most importantly, though, is the inability of the local authority to dispose of properties as part of wider asset management strategies, where PV obligations have been entered into. This is a very serious issue, as authorities are disposing of vast arrays of all kinds of civic buildings on an ongoing basis, as they seek to make cuts to their operating budgets. Schools rarely empathise with this standpoint, particularly if they have been offered free PV systems and lower energy bills as a result.

The simple way round all of these problems is for a local authority to offer to fit solar PV to all of the schools in its area that are suitable. The council can borrow the money to do this and can then repay the loan with the income from FITs or ROCs. Meanwhile, the school gets the electricity and educational value of the renewable energy.

It is also the case then that the work can be programmed into the normal maintenance schedule and everyone is happy. Peterborough City Council is a good example of this, although unusual in the sense that the local authority does not give the electricity to the schools free, but charges at a discounted rate. Most of the schools have taken up the offer.

However, many local authorities are reluctant to do this because of national educational policy. In simple terms, a school could apply to become an academy and leave local authority control at any point. If it did, there would be no guarantee that the Council would recover the value of the investment that it has put into the asset, as the school buildings normally transfer as they are. As a result of this, many councils have not taken any action to install solar PV on their schools. However, pressure was mounting from 2014 for this to happen.

It is often the case with buildings-based systems that the council effectively calculates what it can afford in terms of a solar programme and then the buildings required for that level of installation are identified. It may be that when grid parity arrives, that all council buildings of every type have a solar installation and that time may not be more than a few years ahead.

Conclusion

As mentioned above, the nature, type and size of solar PV installation will depend on the strategy of the authority concerned. The question should always be in the background – what does the council want to achieve?

An early analysis of all of the matters examined in **Chapter 5** will soon identify the best way forwards. For now, most authorities have gone for buildings-based systems, often modest in size. There is no reason, however, why a local authority could not determine that it will develop a solar farm instead, or even in addition, to its buildings based work.

Key Learning Points

- *The choice between land and buildings is an important one*
- *They are normally motivated by different things*
- *A land based solar PV farm is a sizable commercial transaction, requiring substantial finance and careful planning*
- *Buildings can be done at any scale, but if a substantial buildings programme is undertaken, this is closer to the solar farm experience*
- *Some decisions will be key to the business case, for example using the electricity on site for buildings and how to sell it for solar farms*

Introduction

Community energy is likely to be one of the big growth areas in renewable energy over the next decade. However, it sometimes causes confusion amongst the public as to what is genuinely 'community' IE promoted by the community itself and what is 'civic' (promoted by the council). For the purposes of this work, it is only civic projects that are of interest, although it is possible for the areas to overlap. For this reason, a brief consideration of community energy is included below.

Linked to the notion of community though are two other concepts. The first is community engagement, whereby a local authority communicates with and consults the community over its own plans for a project. The second is the notion of community benefit, which denotes some particular reward coming to the community that hosts a renewable energy facility. Both of these notions are also considered in this Chapter.

Community Energy

Community energy has been around for some considerable time now, with some communities pioneering a community approach to a renewable energy facility. However, in the UK this has been rare and that is to be contrasted with EU neighbours on the Continent. There, community energy is much more ingrained, for example in Germany, and is seen as the norm. Denmark is another good example, where the vast majority of heating is delivered via community heating projects.

Decentralised energy systems have been held up as a good model and community energy is a direct way to achieve that goal. Accordingly, the Government eventually realised that this would be a policy aim worth pursuing in the UK. Prior to that point, community energy would only really have happened organically over a very long period.

The situation changed with the publication of the very first Community Energy Strategy by DECC on 27 January 2014. In the Foreword, Ed Davey, the Secretary of State for Energy and Climate Change, described community energy as being 'at a turning point'. He said that the Government wanted to play to the advantages that community based action offers energy and climate policy. This is indeed a goal worth pursuing.

The Strategy, spanning some 100 pages, made clear the Government's support for community level energy but demonstrated that it has little understanding of it. In some ways, it was what the Strategy did not say that was most noteworthy.

It focussed on issues such as capacity, resource and finance and asked how these can be helped? It pointed out some of the barriers to more deployment, such as the regulatory issues (including grid connections and procedures) and licencing under the Electricity Act 1989. However, it displayed a lack of understanding about how communities could be motivated to take action and also on the role of local government in helping them do so.

It chose a very narrow definition of 'community' in the first place, excluding all projects that are promoted by a local authority for a start; but also excluding crowd funding and financial bonds as a way forwards. The reason given was that these promote individual ownership, rather than community ownership. Seeing as it was starting from such a very long way back, it might have been expected that DECC would welcome any sort of ownership that brought members of the public into renewable energy schemes.

It then settled on one particular way of trying to get the community in to energy projects – and that was to force commercial developers to relinquish part ownership of their projects. This was criticised at the time as being too narrow but has remained a central plank of Government policy.

Types of Renewable Energy Projects

In the view of the author, there are three types of renewable energy facility: 'commercial', 'community' and 'civic'. Commercial projects are driven by profit and are developed by companies skilled in deployment of large-scale facilities at risk. They are funded by private sector capital, and their developers expect to make a profit on their investments. These are the projects that are driving the UK towards its emissions and renewable energy targets under the Climate Change Act 2008.

Secondly, there are community projects, which tend to be smaller and more rooted in social value, rather than just profit. In the past, most community projects have been small and focussed on a particular area. Examples might be a small solar PV installation on a church roof or a wind turbine to provide electricity to an outlying community. These are not commercial projects and are not driven by profit. They take a long time to come to fruition and are negligible in the overall scale of renewable energy at the current point.

Finally, there are civic projects, developed and operated by a local authority, which are still funded by the public (and for indirect public benefit) but operated more like commercial developments. These are an important half way house. The projects are funded from the public purse and are therefore rooted in the community. However, thy also have a close nexus the other way, as such projects are run similarly to commercial enterprises, with the money being recycled back into public sector coffers.

The contents of the Community Energy Strategy suggested that this was a distinction that DECC did not fully appreciate. In other words, civic projects are different to community projects but there are many areas of overlap. Instead, its wording confused the two. Moreover, it missed the point that the local authority, whilst wanting to pursue its own projects on its own land and assets, could still help community groups undertake their own projects.

The Shared Ownership Taskforce

Notwithstanding the views expressed above, it is necessary to briefly cover the Government's subsequent proposals on shared ownership, if only to conclude that they do not impact on local authority schemes.

This Shared Ownership Taskforce was set up under specific provisions in the Community Energy Strategy. These state that the Government will force commercial developers to offer community ownership of their schemes to the public if they do not embrace this aim voluntarily.

The Community Energy Strategy specifically states:

"We expect that by 2015 it will be the norm for communities to be offered the opportunity of some level of ownership of new, commercially developed onshore renewables projects. We will review progress in 2015 and if this is limited, we will consider requiring all developers to offer the opportunity of a shared ownership element to communities." (at page 36).

So the principal aim is to force commercial developers to give stakes in their commercial projects (for example, wind farms or solar farms) to community groups.

As part of this process, the renewables industry and the community energy sector have committed to work together to facilitate a substantial increase in the shared ownership of new, commercial onshore renewables developments by 2015. The renewables industry has agreed to lead a Taskforce, made up of representatives from industry, community energy groups and Government.

This was in response to another paragraph from the Strategy:

"The Secretary of State for Energy & Climate Change has asked an industry taskforce to work with the community sector and report back to him by summer 2014. This report will include a robust framework and timetable for implementation. In addition to identifying measures to increase community ownership of new commercial developments, the taskforce will work with community energy groups to set an overall level of ambition for community ownership of new renewables developments (including both wholly and partly community-owned developments)."

The Shared Ownership Taskforce was appointed in the summer and met four times before the publication of a preliminary report in June 2014. The Taskforce subsequently met in September to finalise its report, which was released in October 2014.

The plan is to conduct a 'light touch' review after six months, and then have a full annual review after 12 months. As this will be after the General Election of 2015, it will be up to the new political administration to decide how to take this forward and whether to follow up on the pledge to use legislative means to enforce community ownership if progress is inadequate.

The membership of the Taskforce was wide and varied and featured most of the leading figures from the community side, including Pure Leapfrog, Energy 4 All, RegenSW and Community Energy England. However, not one representative of local government was invited to sit on this body, which in the view of the author was a mistake.

So far as the types of project that would be subject to this voluntary code (and be the subject of legislation if the market did not respond positively), the following was proposed:

"Commercial project developers seeking to develop significant renewable energy projects (above £2.5m in project costs) for the primary purpose of exporting energy on to a public network should offer interested communities shared ownership."

This means that the provisions will not apply to a local authority, as it would not constitute a 'commercial project developer' for this purpose.

The final report of the Shared Ownership Taskforce was published in October 2014 and by this time had appreciated that local government would have to be part of the solution for community energy, despite this glaring omission from the Government's Community Energy Strategy. As a result of pressure from the public sector, a new paragraph on local authorities was added to the final report, recognising the 'vital' role that they can play in the facilitating the deployment of renewable energy.

There are various ways in which this can be done:

"....including developing their own projects, supporting community groups , linking developers and community groups, or buying into renewables schemes themselves ..."

The wide coverage of this paragraph was welcomed and for the first time there was a recognition of the benefit from local authorities actually undertaking civic schemes, which have a clear community benefit as well. The Taskforce now encourages central government to support these local authorities working in this area.

It is not necessary to go into any further detail in relation to the Shared Ownership Taskforce, save to mention the models that are put forward for consideration.

As the Taskforce pointed out, the 'limited examples of shared ownership seen to date tend to fall into three basic categories'. These are:

• Split ownership, in which a legally constituted community enterprise buys a proportion of the development's physical assets – for example, one wind turbine or 30 PV panels;
• Shared revenue, in which a legally constituted community enterprise buys the rights to a future virtual revenue stream which will be calculated as a specified proportion of the output of an energy production plant (less agreed operating costs and generally less virtual debt service). This revenue stream will be calculated as if the community had acquired the underlying infrastructure;
• Joint venture, in which a commercial operator and a legally constituted community enterprise work together to create a joint venture to develop, own and manage a project..

The reason that these models are mentioned in this work is that there is nothing to prevent a local authority voluntarily entering into a relationship with a community group, to procure a joint local authority / community project in exactly the same way.

Indeed, bearing in mind the changes to the rules under the Renewables Obligation in 2014, described in Chapter 8, removing the RO from solar schemes over 5 MW and the fact that Feed In Tariffs only go to 5 MW capacity, this may be the only way of promoting a larger solar farm (that is, unless a local authority wants to utilise the contracts for difference regime).

So community energy has had a boost and that is why it is stated that it will be on an upward trajectory for some time. As can be seen, this is not directly relevant to the subject of this book, although there are many overlaps. The foregoing is therefore only intended to be a guide to the community side.

The Communications And Engagement Plan

Consideration therefore returns now to local authority promoted schemes. Here, one of the most essential parts of the process is considered: the communications plan. This might be greeted with some surprise. There are lots of strategic and technical matters to be organised and arranged by the council and surely these take precedence? However, these are almost all 'inward' looking and, at some stage, the council or public body has to look 'outward' to the public and the community. No scheme takes place in a vacuum and as these projects are funded by public money, they will be scrutinised externally. If the council does not get across the right messages, then the scheme may not be a success.

Many people do not believe in climate change at all and are concerned – if not alarmed – at the cuts in public expenditure taking place. It is a natural conclusion, therefore, that some anxiety may be expressed at a large capital sum being expended on an environmental project in such a climate of financial austerity. It is essential that the message is communicated effectively - that this is a sensible and prudent project, in line with the council's stated goals and strategy. And more importantly, it is one that will bring considerable benefits in the future. Enter the communications strategy.

Developing A Communications And Engagement Plan

So, the authority is considering options for a 'civic' renewable energy scheme in its area, whether solar, wind, biomass, anaerobic digestion or whatever, to be sited within the council's area.

Depending on how ambitious and ground-breaking the project is (for example, there are currently no anaerobic digestion plants owned and operated by a local authority in the United Kingdom), the communications strategy will need to be tailored to the scheme. If it is a relatively straightforward exercise to fit solar PV to some of the council's civic offices, at a relatively modest cost, it will differ greatly from a 5MW free standing solar farm costing £5m.

The audience for the communications strategy will also differ. The strategy for a large social housing scheme is really focusing on the tenants, rather than the public, as it is primarily them who need to be won over. A more major development of a solar farm is really addressing the issues for those living nearby over its impact on the area and the wider council taxpayers over the costs.

The depth of the communications strategy may also depend on whether there is likely to be public opposition in some form or other. If concerns are raised, then time and trouble has to be taken to effectively answer those concerns. This is particularly so in relation to wind farms.

Strategy

The starting point is to consider the role of the communications strategy in the overall process. This means considering its aim and objectives, the messages to be conveyed, who to convey them to and how. Whilst this may sound straightforward, it is anything but, and internal public relations teams might need some external support to prepare such a plan.

> The aim of the strategy is to communicate to, and engage effectively with, the designated audience, on the benefits of the project and the process of public consultation that will be followed.

Figure 13.1 – The aim of the Communications Strategy

One of the early decisions will be to decide if the project is sizeable enough to merit an 'identity' in public relations terms. This might be comprised of a suite of graphics that are easily recognisable. Part of this might be a logo or name used to define the project. This was well illustrated by the Wrexham Council solar PV project, as described in the case study by Creative Concerns. The graphic was used on all documentation relating to the project.

As for objectives, the main one is to be open, honest and transparent about the consideration of renewable energy in the area concerned. There has to be a genuine intention to use all appropriate channels to communicate, listen and consult on options for the use of renewable energy and the projects under it. This will involve clear identification of the costs of such energy projects, but also the benefits – both financial and non-financial - that will flow from that and how these can be used to benefit the area. **Chapter 5** considered the necessity to develop a robust and clear strategy for renewable energy in general and it is now that this really starts to come into its own. The council needs to demonstrate clear political leadership and support for the renewable energy project and a strategy that is being implemented in a professional and appropriate manner.

Regrettably, the converse is also true: if the council does not have a robust and well though through strategy, projects can soon unravel as this will become apparent when the media analysis really kicks in. Difficult questions, inconsistencies in answers and the ability of the mischievous journalist to portray a council as not having planned a project properly can be fatal in this area. Once member support for a project is lost, it is usually lost for good.

Who to Communicate To?

Some audiences for a particular exercise are set down by law, for example the statutory consultees in a major planning exercise, as discussed in **Chapter 14**. Here, however, it is down to the local authority itself to whom it wants to convey the message.

It is good advice to always be on the 'front foot' regarding communications ie: be proactive - early, up front and open about what the authority is doing

The alternative, being reactive, or on the 'back foot', which means that the authority will always be responding to the comments of others, firefighting, answering hostile questions and so on.

If the proactive approach is followed, this implies that more rather than less consultees are appropriate. Even though this might tease out potential pockets of opposition, this is what is needed. If there is going to be a problem with a renewable energy project in this area, this needs to be apparent now, not when the whole process has travelled much further down the project management path, with attendant costs in time and resources.

The early part of this exercise is referred to as 'stakeholder mapping' IE: the identification of all of the various elements of society that need to be part of the consultation/ information process. **Figure 13.2** below considers some suggestions as to who might be involved.

- *Elected members – on the council*
- *Elected members – potentially for other nearby councils*
- *Residents of the area (in particular wards including the designated sites)*
- *Residents of other council areas (in particular those close to the designated wards);*
- *Key stakeholders – such as the county council (if relevant) and Chamber of Commerce*
- *Press and media*
- *Community and residents groups*
- *Green groups*
- *Local Members of Parliament (ensuring other MPs are also aware)*
- *Wider local government / green energy community*

Figure 13.2 – The Audience for the Communications Strategy

Key Messages

Having decided who to contact and publicise the project to, the next element is the actual message that is going to be conveyed. Again, this needs to be carefully considered. The message will differ, depending on the strategy, the progress of the project so far – ie: have sites been designated or not? It will also depend on the technology concerned, as some have far wider implications than others. Fortunately, solar PV projects are relatively low on the scale of controversy.

The strategy of going early on the communications should mean that the whole project is not completely fixed and set in stone. This conveys a bad message to the public – this is not really consultation, they are just being 'told'. It is better to make clear that the project is in the very early stages: the council is only looking at the options at this stage, but has a preliminary view that a solar PV project would work. Then it can be made clear that the council is consulting with the public and will listen to its views before making a final decision.

It is important as part of this process to effectively refer back to the climate change strategy and make the case for the need for action. Confirming that the council is committed to tackling issues of climate change is key, with a link to the need to introduce green energy and its important role in this.

Having a wider strategy allows the authority to say that it is looking at more than one area and that no decision has yet been taken. The council will determine in due course that the project is appropriate in relation to its overall strategy and is cost effective. Pointing out that there could be significant economic benefits to using renewable energy in the area is an important part of the message. It is also important to highlight that the benefits could include jobs and money coming into the area that could help to run public services and reduce the burden on tax payers.

The council will also need to deal with the actual process that it is going to follow. For example a robust feasibility study will be undertaken (or has been undertaken), a trial to see if conditions would be suitable etc. before any planning application will be submitted.

The council will need to deal with the subject of how it will raise the money too. It could invest in the renewable energy project from its own reserves or even by borrowing money on a payback basis. Either way, it needs to point out that there would be no effect on frontline services and the council would only go ahead if it was clearly in the best interests of local tax payers to do so. **Figure 13.3** below considers some possible key messages, using the fictional local authority, Barchester Council.

• This is a civic project, which is publicly funded but with all the benefit coming back to the area of Barchester
• It is a 'not for profit' project, in the sense that whilst there will be surpluses of income over expenditure, they will all be re-invested in one way or the other for the benefit of the people of Barchester
• The council is proceeding with the project because, even at a time of great financial austerity, it is financially sensible to do so. The project will deliver a large number of non-financial benefits (see below) but also considerable income to fund future council services
• The wider benefits to Barchester are:
• Community leadership
• Energy security
• Carbon benefits under the CRC
• Economic benefits
• Effectiveness and efficiency
• The project has across the board multi party political support on the council
• But it is not just about us and our project, its about the climate change requirements of the area
• The council, as the democratically elected body for the region, will decide on the exact nature and scope of the project, and the re-investmentof the surpluses, but will consult the community widely
• The project will be pursued diligently and in accordance with good industry standards. A timetable has been agreed; this will allow ample time for full consultation and discussion with the statutory consultees in the planning process

> • *The council has no former experience of this type of renewable energy project (there are no local authority projects of this nature anywhere in the UK yet) but will procure expertise to advise on the delivery of the project*
> • *Risk will be carefully managed. The council will not expend any money unnecessarily, and particularly in the early stages whilst the viability of the site and other key matters, such as planning consent and a grid connection are being determined*
> • *The council has a longer term aspiration to be a leading 'green' council and to own and operate a local energy services company (ESCO). This is because the council believes that such a venture would help energy security, save millions of pounds in energy costs in the longer term, create local jobs and supply chains and help to remove fuel poverty. This project is the first step towards that goal but will be followed by other similar projects, whether wind, solar, or biomass in nature or the development of heat networks.*

Figure 13.3 - Key Messages for a Solar PV Project in Barchester Council

The Method of Communication

This will differ, depending on the audience and the nature of the scheme.

• Residents

Public consultation can be held via public meetings, organised by the council. These are best in council buildings or community buildings (church halls, schools, or community centres). The message is not just verbal. It needs to be conveyed in pictures and photographs, graphs, charts and billboards.

These concepts can also be put on display in other places, for example, a roadshow using locations such as libraries, shopping centres and community centres.

Some authorities have used the model of an e-survey to let residents have their say, or give their views online. A Citizens Panel of some sort is another potential idea.

• Elected members

Member briefings can be written and distributed to all members the council. However, it is essential that there are also meetings and briefings of all members by the key Portfolio Holder and officers dealing with the project.

If the scheme might affect members in another authority, for example where a solar farm is on the boundary of two local authorities, then specific briefings of members in the other authority should be contemplated, particularly relevant ward members. This would need the consent of the other authority.

• Key stakeholders

One to one meetings or briefings can be arranged with key stakeholders, as identified by the stakeholder mapping exercise mentioned above.

• Publicity materials required

A wide array of materials will be required for a large project, such as a solar farm or a major social housing project. This may comprise a fact sheet, giving simple facts about renewable energy, the benefits and the process. This could mirror the display boards used at the public meetings.

Display or interpretation boards will be necessary, setting out the concepts, using visual materials, photographs, charts and written facts. **Figure 13.4** describes some of the display boards prepared by Cornwall Council for its solar farm proposal of 2010. The idea was that anyone visiting the open day or presentations could simply walk along the boards and get the full story of what was proposed.

- **Board 1** – *What is Climate Change?*
- **Board 2** – *Cornwall's Energy Statistics*
- **Board 3** – *Renewable Energy*
- **Board 4** – *The Green Cornwall Programme*
- **Board 5** – *Solar Photovoltaics*
- **Board 6** – *The Newquay Solar PV proposal*
- **Board 7** – *The Community Benefits*
- **Board 8** – *Details of the First and Second Consultation*

Figure 13.4 – Display Boards for Newquay Solar Farm

A timeline setting out the milestones to show the various steps, from decision making to construction and commissioning will also be necessary.

Some technologies, particularly wind energy, might also need 'myth busting' fact sheets, giving dedicated information about issues of concern, for example noise, wildlife, flicker/strobe effect, views and effectiveness of wind power. An example in relation to solar energy is that 'it is not sunny enough in the UK to make solar panels worthwhile'.

Leaflets might also be delivered to nearby residents, outlining facts and how to have their say in the process.

• Web and new media

The council will have a website for normal council business and this needs to host dedicated web pages for the project, with links to suitable other websites for the technology concerned.

Complimentary new media support, might include a video or film, setting out what the council is trying to achieve, which might be viewed on Youtube, and new media links to Facebook or similar sites should be considered.

Different authorities will take different views as to the use of social media and it has to be recognised that negative effects can also ensue. The council does not want a momentum against the scheme to grow on Facebook or Twitter, and so may wish to use the social media tools carefully.

• Press and media

It was mentioned above that a proactive strategy means openly engaging with the press and other media and seeking coverage for the project. This means providing necessary information to local papers, blogs, the BBC and ITV, local radio stations and so on.

A series of formal press releases will need to be developed and released at key stages in the process.

A press conference, where the media can ask questions of the key members and officers is also a good way of disseminating messages and engaging with the press.

• School Engagement

Schools have many advantages in relation to renewable energy. Children and younger people are far more concerned about damage to the earth than are older people and are therefore more likely to support eco action. Renewable energy can also be a good part of the curriculum and used as a learning tool.

It is therefore worth seeking to engage with schools about a local project that will have significant press interest and where the benefits and implications can be discussed.

• Other matters

It will be necessary to assess the impact of the communications strategy as it progresses, including the success or failure of different communications activities. It will then be necessary to amend or adapt the messages and tactics as appropriate.

• Spokespeople

In the chapter on strategy, the importance of strong, clear and accountable leadership from the council on renewable energy and climate change was emphasised. It is even more important with the communications strategy for the council to be able to demonstrate that it is speaking with one voice on its policy.

This means that the key individuals will need to be fully 'on message' relating to the project. They would include: the Leader of the Council; the Cabinet member for environment and sustainability; the Chief Executive; the Director of Environment and any external advisers that the council is using.

It would be normal to form a media protocol to control who is able to speak formally on behalf of the council in relation to the project. It has to be made clear to others in the council that they are not able to do so.

Budget

Such a communications strategy will have budget implications. These should be carefully assessed and worked up with other elements of the project costs. However, it is worth bearing in mind that for a large project, with a substantial capital cost, these costs might be more substantial than would be the case in relation to a non-renewable energy project. As mentioned above, external assistance may well be required.

Scale of communications strategy

As mentioned above, the scale and depth of the communications strategy will depend greatly on the project concerned. Obviously, a smaller project will not require the level of input mentioned above and to do so would definitely be overkill. However, **Chapter 12** indicates that local authorities are considering larger solar farm type contracts, or substantial social housing contracts, and these will need to be carefully assessed. It is often the case that the communications strategy is not seen as vitally important, but experience demonstrates that it might just be the difference between success and failure.

Community Benefit Issues

Community benefit is another loose and rather unsatisfactory term, which is often misconstrued. In law, a community benefit payment is a voluntary payment made to a community group that is not linked to the specific granting of a planning permission. It therefore has a relatively narrow meaning. However, community benefit more generally could denote any value that the community (the public) gets from a renewable energy project. This has particular relevance to local authority schemes.

In this regard, the wider community benefit of the project is closely linked with the communications strategy. That is essentially what the message is about. What will the public gain from this? How will the people of the area, the council taxpayers, business community, ordinary voters and the like feel about this scheme? If public money is to be expended on a project of this nature, the council has to have thought through how the benefits will filter back to the people and the community. It would want to publicise this anyway, for reasons explained above, but there is often the view that as everything a local authority does is funded by the public and essentially for the public, the public will support it, but that is not necessarily the case. A coherent and planned approach to community benefits needs to be developed and, in tandem with the communications strategy, forms a powerful force to garner public support.

So in the wider meaning, it is necessary for the local authority to demonstrate community benefit in order to win over public opinion and ensure that it obtains planning consent for its scheme. This will probably mean that it has to differentiate its project from others, particularly profit driven, private sector schemes.

The council cannot rely upon its role in civic governance to persuade everyone that the income derived from such a project automatically goes back into community coffers. A special effort will therefore be necessary to drive home the message about the benefits of the project to the community. It goes without saying that the greater the benefit from the project, the greater public support it will have, and the fewer objections there will be to planning permission being granted. This is vital to the role of members generally and ward members in particular.

In its more narrow, technical planning meaning, community benefit is perhaps best developed in relation to wind energy schemes, where guidelines are available from Renewables UK as to how much financial contribution should be given to the community. The principles of community benefit apply equally across other technologies, though, all of which will have an impact on the public one way or the other. Most of the other technologies have now adopted the Renewables UK community benefit provisions.

Community benefit can be measured on a scale from virtually none (unlikely to be acceptable) to significant (for example, both local and general benefits provided to the public) and can even go wider than that. The issue for each council is to choose where the line should be drawn.

Small Community Benefit

It is not really possible to give no community benefit at all, and so a small benefit normally entails some form of monetary contribution to the local community. This might be to an existing community group or organisation. Or a new community trust might be established for the purpose.

In a wind energy project, the guidance produced by Renewables UK is that a developer should agree to provide at least £5,000 per MW of energy created by a wind farm development. IN the past, this figure was £1,000 but it was recognised that this was not very effective and was often not received well, largely due to the fact that there is much greater awareness now of the level of income and profits being generated by such projects. Accordingly, the figure was raised substantially. In relation to non-civic projects, the perception that an outside party is using local land and making big money, without any real benefit going to the local community, can be both powerful and fatal to public support.

A Higher Community Benefit

However, a council could strive to be exemplary in developing a leading comprehensive benefits package, which will help promote both the scheme and the council at the same time. This starts by transparency on the income and profit from the project and an emphasis on its benefits to the local community.

Such a package might be split into two parts: local and area wide. For the purposes of illustration, the comments below relate to a major solar farm development (5MW+) on council owned land in the fictitious local authority of Barchester.

The first part is the local part. This is for the exclusive benefit of the nearest community to the project. If there is a housing estate within a reasonable distance of the site (say within 1-2 km), and overlooking the site, then the council could determine that it will allocate some of the income to give those residents a 'green' benefit in consideration of their proximity to the site.

The obvious project would be to offer a type of Green Deal makeover to all of those houses, free of charge, up to an agreed amount (for example, £10,000 per house). This would then give the householder choice over what measures are fitted, such as cavity wall or loft insulation, doubleglazing or their own solar panels. This way, the council gets to promote Green Deal (also part of its green strategy) and get valuable experience, whilst winning over the local community. This could be in addition to a sum contributed to a local trust, to be spent on that particular area. There are numerous other variations that could be considered. It may also be the case, of course, that the Council can raise other monies for such work, such as from the ECO provisions. This might apply if the houses were to receive external wall insulation or the like as part of the process.

The second part of the package is the area wide benefit. Obviously, under normal rules, the council itself would decide what to do with the money generated from such a substantial project. This might be anything from the reduction of the council tax (or freezing increases in the future) to spending money on new projects.

One way to gain good engagement with the public would be to offer them a say in how some of the money is spent. A list of potential projects could be drawn up, from revamping council buildings to new community centres or transport links, with a very public consultation exercise embarked on as to which has greatest public support. This is an excellent way of linking the benefits to the necessity to build the project in the first place. If the project does not go ahead, the benefits do not materialise. This second way of giving benefit is stronger than the council, as the elected body, simply deciding how the money is spent, although this is, of course, completely legitimate.

There are many other possibilities that could be considered by a council in this position. One is the potential for income from the project to be used to create an 'energy park' in association with the project, to create a centre of excellence in the area and create new jobs. This could include educational facilities and training workshops, perhaps in conjunction with the local universities or colleges.

Tourism is another potential benefit here. The site could have viewing platforms included, a visitor centre attached and so on. Wind farms and solar farms have provided examples of this, such as the Ecotricity wind farm in Suffolk, where the viewing platform on the top of the turbine is very popular with tourists. At the Milagro solar farm in Navarra, Spain, described in Chapter 12, there is a viewing platform and visitor centre, showing the layout of the site and illustrating the power being generated there.

A More Outward Approach

All of the foregoing concerns the council itself and its projects and developments. A different approach, either alone or in conjunction with the above, would be to look outwards. There are two relevant areas here: helping the community undertake schemes and doing something to benefit the wider economy of the area.

• The Community

Community energy is considered above and it is noted that this is a rapidly growing area. The Government wants to see much more community energy in the UK and has published a Community Energy Strategy to promote this. However, the notion of community energy is not new, and has existed for many years. Those authorities that are active in the green space will probably already have considered how they can take steps to assist community groups to undertake their own projects and gain a wider community benefit as a result. As ever, the problem with this proposal is funding. It is this element that DECC could change under the Community Energy Strategy.

An example of how a local authority might assist community groups would be to create a new post of 'community energy officer' in the council, which could be a fixed term for two years. This officer would then be available to assist any community group in the area that wants to pursue a renewable energy project to help it along. Obvious areas are approaching banks to borrow money, developing business cases and completing the forms for planning permission.

A report by the Energy Saving Trust entitled Power in Numbers – the Benefits and Potential of Distributed Energy at the Small Community Scale examined this area and concluded that a relatively small amount of assistance could have a significant effect on ensuring that more community schemes come to fruition.

The reason that more local authorities have not gone down this route is simply due to a lack of funds. Here, however, the council will be generating funds that could make a big difference in this way. If the salary and on-costs for the post were, say £50k pa, then a fixed sum of £100k would be required to fund this for two years. The council could then appraise the performance of the service and decide whether to continue funding it in later years.

One of the advantages of such a move, would be that the council could always point to the fact that it is not just about the council and its project, it is about the carbon footprint and economic vitality of the whole area.

• *The Wider Economy*

This builds on the last point. Whilst that involves the council looking outwards, its gaze only goes so far as community groups. The suggestion is that it could come up with a proposal that is far wider. The other part of the economy that has not yet been considered is the private sector and the council can also help it with money from a substantial project.

A simple example would be to publish planning guidance (special planning documents) that gives assistance on how to apply for planning consent for renewable energy projects. Cornwall Council, for instance, has issued a series of such documents. *Renewable And Low Carbon Energy – Supplementary Planning Document* (June 2010) is one of its suite of documents in this area.

Another example would be a Community Infrastructure Levy scheme, making clear that some of the benefits will go towards energy infrastructure that will help green energy developers. Under such a scheme, a levy is placed on qualifying new development and sums paid into a fund. The fund can then be used for designated purposes, such as green infrastructure. A district heating network could be an example of this, whereby the council funds the pipe-work on the basis that private finance is raised for the Combined Heat and Power or other heating infrastructure.

Again, this gives the council an excellent standpoint in terms of its 'giving the benefit back to the people' argument.

Naturally, this would not be done quickly – a Community Infrastructure Levy scheme would take over a year on its own. However, if a commitment was to be made towards this, then the council could start reaping the benefits in PR terms from the word go. It could also refine the plans and extend them (for example, ultimately creating some form of enterprise zone) as time goes on and more council-led renewable energy projects are determined.

Conclusion

Community energy is likely to be on a steep upward curve for the next decade. As awareness grows of energy issues, and concern over costs also grows, more and more groups are likely to want to deliver a project of their own. This movement, whilst separate from what local authorities are doing themselves, is nonetheless important to their overall areas.

In so far as the local authority's own projects are concerned, the two factors above of good communications and engagement and community benefit are central to winning 'hearts and minds' to get the project delivered in the first place. The more support the project has, the easier and quicker it will be to build it. This is an essential step in that process.

The council therefore needs to start the early process of thinking about the options for communications and community benefits and putting them to members, so that a formal position can be determined. Both the communications strategy and the community benefits decisions need to be completed before any physical work commences.

Key Learning Points

- *The communications plan is much more important than is generally realised*
- *Member support is crucial and so public criticism is problematic*
- *Much opposition to renewables is caused by a position of ignorance*
- *The communications strategy is to inform and educate about the benefits of the project*
- *A clear plan is required, setting down the message, the audience, the tools for dissemination and so on*
- *This will take time, effort and money*
- *If this work is not done, the council risks negative publicity and lack of support for its project*

At the heart of the conversation around communicating renewable technology is a narrative about climate change. On this subject, there is an excellent store of intelligence and knowledge on what works and what doesn't, from that published by Defra on pro-environmental behaviours to both business and the general public, to the Sustainable Development Commission (I Will If You Will), to the IPPR (Positive Energy) to the Consumers Association (An Environmental Contract).

In brief, the consolidated understanding on climate change communications can be boiled down to a few key points.

Actions count

Awareness is growing, but pathways to action are still not clear. While up to 90 per cent of those people and businesses asked cite climate change as a clear and present threat to our economic, social and environmental future, as few as 9 per cent can clearly state where they feel they should be taking action.

Although bridging this gap between awareness and an understanding of how each and every one of us can make a difference is important, so too is the role public bodies can play in leadership as exemplars through their own carbon reduction activity.

There should be no fear without agency

The urgency and immediacy of the threat can be used to grab attention but it must, at all times, be twinned with the message that something can be done, from the humblest domestic action on energy efficiency to bold measures to increase our technical response, particularly in the area of renewable energy.

The time is now

A key theme in climate change communications has to be the immediacy of required action. Most of the tools and solutions we need to meet our targets on reducing carbon dioxide emissions have already been identified. The challenge is to make the case that now is the time for action, and that investment in renewables must not be delayed.

For some, the advantages of renewable technology speak for themselves: a clean, limitless source of energy that allows us to gradually phase out our reliance on fossil fuels. For others, doubts still persist over effectiveness, reliability, cost - and even necessity.

From a communications perspective, it can be useful to think of your audience as being on a sliding scale of attitudes and perceptions. At one end are the people who get it. Perhaps they are concerned and well informed on the challenges of climate change and energy dependence, perhaps the economic argument resonates. At the other end of the spectrum are those that will never buy into a renewable project, people with deep-rooted distrust of the industry, and in some instances, climate change itself.

In reality very few people fit into either of those groups and, more often than not, very little can be done to change entrenched opinions with even the most exceptional communications campaign. The vast majority will sit somewhere else on the spectrum. They might lean toward skepticism but not be totally convinced by the anti-argument. They might broadly support the idea of renewables but have lingering concerns. They might be slap-bang in the middle without strong feelings either way.

Of course, good communications should aim to engage and inform all audiences, but in truth it is the majority group that are neither 'dead set against' nor 'wholeheartedly support' renewables that hold the key, and can make the difference between success and failure. A campaign that fails to make a coherent case risks allowing people to slip down the scale into the 'anti-category' or from a 'lukewarm' to 'cold' position which, if allowed enough unopposed momentum, can totally derail a project.

Good preparation is fundamental. A great deal can be learnt during the development stage that will direct the rest of the communications and help get under the skin of a project. This is an opportunity to look at, and learn from, the successes and failures of others as well as a review of previous consultation activities in the area and the methodologies used to ensure the project team is aware of any key concerns and the relevant interest groups.

From the research, a stakeholder mapping exercise can be undertaken, a full audit of stakeholders and what level of communications detail they require. This is also the stage that the messaging matrix can be evolved – tailored messaging for different audiences depending on the information they need. A key outcome of the above will be the production of a stakeholder map. Identifying exactly who needs to be consulted and at what level is critical at the inception of a successful engagement process. Failure to identify and speak to a group, individual or organisation in the early stages can deal a blow to credibility, and waste time and resources.

To take Wrexham County Borough Council's project to install around 3000 Solar Photovoltaic panels onto its domestic and non-domestic property portfolio as an example, the messaging had to be sensitively targeted. For residents that would receive panels, it was crucial they bought into the project and understood how to get the most from the technology for their own benefit, as well as for the council's. For those whose homes were not suitable, it was more appropriate to explain the selection criteria and offer a viable alternative by which energy savings could be enjoyed. For other audiences including staff, stakeholders, the media and general public, we wanted them to feel supported and informed, to see how the council is leading on this issue, and to inspire others to take energy saving action.

Some key features of our messaging in this campaign were:

One. Local equals powerful.

When climate change is presented as a global, planet-threatening issue it can be simply too big and too intimidating for many people to deal with it, either in a professional or personal way. The scale can be paralysing and the actions to take can seem too small and too insignificant. Localism can deconstruct this, powerfully. In the solar project, we talked about the impacts and benefits directly relating to Wrexham.

Two. *I will if you will.*

It's classic social proofing. People are more likely to take action if they see others doing so also. Only 10-15% of us are self-starting altruists or activists on issues like climate change, the vast majority are consensual and need to be shown that others are doing it too. Once the solar project gained buy-in among residents, the momentum helped the installation process run smoothly.

Three. *Pride of place.*

If you fuse civic pride with an essentially environmental call to action, it becomes an entirely different proposition. Do it for the planet? Maybe. Do it for Wrexham? Definitely!

Four. *First steps on a big journey.*

At the local scale, the steps on the journey are real and tangible. You can see action taking place, you know who to call or where to ask for help. Action can spread through social networks, neighbourhoods, schools and businesses.

To address a number of audiences and lines of communication and given that each audience may need to undertake varying courses of action, a branded campaign identity is of great benefit. The concept is tried and tested. Any overall campaign identity needs to allow the communication of different messages to different audiences via different channels within one overriding identity. It also needs to be in the imperative mood, be empowering and, preferably - it needs to be fun. Our brand for Wrexham was built on the 'People Power' brand we had previously developed (a campaign based on encouraging individuals to take action), and simply called 'Solar Power'. It was an accessible, colourful and playful brand that allowed us to talk about climate change without being corporate or overly authoritarian.

With the visual brand and messaging in place, we move to the deployment phase. Good communications planning fuses together methods that deliver a high level of personalised contact with those that offer a greater 'reach' through a bigger audience, such as online communications tools, door drops or media relations.

For Wrexham a targeted suite of literature, film, events and online communications were used to give tenants receiving panels help using the technology (which also helped increase income for the council). Those not receiving panels were provided with an explanation of the selection criteria, and the offer of a Green Doctor visit that would make their homes more energy efficient and help them save money. Internal council support came through council publications and newsletters, and a full PR campaign was run to raise the profile of the project aims.

All audiences were informed about the economic benefits individually and to the council, and the global climate change context was explained, with Wrexham Council positioned as a leader on the issue.

A key success for the campaign was that the council did not experience any difficulty accessing properties to install the solar panels – access had been a problem on other projects. Residents bought into the project to the extent that prevented access was a non-issue. In addition the Green Doctor offer became oversubscribed during the course of the installations, which went further to reducing the overall carbon footprint of the region.

Andrew Peacock
Senior Advocate
Creative Concern
www.creativeconcern.com

The delivery phase of a solar PV project

14

Introduction

In each solar PV initiative, there will be a series of phases that will comprise the whole transaction. Sometimes these will take years to come to fruition; on other occasions it might all come together fairly quickly.

The various phases are illustrated in Figure 14.1 below.

1. **Scoping**
2. **Strategy**
3. **The project & risk management**
4. **The business case & funding**
5. **Political approval**
6. **Procurement**
7. **Construction & Commissioning**
8. **Post Construction Matters**

Figure 14.1 - Stages In A Solar PV Project

All of the different aspects of these phases have been covered in previous chapters. There are only a few miscellaneous areas that did not fit elsewhere that need to be covered here. However, the purpose of this Chapter is to take a 'helicopter view' of the whole series of events and to attempt to put it in some form of chronological order. This material should be taken in the spirit in which it is intended and not as a rigid, set timetable. Local government does not work that way and sometimes elements may be approached out of order.

The Scoping Stage

The scoping stage is the start and covers a number of different aspects of a particular project. The idea for the project usually came from somewhere. One of the officers or members went on a course, read an article or a book or heard about another authority's experience in this area.

Sometimes it is the professionals within the authority who suggest projects, such as the energy manager, sustainability officer or environment director.

The idea has to germinate into a concept in order to be promoted. This might be climate change related or based on the economics of renewable energy projects. These issues depend greatly on the authority concerned. The background for this activity is the current situation with climate change on a global scale. This is discussed in **Chapter 2** and against this background, many authorities have determined to act. But what should they do?

If any local authority has considered the different renewable energy technologies in detail, it will have become apparent that solar PV is one of the easiest to progress. It does not take as long as wind, is less controversial and every local authority has numerous buildings that need energy. Many other local authorities have already fitted some solar PV and so there are good news stories circulating within local government on the subject.

The Strategy Stage

Hopefully the local authority concerned already has a climate change strategy, as discussed in **Chapter 5**. As indicted there, each local authority should develop a holistic climate change strategy, setting targets and goals, building a route map towards them, and coming up with projects that form the steps on that path. Such a strategy should join up the various different parts of the agenda and link them to corporate goals and aspirations. As an example, buildings might include schools, social housing, leisure facilities or civic headquarters, but all have the same issues in relation to energy management and efficiency and the fitting of renewables. A corporate approach is therefore vital.

This should lead to both a climate change strategy and a renewable energy strategy. Often the former exists, but the authority is vague on the latter, perhaps just including some general statements in its climate change strategy.

But the brutal truth is that the only thing that counts is installations delivered, meters turning, and kilowatt hours being generated. Accordingly, it is difficult to avoid having a specific strategy and setting some clear goals, with metrics to demonstrate progress towards them.

It may well be that an authority needs some external assistance on doing this work. Fortunately there are plenty of different advisers at all levels to help, from small consultants to major professional firms.

As **Chapter 5** concludes, an authority will need a robust series of plans if it is to make the most of this opportunity. These will be drawn up in the context of the current policy and legislative framework (examined in **Chapter 3**) and the position of the authority, in particular its finances (**Chapter 4**).

The Project Stage

So, the authority has determined that action is required, either on environmental grounds or economic grounds (to assist with economic development) or both. The various corporate strategies have been put in place, such as a strategy on climate change, a renewable energy strategy and the links with other corporate strategies, such as asset management, have been made.

Next, the authority needs to move into the project phase. This will involve both identifying a project and then planning how it can be brought forwards.

The first decision is to undertake renewable energy, as opposed to – or alongside – energy efficiency work. **Chapter 6** emphasises the hierarchy in this area, with reducing energy use as the most effective and least expensive work, followed by improving energy efficiency and then last of all introducing renewable energy solutions. The authority has gone through that exercise and has decided to undertake both energy efficiency and renewable energy in tandem. Next, it chooses solar PV from those available as its first renewable energy technology. **Chapter 7** fully explains how solar PV works and explains why this is a good choice.

Having decided to go down the solar PV route, the authority next needs to decide if it will fit solar to its land or buildings. There is some detail to this decision and it is considered in **Chapter 12**. Which way a local authority goes, will depend on its land holdings, how many buildings it has and whether it intends to undertake the work itself or via external contractors.

The pros and cons of land based systems as opposed to buildings based systems are set out in **Figure 12.1** and this decision needs to be taken carefully. The first project will always be the most challenging and subsequent projects will be found to be easier with experience.

In the examples below, different scenarios are considered, including the authority deciding to go for a buildings-based strategy and to have a procurement exercise to enter into a design, build and operate contract; a social housing operation, again using a design and fit basis; and the construction of a solar farm.

In each case, the authority will need to determine whether it has the internal skills to procure and plan such a contract or needs to engage external consultants to assist. These might include strategic advisers, financial advisers, legal advisers, technical consultants or experts on grid connections and dealing with Distribution Network Operators.

The council will need to draw up a timetable for the procurement and a 'Gantt' project management chart (or similar format spreadsheet) for the whole project. This will set down each step that needs to be taken and in what timescale. Such detailed project planning is essential to keep a large project on track and ensure that the project team is managing the project effectively.

Figure 14.2 below gives an example of a Gantt chart for a solar farm project. A project of this nature will cover a number of stages, across a timeline of at least a year. Featured below are the basic steps in that process. The exact timing of each step will depend on the project and its progress, for example whether an EIA is required, whether planning consent is granted and so on.

Concept Phase (3 months)

- *The council has an idea and seeks to put that idea into a formal strategy*
- *A report is necessary on how the project might be framed*

Project Planning Phase (3 months)

- *The council needs to resolve to embark on the project, at least until the next stage and identify funds to do so*
- *Site identification – if there is more than one site, works to determine the best one*
- *A communications strategy goes hand in hand with the community consultation process ie: starting to engage with those in the vicinity of the chosen site(s)*
- *The council needs to engage with neighbouring authorities (if relevant) and the county council (where appropriate) about the project*
- *The council needs to engage with the necessary statutory agencies*
- *Engage formally with the DNO regarding grid connection*
- *Preparation of a procurement plan*
- *Submit screening application to planning department to check whether an Environmental Impact Assessment is required*
- *Development of the community proposals goes hand in hand with the communications strategy and the consultation process*
- *The site can now be finalised*

Planning Consent Phase (3 months)

- *The application is made by the council as applicant, to the council as regulatory authority*
- *A 'Chinese wall' needs to be established before this process can commence*
- *Consultants might be used*

- *The statutory consultees will be part of this process, as well as a public consultation, bearing in mind the nature of the project*
- *The council has no right of appeal and therefore only gets one opportunity to obtain planning consent*

Procurement Phase (3 months)

- *The contractor that will design, build and operate the facility for 20 years now needs to be identified*
- *The procurement will be covered by the EU procurement rules and will need to be structured properly*
- *Advice will be necessary on the legalities to be followed*
- *The procurement is likely to be on the restricted procedure basis and this will need careful planning*
- *The result of this phase is the award of a contract to a contractor with the necessary experience and expertise to undertake the work*
- *The Business Case can now be finalized, as the council will have the full construction cost of the facility*

Construction Phase (6 months)

- *This phase sees the actual building of the facility in accordance with its plans, for which planning consent has been granted*
- *The contractor will put in the footings, have the panels and inverters delivered, put them together and fix them into place*
- *The grid connection will then be undertaken, perhaps involving a new substation*
- *A plan for construction might be part of the planning consent and will need to be followed*

Commissioning Phase (one month)

- *Commissioning is effectively the turning on of the facility*
- *It is commissioned when it is capable of operation ie the arrays have been installed, the cabling organized and the grid connection completed*

- *Once the facility is commissioned, it starts earning income from the solar energy that it generates*

Operation and Maintenance Phase (for 20 years* from commissioning)

- *The council will be the owner of the solar farm and will be responsible for its maintenance*
- *Maintenance work will be carried out in accordance with a planned schedule*
- *This aspect will be contracted to the external company that has designed and built the facility*

Decommissioning (after 20 years*)

- *The final stage in any project is the decommissioning at the end of the life of the facility. This is usually after 20 years. The simple choice is usually to remove the arrays and make good the site (often an original planning condition) or to replace the panels with newer models. A new planning consent will be required.*

* Note that the council may not want to decommission after 20 years, depending on planning conditions and the operability of the facility.

Figure 14.2 – Gantt Chart for a Solar PV Project

The business case & funding

In parallel to the project planning will be the work to prepare a business case and plan (examined in **Chapter 9**), taking into account the financial incentives (here the FITs explained in **Chapter 8**). It will need to identify the source of the money (**Chapter 10**) and the full project budget.

If the project is motivated on economic grounds, then the business case will be based on the income that can be received from the project, the payback and the return on investment. If it is based on environmental grounds, then it will be motivated by affordability of the capital to make the project a reality.

As **Chapter 9** reveals, there is a multiplicity of other factors that will determine the business case, such as the energy use in the buildings concerned and whether to prioritise buildings with a high energy use (such as leisure centres) and use the energy on site, to maximise the return.

A good analysis of the costs will need to be done and it is essential here that up to date information is available on market prices for solar PV panels and equipment. It is also important that business cases are realistic and do not include needless extra costs, such as cleaning or unnecessary maintenance checks.

The funding routes will need thorough examination too and this may involve considering different ways of finding the money; perhaps a joint arrangement with another authority or even a public offering?

Risk Analysis

One of the integral parts to the business and financial cases, the project planning and the political approval, is risk management. Any commercial contract involves risk and the council will be familiar with this. However, how risk is quantified and managed is key to the delivery of any such project.

Risk basically involves a series of questions and how these can be answered. These include:

- *What is the risk? What might happen in relation to this contract?*
- *What is the likelihood of it coming to pass? Is it likely that this will happen or fairly unlikely?*
- *What happens if it does? What are the consequences of the particular outcome? Will it lead to financial or other losses?*
- *Who bears those consequences? Will it be the council or another party (such as a contractor working for the council).*

The contractual parties, such as the private sector company that will fit solar panels to the council's buildings or build the council's solar farm, will of course be subject to a number of different obligations, usually under financial indemnification to the council if they default. However, that is a relatively late stage of the process; all of the early work, such as the identification of the site and the obtaining of planning consent is at the authority's risk.

There are a number of different types of risk that will occur during a solar PV project. Any council can protect itself against many of these risks by employing experts in the planning and construction of the facilities.

The overriding principle that should be operated, however, is to minimize the council's exposure to financial risk until it is completely clear that the project will proceed.

The most fundamental risks to any major solar energy project are:

- *Getting a planning consent*
- *Arranging a grid connection*
- *Construction of the works*
- *Timing of completion to fit with degression dates under FIT (depending on business case)*

These may vary depending on the project. The solar farm is the easiest example, as it will always require both planning consent and a grid connection. Non-domestic buildings may require permission (see **Chapter 12**) and will probably require some work to the electrical system to allow connection to the grid. Housing is different again; here there are Permitted Development rights in operation and the grid connection might not be an issue. However the authority will be concerned with programming issues, which can be complicated when thousands of houses are concerned.

In general terms, planning consent is considered in **Chapter 12** and, for solar farms, is closely linked to public perception and the communications strategy (both internal and external). Grid connections can be explored with the local Distribution Network Operator (DNO) and an indication given in advance of a formal offer. **Chapter 11** explores those issues.

Procurement and construction risk is offset by the council undertaking a well run procurement exercise, supported by external expertise and requiring appropriate experience and capability from applicants, as discussed below.

There are a multiplicity of other risks, as is the case with any construction / engineering project. These include:

- *Raising finance*
- *Income risk / technical performance*
- *Supply chain issues*
- *Site based issues – including flooding, access, topography or roof strength*
- *Contractor failure / insolvency etc.*
- *Weather damage / storms etc.*
- *Warranties*

All of these risks can be managed, for example by careful choice of sites, focus on the supply chain and so on.

Of more interest might be those relevant to local authorities, such as:

- *Change in political control*
- *Change in Government policy*
- *Loss of key personnel internally*
- *Leakage of corporate support, political or managerial*

These might be more sensitive, but can be managed. It is important that the council members view a large solar project as an essential project to deliver growth and therefore not politically driven. Accordingly, it should not lose political support if the council's membership changes in subsequent local elections. This is entirely possible, when projects are in gestation for a period of years.

It would be normal practice for the council to undertake a full risk analysis as part of its work on this project. However, it would seem sensible to obtain the support of the Corporate Management Team and also have Cabinet approval to move the project forwards, before such detailed work is undertaken.

The first steps are to review the suitable sites and consider the planning and grid issues. The main issue at this early stage is to minimise the council's exposure to costs, until these fundamental issues have been resolved in the affirmative, as they threaten the viability of the project.

A full risk profile can then be drawn up at a later stage, when it is clear that the project is possible, with each risk examined, graded and given a priority level and added into the council's risk register.

Enable
- Financial risk
- Income risk
- Procurement risk
- Technical performance
- Resident engagement
- Staff engagement
- Ownership of properties / ability to change
- Planning permission
- Grid issues / DNO
- Legal issues re ownership etc.
- Tax issues
- Supply chain issues
- Local benefits issues such as employment

Install
- Roof integrity
- Resident support
- FIT income
- Surveys
- Latent problems

Maintain
* Storm damage
* Vandalism
* Theft
* System malfunction
* Contractor failure / insolvency etc.
* Insurance
* Warranties
* Remote monitoring

Management Of Risk
* Which risks are best managed where?
* Which risk are better with the council?
* Which risks will the contractor price prohibitively?

Figure 14.3 – Risk Matrix for a Housing Solar PV Project

Political approval

If an authority is to make a major push forwards with renewable energy, this has to have political approval at the highest level. The Cabinet will determine the priorities of the council and if climate change can be included, so much the better. Moreover, if the Cabinet wants to inject some activity into the local economy and believes that the green agenda can be that catalyst, then again it is likely that ambitious projects can be considered.

The Corporate Management Team also needs to be fully in support. This includes the Chief Executive and Director of Finance, as well as the Environment Director. As such projects need considerable funding, the finance personnel are particularly important and if the Director of Finance is very cautious, it is unlikely that a major project will come forwards.

The politicians need to be fully in the loop as the project moves from idea to concept, and from proposal to project elect. Usually this is by informal means, although at some stage the members will need formally to take a decision to proceed. This might be to put a scheme in the capital programme, to provide a budget for it or whatever. At that stage the proposal will need to have crystallised into a fully thought out plan, supported by a business case and full costings and necessary technical and other advice.

The normal way of proceeding is for the Cabinet to resolve to undertake the project and then to delegate the day to day running of it to the officers, subject to budgetary or other mechanisms as appropriate. There is normally a reporting back agreement if there are problems, if budgets will be exceeded or for information at various intervals.

The Procurement Stage

This is one of the stages that requires a little more information, as it has not been dealt with elsewhere. There are three elements that need to be considered here: the form of procurement that needs to be undertaken; the exercise to choose the successful contractor; and the contract to which that contractor will be bound.

It is necessary to appoint an internal team to work on these issues. This will need representation from legal and finance departments, as well as environment, energy management, sustainability and policy. If the team is well chosen and works well together, it will ensure that the complex but important issues in this stage are properly completed and knitted into the overall strategy.

The Procurement Exercise

There are a number of ways that a procurement exercise for solar PV could be structured. However, an authority will need to be guided by legal advice as to what the requirements of the EU procurement regime might be. The regime will apply to all procurements with a total cost of just over £170,000 (or £4.4m for works) and so all but the very smallest facilities will be caught by the regime.

The procurement regime works on the basis of contracts for works, services or supplies that qualify and are entered into by a public body that is a contracting authority under the rules. Normally, this requires a competitive tendering exercise, following advertisement in the Official Journal of the European Union. It may be possible to save some of the procedural steps by 'calling off' under a Framework, which has been put in place under the procedure. However, the advantages of this would need to be weighed against the fact that such frameworks may not be specifically tailored to the specialist needs of a PV project; the criteria for award may not reflect the authority's priorities; and the contractors on the Framework may not be specialists in this field.

If a bespoke procurement is to be undertaken, the main distinction to be made is whether a procurement uses the 'normal' rules ie: the open or restricted procedure, or 'special' rules, such as competitive dialogue or negotiation. This will need specialist legal input but in general terms, depends on whether there is a straightforward solution to meet the authority's needs. The exceptional routes cater for situations where it is not clear what the scope and extent of the contract will be and this therefore needs dialogue or negotiation. However, it will normally be the case that the standard procurement routes will be suitable for solar PV procurements.

In a procurement for design and fit services for domestic or non domestic installations, the council will know enough about what it wants to prepare an 'output' based specification. This is a specification that defines the end product, rather than the method of getting to it. So an authority could indicate that it wants between 1.5kw and 4kw of solar power from at least 500 roofs in its inventory of all its social housing. This means that the choice of which houses to use, design of the systems, capacity of the systems and make of the panels, would entirely be up to each bidder. This way, the council can simply evaluate the bids that it receives from each contractor in a transparent way that has been published in advance.

The alternative might be problematic. This would involve the council specifying the systems that it wants, where it wants them and how the work is to be carried out. As the council is not an expert in such matters, it would be counter productive to do this and would also mean that the authority would miss the chance to rely upon the main advantage of the earlier way – the fact that the contractors are the experts and can be legally bound to the promises that they make about the design and operation of the systems that they fit.

A solar farm will be different again. However, there is no reason why the restricted procedure cannot work here too. By the time the process described in **Chapter 12** has been completed, the council will have a site, a planning permission (probably with conditions attached), a maximum capacity and a grid connection all sorted out. When these are set, there are not many variables in the solar farm left to determine – only the siting and size of the arrays, the make of the panels and inverters and the like. There is not insufficient uncertainty to even mount an argument that negotiation or dialogue is necessary to iron out the details of the contract.

Selecting the Contractor

The council will want to look carefully at the bids that it receives in the procurement exercise. Assuming that it has determined to go for a design, build and operate route, it needs to be sure that the contractors bidding have the right experience and expertise for the work and an understanding of the requirements of the client. Local authorities also want to try to promote the local supply chain where legally possible to do so.

There are two stages to every procurement exercise, the first focusing on the actual applicants for the work and the second focusing on their proposals to undertake it. Most authorities have standard procedures for bidder selection that it would use for a solar PV contract. However, it would be sensible to check that those procedures are tailored to the needs of such a contract because this is the only stage in the process where the experience, technical ability and financial strength of the bidders can be taken into account.

However, the criteria to select the winning tender will need both careful forethought and dedicated legal advice to ensure that they reflect the authority's needs and priorities. They will also need to be settled before any tenderers are invited to bid. It is also sensible to have them signed off by key stakeholders in the project, as they cannot be changed subsequently. The bidders will know what the criteria are and will use them to shape their bids.

The first decision is the split between price and quality. This is often 50/50 but here the council may consider the risks higher and therefore justify a 70/30 split between quality / price, or even higher.

So far as price calculation is concerned, the price per kw installed is the figure that needs to be identified and used in the evaluation. Most authorities have standard procedures for allocating points in relation to price; these normally award the maximum points to the lowest price, with a lesser number of points to other bids, based on their relationship to the lowest priced tender. It is important that the tenderers were asked to set their prices out in a way that enables a price per kw installed figure to be arrived at, and the comparison of like with like.

In terms of criteria for quality assessment, this will be up to the authority to decide. The following are some suggestions of what might be included:

- **Technical factors** – *this might include the nature of the panels (monocrystalline or polycrystalline), their efficiency ratio or maintenance requirements*
- **Supply chain factors** – *the nature of the supply chain, delivery and storage of materials, access to equipment, or carbon reduction arrangements*
- **Commercial issues** – *the relationship that the contractor has with the DNO and OFGEM, the proposed resourcing of the contract (numbers and qualifications of staff, time on the job etc.) and any 'added value' on offer*
- **Management of the contract** – *the management team in place, their roles and organisation; the skills and experience of the personnel and operation on other projects; and the depth and quality of the installation programme submitted as part of the tender*
- **Employment** – *the training of employees, apprenticeships and arrangements for training the council in maintenance work etc.*
- **Site arrangement**s – *this might include communication channels, method statements about how the work is to be undertaken and demonstration of previous projects with well run site arrangements*

The council might wish to set a minimum quality threshold – for example, a contractor has to achieve a score of 60 to be considered. Again, it is up to the authority concerned.

The final weighting is arrived at by calculating the individual scores in the price and quality components and then applying the price / quality percentages. The council might want to arrange presentations to confirm the rankings on the paperwork are broadly right.

If the exercise is undertaken diligently and with the right advice, it should pass off without a problem. The successful contractor is then invited to enter into a formal contract with the council.

The Contract

This is a vital part of the arrangements. If the council goes to some trouble to find the right contractor to undertake the work, but does not then tie them down tightly into contractual arrangements, then its efforts may have been wasted. This is particularly so if there is an output specification in play as the contractor has pledged the design and suitability of the equipment to be fitted.

Irrespective as to whether the local authority has plans to develop a land based Solar Farm or a single roof top installation or series of such installations, there are a number of issues which they will need to consider. The authority will need to engage, either through its internal resource or externally through a consultant, a Project Manager to oversee the project on behalf of the council. This is a key role and will not only certify payments due to the Contractor but also to inspect the works on an ongoing basis for defects, deal with any Contractor queries and/or claims and be present for the commissioning of the relevant installation. It is therefore imperative that the Project Manager has sufficient time and experience to manage the project.

Another key member of the team will be the technical adviser. Again, the technical adviser may be sourced from the local authority's in-house team or alternatively an external adviser may be engaged.

If an external project manager and/or technical adviser is engaged, then their appointment will need to set out clearly the scope of their role and their ongoing responsibilities during the project. The standards to be expected from the consultants in undertaking their roles and any limitations of liability on the consultants for failing to undertake their obligations should be set out in the contract.

The next issue to consider when engaging the Contractor will be the contractual model for their engagement. Both the legal and technical advisers should be consulted for advice. For example, it may be that, at the outset, the exact number of projects may not have be identified (eg: the local authority may be waiting for structural reports and/or planning permission for some of the schemes, whereas others may be ready to go ahead) and therefore the local authority may consider entering into a Framework Agreement with the Contractor to call off specific projects on pre-agreed terms and conditions as projects come online.

The form of the construction contract may take a number of forms and there will be a number of drivers which will influence the contracting model including cost, experience, appetite for risk and the level of involvement the council wants over the short and/or medium term. For example, the local authority may wish the Contractor to take all of the construction risk on a "turnkey" basis, but may wish to utilise its in-house resource to undertake the maintenance of the solar farm over the long term. Alternatively, the local authority may wish to have greater certainty over the performance of the solar farm (including generation and access to spare parts), and so may contract with the Contractor to carry out both the construction and operation and maintenance of the installation for a five to ten year period.

Furthermore, the local authority may wish to engage certain contractors directly, for example the panel supplier or the mechanical and electrical contractors, and may not want the additional cost of the Contractor providing a turnkey solution. However, this may involve greater project management and the council may have to incur additional costs for external project management to oversee the multi-contracting approach.

Regardless of the form of contract model, there are a number of inherit risks which the Construction Contract will need to specifically deal with. These will include the following:

- *the security package offered by the Contractor including parent company guarantees and performance bonds, in the event that the Contractor fails to carry out the project (for example, due to insolvency)*
- *the performance guarantees offered by the Contractor. If the Contractor is wrapping the entire project, including the maintenance, then the local authority is more likely to receive a higher availability and performance guarantees than under a multi-contracting approach. However, this will need to be considered in the initial cost savings when selecting the form of contract*
- *parts availability*
- *maintenance obligations*
- *the programming of the works*

In addition to the general points set out above, there are specific considerations for ground and roof mounted projects which the council will need to consider.

In relation to roof top schemes, the council may have already engaged a structural engineer to assess the condition of the relevant roofs to withstand the additional weight of the Solar PV installation. The local authority may have engaged external consultants or used its own in-house engineers to undertake these assessments. If the Contractor is not able to rely on the structural engineer's report, but is responsible for any damage caused to the roof as a result of the Solar PV installation, the Contractor may have to carry out its own structural report which will inevitably increase costs. Alternatively, the local authority may allow the Contractor to rely upon the report already produced and therefore a contractual link (ie: a collateral warranty) will need to be entered into between the Contractor and the structural engineer, to allow the Contractor to pursue a claim against the structural engineer in the event that the report was negligently prepared. However, in neither case will the Contractor accept liability for latent defects in the property, which could not have been identified by an inspection of the relevant property (eg: foundations not being constructed in line with any drawings produced). So the current insurance policy for the building should be checked to ensure that any damage caused can be claimed for under the relevant policy.

Responsibility for gaining access to the relevant properties for the Contractor to carry out the installation will need to be established, as the Contractor may have a right to claim for an extension of time and additional money if the local authority fails to get access for the Contractor in line with the programme. In addition to access, consideration will need to be given to the storage of the panels and the security arrangements at the site.

The Contractor will also need to indemnify the local authority for any damage caused to the roof during installation (which may include leaks in the roof and any electrical problems which arise as a result of the Contractor undertaking the installation).

In relation to ground mounted schemes, if the local authority has selected an EPC/turnkey solution, the Contractor would be expected to take ground conditions risk (ie: of any delays associated with unexpected ground conditions at the site such as archaeological finds or unexploded ordinance). But on a multi-contracting approach the relevant contractor is unlikely to take these risks and the local authority may need to build in time and costs and/or undertake a thorough examination of the relevant site to mitigate these risks. Similarly, access to the site will need to be considered, as many of the sites proposed for ground mounted schemes are greenfield sites and may not have sufficient access roads or hard standing for large vehicles and so deliveries may prove problematic.

Construction & Commissioning

Assuming that the local authority has gone down the external contractor route, there are a number of areas concerning the contractual performance that will be of interest.

If the scheme is a land based solar farm, then it is a straightforward situation of inspecting the works and the grid connection and other facilities. This will be relatively easy and be the final stage, at the end of the construction period.

However, if the arrangement is for a social housing project, then houses will be completed from the first week on site to the last week. Here, some form of sign off arrangement needs to be put in place, which is linked to both the contract and payment. The contractor needs to know that a domestic installation is in accordance with the contract and also needs that particular part of the contract to be released for payment.

This need not be difficult but will take some thought. In a large contract many houses may be fitted per week and so a Clerk of Works role might be justified. This person will inspect the completed work and verify that an installation has been fitted, is operational and is working in accordance with the contract. The contractor's representative will need to be present for this and agree the sign off. This will then trigger payment.

A non domestic series of buildings will probably be in between those two extremes: a number of buildings to be inspected, but less than in a housing contract; installations less than a land based system but bigger than domestic sized installations. Here again, arrangements need to be made for inspection and sign off.

In law, the installation needs to be 'commissioned' (ie: capable of operation) and the correct application for FITs made before the tariffs can be claimed. It is therefore essential that the authority confirms that the system has been correctly fitted and is operational, with the correct FIT application having been submitted, before payment is made.

Post Construction Matters

The main issue to be addressed post construction is monitoring and reporting. There will also be an element of maintenance, although this will not be substantial.

On the reporting front, the council should have given consideration to the level of monitoring it requires and how reports will be presented. If there has been a competitive tendering exercise, this normally forms part of that. The tenderers will be asked to confirm what method of monitoring and reporting they are proposing to use to meet the contractual requirements. Then each system forwarded by a bidder can be appraised.

The council will normally want regular monitoring, to ensure that all is well with the installation and periodic reporting to officers and members. Such a system might entail default monitoring ie: the system throws up an alarm if the energy generated is not within pre defined levels. This might mean that a panel has been damaged, stolen or is otherwise not working.

As **Chapter 7** reveals, due to the way solar power works and the wiring of the inverters, a non performing panel may have a much wider impact on the performance of the system and so needs to be identified quickly. If a string system is in operation, the failure of one panel can ensure that the output from the entire string is lost. Furthermore, as the contract has a defined financial income stream, it is important that losses are kept to a minimum. Normally, such an alarm will be automatic ie: monitored remotely and using technology. This will then prompt a further remote check on the system concerned and then a physical visit to the site to check on the system.

If work is required, this will come under the maintenance arrangements. What arrangements have been put in place for maintenance will depend on the way that the contract has been set out. Sometimes, maintenance is left to the contractor for the whole of the contract term. This is usually the case for a solar farm.

However, for a social housing contract, it might be that the contractor assumes responsibility for maintenance for a specified period, such as two years, with the council's Direct Labour Organisation (DLO) taking over responsibility after that. Indeed, it can be part of the contract that maintenance is handed over smoothly, including the training up of the council's team towards the end of the two-year period. As the curve in relation to solar PV tends to be the shape of a bath tub (ie: failure is almost always at the start or the end of the arrangements) it is very cost effective to assume responsibility for maintenance in the main part of the contract term. All the authority needs is Microgeneration Certification Scheme accredited and trained electricians and other personnel and a supply of replacement panels, inverters and wiring.

Conclusion

It is difficult to generalise on the average time for delivery of a solar PV contract, as there are so many different types. **Chapter 12** has shown the difference between land based and buildings based systems and illustrated that they are very different contracts. Even within buildings related contracts, there are small contracts for a few non-domestic buildings or very large contracts for thousands of houses. Each has different characteristics.

However, what this chapter does illustrate is that all procurements, projects and contracts are approached the same: time in the timetable for proper planning, based on a defined strategy, with proper advice, against a robust business case; involving a soundly planned procurement exercise, a well drafted contract and sensible payment mechanisms. These things are not thrown together overnight and take time to arrange properly. If it is done properly, then the prospects of a well functioning system, reduced risk and client satisfaction are greatly enhanced.

Key Learning Points

- *Each project will go through a number of defined stages and the better these are planned in advance, the more smoothly the project will proceed*
- *A Gantt type chart will be necessary with a clear timeline to avoid project drift*
- *A thorough risk analysis will underpin this work*
- *The procurement of contractors, the choice of the most economically advantageous tender and the contract that the company is required to enter will need careful thought*
- *The construction and commissioning phase will include all necessary registrations under the financial incentives and will need appropriate time in the timetable*

Developing a revolving fund for
solar PV work in local government
via direct services

15

365

Introduction

In the course of this work, a number of different elements of strategy and practice have been considered. There is, however, one last decision to be taken. In fact, this does not come at the end at all, but for the sake of structure of the book, it has been left to the last substantive chapter. This issue is whether to employ others to undertake the solar fitting work for the local authority, or whether to develop those skills in house. This only refers to buildings based solar PV work and not to the development and construction of solar farms.

In some ways, that last statement might be misleading: what is being suggested here is not a simple matter of training up a few electricians and other personnel to be able to fit solar panels, but creating a wholly new and comprehensive in-house solar PV function that can become self funding over time. This is perfectly feasible and should be seriously considered by any local authority or public body considering the solar PV route.

Other chapters have outlined the necessity to think carefully about the whole operation. Each local authority should develop a holistic climate change strategy, setting targets and goals, building a route map towards them, and coming up with projects that form the steps on that path. Such a strategy should join up the various different parts of the agenda and link them to corporate goals and aspirations. Buildings might include schools, social housing, leisure facilities or civic headquarters, but all have the same issues in relation to energy management and efficiency and the fitting of renewables. A corporate approach is therefore vital. Part of this corporate approach will be the authority's attitude to direct services, as opposed to outsourcing, partnerships and other forms of service delivery.

In some ways, it might have been considered that direct services were on the wane. Many different public policy initiatives have been introduced by successive Governments, such as the Private Finance Initiative, Building Schools for the Future and trunk road de-regulation, that have all steered public bodies away from direct services and towards private sector provision.

However, when the financial crisis examined in **Chapter 2** hit in the late 2000's, many authorities questioned the flexibility of long-term arrangements with private sector providers, based on fixed reward structures. It did not make finding cuts in expenditure easy. As a result, many services are coming back in house, as illustrated in the Association for Public Service Excellence (APSE) paper Insourcing: A guide to bringing local authority services back in-house. In relation to solar PV, the decision as to whether to do it yourself should be an economic and organisational one, rather than one based on ideology.

Chapter 5 explained the substantial advantages that engaging in renewable energy can bring to a local economy and its supply chains and these are summarised in **Figure 15.2** below. Local authorities have everything that they need to engage in solar PV activity: buildings to convert, workforces to undertake the work and the capacity to borrow money to fund such works. Another APSE paper: The Virtuous Green Circle: Creating a Revolving Fund for Solar Energy contends that solar PV is a chance to create an opportunity out of the recession and make changes that benefit areas and are self -funding. It is described as a 'once in a lifetime' opportunity.

This Chapter suggests a way of doing this – to lead the way on introducing buildings based PV to local authority owned buildings and to undertake the work by some form of direct service team and financing by the local authority. In so far as the exact nature of the team is concerned, this is not really relevant to the concept. Over the years, many new types of organisation have sprung up – whether ALMOs, RSL's, trading companies or Limited Liability Partnerships. The principles are the same for all of these different types of organization as they all employ their own staff.

By doing this – and doing it this way – maximum gains are achieved for the local area.

Figure 15.1 summarises what is needed in order to take this route.

The following are required:

- *A commitment to in house services*
- *Experience of in-house services*
- *An existing in-house building maintenance function*
- *Access to the authority's buildings via a corporate plan*
- *The ability to borrow money to fund the operation*

Figure 15.1 – The 'Do It Yourself' Route to PV Installation

Some of the issues in **Figure 15.1** are crucial. As an example, if an authority no longer has an in-house building maintenance team, comprising electricians, builders, roofers and scaffolders, then it will struggle to introduce the PV fitting operation described below. Moreover, if the authority is not prepared to fund the operation via borrowing, it is unlikely to get off the ground. There might always be alternatives, for example undertaking a joint operation of some sort with a neighbouring authority, but the comments below are predicated on the basis that the authority has the essential elements already and a desire to capture the benefits from this operation.

If a council pursues a renewable energy scheme, there are a variety of benefits that will arise. These have not been widely acknowledged, but were explained in **Chapter 5**. They are repeated in **Figure 15.2** below.

- ## Community Leadership

Local authorities are encouraged to 'lead from the front' and to provide an example to their local areas.

- ## Energy Security

DECC has already confirmed that there are likely to be power cuts in the next decade, and any area that might be affected by such cuts will be in a stronger position if it has its own renewable energy sources.

- ## Carbon Benefits

The Government is legislating to place ever more stringent targets in relation to greenhouse gases. The CRC Energy Efficiency Scheme will require local authorities to purchase allowances in relation to their carbon emissions.

- ## Effectiveness and Efficiency

The renewables option gives the local authority the chance to save money by using the energy that is generated from its own sources, thereby meaning that external energy costs do not have to be incurred.

- ## Economic Benefits

The green agenda offers the best potential for growth at the present time, by positively stimulating local supply chains.

- ## Income Generation

The green agenda is an important way to generate further funds, via the income streams from the financial incentives and the sale of excess electricity into the grid.

Figure 15.2 – Benefits of a Renewable Energy Scheme

However, in order to ensure that these benefits are maximized, the council needs to retain control over the process. It can do this by using the do it yourself route.

Skills And The Supply Chain

The benefits that can be gained from a solar PV installation scheme are such that this might be the key reason that a local authority decides to go down the solar route. It has often been mentioned that not everyone is motivated by the need to 'save the planet' and the economic arguments often play more strongly with some officers and members. It does not really matter what the motivating factors actually are, so long as the local authorities and communities obtain the benefits.

But here it is necessary to contrast two different ways of proceeding. The first is to procure, via an Official Journal of the European Union advertisement, a contractor to install solar installations on its buildings. The council can only have limited influence via the contract on the supply chain and specialist contractors might use their own equipment, people and supply lines. In these circumstances, the impact on the local economy might be limited, even though the authority is subsequently benefitting from the facility. In many ways, the local authority benefits (the free energy and cost savings etc.) are a given; it is the wider benefits to the local economy that will make the difference.

To achieve these, there is a different way of doing it. This can be referred to as the 'do it yourself' or DIY option, where the authority literally does the fitting work itself. This means that it recruits and trains the people who will do the work, both preparatory and delivery; obtains the supplies and equipment itself, using its existing sustainable procurement processes; and gives active consideration to how the local economy can benefit at every stage.

The benefits that can accrue to the local economy depend, to an extent, on the nature of the work. It is therefore necessary to consider the skills required to undertake this work.

These are illustrated in the box overleaf.

- *Procurement work, to obtain the PV kits and associated supplies*
- *Surveying / engineering / and calculation of roof bearing loads*
- *Financial work, such as funding and running the accounts*
- *MCS accreditation work, recruitment and then training as competent persons; also MCS accreditation of products used*
- *Vehicles and equipment logistics*
- *Planning permission, building regulation consent and liaison with DNO*
- *Energy management and energy efficiency work*
- *Electrical fitting (of the panels and wiring etc., together with meters);*
- *Roofing work*
- *Scaffolding and access*
- *Building maintenance work, including health and safety planning and repairs and making good*
- *Monitoring of performance of the equipment against projections*

Figure 15.3 - Skills for a Solar PV Fitting Operation

If a local authority – or relevant organisation - still has a building maintenance operation, then most (if not all) of these skills will be available to it, subject to training on PV installations. If it does not, it can recruit a team specifically for this purpose. Another alternative is for joint arrangements to be sought, for example between a county council and the districts within its boundaries where some authorities have personnel and some do not. Such joint arrangements can also offer economies of scale on the price of the PV kits.

The mix between the public and private sectors is also completely flexible. As an example, an authority might use all directly employed personnel on such a job but use local skip hire, scaffolding firms and surveyors.

In October 2011, a paper published by Unison, supported by the TUC, examined the issues relating to skills and employment in renewable energy schemes. The New Green Team: local government, sustainable energy, jobs and skills, concluded that local economies can be impressively boosted by direct action of this type.

On a specific level, the smaller PV schemes are subject to the Microgeneration Certification Scheme (MCS), which is a scheme introduced by the Government in order to protect consumers that have renewable energy systems fitted.

The MCS is an internationally recognized quality assurance scheme that is examined in **Chapter 11**. In particular, both personnel involved in solar PV work and the products that they are fitting have to be accredited under the MCS.

The Proposal – Creating A New Green Team

Having determined that there is much to gain from a strategy to fit solar PV to an authority's buildings, and that it is preferable to do this via a directly controlled operation, the dreaded issue of funding arises. As detailed above, these are difficult times and therefore further expenditure is likely to be severely constrained. **Chapter 10** considers all of the issues in relation to funding.

However, this expenditure is different to most other expenditure that the authority is concerned with: this is because this expenditure has a guaranteed income stream in support of it. This effectively means that there is no long-term effect on the council in incurring further debt, as such a scheme is self funding.

Figure 15.4 below contains an illustration of how this might work.

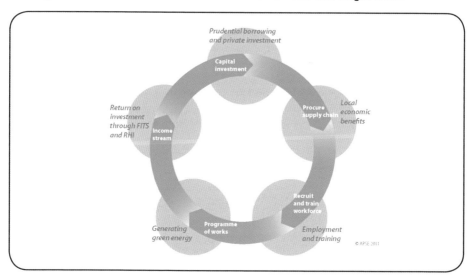

Figure 15.4 – The Green Team

The best way for the authority to raise the money for such a scheme is to use reserves or to borrow the money. So far as reserves are concerned, as **Chapter 10** notes, local authorities have for decades closely guarded their reserve accounts. These are a 'safety net', allowing a council to know that if unexpected circumstances occur, then it will have some financial cushion against unforeseen demands. However, the amount of local government's reserves has been criticised by the Government, and it wants some of that money spent in order to help get over the recession. Whilst this may not be particularly palatable to a local authority, what better way is there to invest reserves than in an income-generating project?

Alternatively, a council can borrow money from the Public Works Loans Board for this purpose. The rate of such borrowing is still very competitive, particularly in the light of the cost of private sector money.

But even so, the authority still wants to get the maximum value out of its project. To achieve this, it needs to create a revolving fund, where the money is recycled time after time to achieve maximum effect.

Here is how such a project might be structured:

- *capital into the new buildings PV account. It is up to the authority how much this is.*
- *The council would recruit (or redeploy) a manual workforce that is tasked with the job of fitting solar PV to all of its buildings in accordance with a pre-agreed plan of work.*
- *The workforce needs to be recruited and trained to a requisite standard and meet the MCS Accreditation standards (necessary to claim feed in tariffs for projects of this size).*
- *All of the necessary equipment and tools that will be required need to be assembled in conjunction with the workforce.*
- *The council needs to develop a schedule of its buildings and work this into a work plan whereby the installation team or teams would move from building to building installing pre determined PV kits in much the same way as the private sector offers to individual householders.*
- *Arrangements need to be put in place to procure the kits and other equipment necessary for the work to go ahead. Lately, kits have become available in varying sizes which include solar panels, inverters, fixing brackets, wiring and so on ie: everything necessary for a PV system in a box.*
- *The work plan needs to determine the priority of buildings. One suggestion is that schools should be the first priority, meaning that the early installations*

undertaken by the team would all be on school premises; others suggest housing tenants should head the queue. It is up to the authority concerned to determine its own priorities.

• The need to obtain planning permission for non residential PV installations might also be a relevant factor for the work programme; applications for planning permission on other buildings need to be prepared and submitted.

• As installations are completed and linked to the grid, the FIT income would start to accrue to the Council's PV account (mentioned above). There would also be Power Purchase Agreement sales from selling electricity, if the Government's export tariff was not used. The occupants of the buildings (whether the council's officers or members, schools or tenants) would get the energy created by the PV panels at no cost. This makes it attractive for them.

• The fund is sustainable in the sense that the full costs are met many times over from the income created. The revolving nature of the arrangements allows the authority to re-invest the gains from the solar PV equipment into this – or other – green measures. Whilst the FIT payments are unlikely to ever meet the full costs of the installation team or teams, these costs will be met over time. If the full income from the FIT is directed towards the costs, these will reduced on a sliding scale as more installations are completed.

• Calculations need to be undertaken as to the value of the initial capital investment, as opposed to the size and speed at which the teams would exist and operate; that calculation can be undertaken to demonstrate what the investment will need to be. This will also be effected by the degression rates under Solar PV feed in tariffs, which are explained in **Chapter 8**.

• As the project progresses, the benefits increase. The Council could continue to fit solar PV until all of its buildings are completed, if it has sufficient up front funds to do this. Alternatively, it could undertake some of the work and then take a break until the income has provided funds for a further stage of fitting.

• Once the council's own buildings are all fitted, the in house team can offer its services to other public bodies (under powers in the Local Authorities (Goods and Services) Act 1970 and to the public at large under powers to levy charges for discretionary services (in the Local Government Act 2003). In this way work for a number of additional years may be obtained for the highly trained, skilled and experienced workforce that has been created.

• Once the work is complete, the income will still continue to accrue to the council's PV account and can be invested in other green projects.

The Business Case And Plan

In any renewable energy project in local government, there needs to be both a business case and also a business plan, as explained in **Chapter 9**. The business case is the rationale for doing something, with a high level explanation and supporting information. This is the sort of document presented to members in order for them to take a decision on such a matter.

The business plan is the detailed financial assessment, including the breakdown of the costs of the installation and also the projected income from it. This will have a lot of detail, including efficiency rates, depreciation and the like.

This proposal needs a one off capital payment to start the fund or a series of annual payments to ensure that the fund has sufficient resources to roll its work forwards. This initial capital payment or payments can be raised from either reserves, borrowing or slippage on other projects. But to determine the size of the payment, a financial calculation needs to be undertaken. This takes the plans for the number of properties to be fitted, the costs of the team and the income from the FITs and works out the financing costs. In this way, sufficient finance can be injected into the fund (and at the appropriate intervals) to ensure that the full number of properties are fitted with PV panels. **Figure 15.5** gives an explanation of the contents of such a business case, prepared by Swindon Commercial Services (SCS) in 2010, that featured in the ASPE paper mentioned above.

SCS has developed a financial model to enable it to cost and produce the financial measures and outputs for individual and large-scale PV rollouts. The model can be used for domestic housing as well as commercial buildings.

The summary produces the output of the model in a single, easy to understand format. Behind this summary are the detailed cost information, financial and non-financial assumptions as well as the calculation of energy production, FIT revenues, investment appraisal and Profit and Loss output.

The summary shows the figures broken down into 3 main areas. These are:
* the input figures and assumptions
* a summary of the investment appraisal analysis
* a profit and loss before tax summary

The input section summaries the key costs of the investment. This shows the total value of the investment, which is built from the costs of the rollout: panels, the inverters, the mounting kits costs etc. In addition to this the installation costs: scaffolding and the cost of labour.

Whilst the ongoing cost of the installation should be low there will be inverter failure. Whilst inverters are getting more and more reliable and therefore should last longer, they will fail at some time and costs will be incurred for replacement. Similarly some panels are likely to fail during the 25 years of the project and allowance has been made in the model for their replacement. The models allows for the costs of ongoing maintenance and monitoring should that be requested by the client.

The next part of the outline shows the total number of panels installed and what this represents in kW and the annual output of all the panels in kWh. The model allows for deterioration in the panel efficiency over the 25 year life by 20%. The rates used for calculating the revenue benefits are shown. This includes the FIT rates, the electricity saving tariff, the rate used when exporting surplus electricity to the grid.

For some installations there may be a cost to pay a lease payment to the owner of the roof(s). Costs and revenues are affected by the rates of inflation, Retail Price Index etc. The rates used in the model are shown here.

The investment appraisal summary shows the Internal Rate of Return for the project and Net Present Value of the project at different discount rates: 5%, 7%, 10% etc. to help understand the relative risk. The payback is shown which is also discounted at the different rates. The cash flow at the different discount rates is shown graphically at the bottom left.

The assumptions for the profit and loss are shown: depreciation assumptions for the installation and the inverters as well as the interest rates used in the model. The profit(loss) is shown at year 5, 10 15 etc to show how the profit (or loss) develops over time. Finally the operating return is shown along with the annual investment return.

The cumulative profit and loss is shown graphically. This helps not only the effect at the end of the project but also shows how the profit builds during the life of the project. It can highlight losses or profits in the early years to enable funding decisions to be reviewed and a view on loan repayment or loan financing taken.

Summary

- **Investment: £5m**
- **575 Houses with around 2.5 kWp**
- **Profit & Loss account profit of over £10m after 25 years**
- **Average annual return on investment of over 8%**
- **NPV @ 7% is over £2m**
- **Payback within 9 years**
- **Annual estimated output over 1,218,000 KWh per year**

Figure 15.5 - Swindon Commercial Services Ltd PV Model

To do this a full cost/ benefit analysis needs to be constructed, taking into account all of the various costs. However, it is vital to include in the cost / benefit analysis the non-financial benefits, such as community leadership, energy security etc as these are also highly relevant to the decision whether to proceed with any such scheme.

Once this analysis has been done – with appropriate local factors and weightings being used – the result should be an overwhelming case for action.

The "icing on the cake" is the fact that the original capital payment can also be recouped at the end, as the FITs continue to be paid for some time after all fitting work has been completed. This effectively means that a local authority that does this achieves the fitting of solar PV to all of its buildings (with all of the associated other benefits) for nothing. Or to be more accurate, paid for by HM Government.

Phasing Of The Work

Any local authority that resolves to go down this path will need to engage in proper project planning. The various steps will need to be phased and **Figure 15.6** below gives some suggestions as to how this might be achieved.

Preparatory Phase

- *Members decision and approval*
- *Identify funds and / or arrange borrowing*
- *Seek MCS accreditation*
- *Apply for planning permission (where required)*
- *Procure PV panel kits*
- *Conduct a full survey of the buildings*
- *Undertake calculations as to loads on roofs, and size of installations*
- *Advertise for staff or redeploy workforce*
- *Procure other supplies, vehicles and equipment etc (requires a shorter lead in time than PV panels)*
- *Set up accounting procedures and methodology of checking performance*

Delivery Phase

- *Train up team and allocate responsibilities*
- *Put in place QA procedures for operation*
- *Register with OFGEM for FITs*
- *Finalise plan of prioritization of buildings*
- *Put in place regular reporting arrangements*
- *Audit payment of FITs*
- *Undertake PR phase*

Figure 15.6 - Phasing of the Project

Scale Of The Operation

One of the strongest points about this concept is that it can work at almost any scale. One authority might only have a modest investment to make and want to secure the employment of a very small team of installers. By contrast, a larger authority might want to enter this market in much larger fashion. The concept is the same for both, subject to the preparation of a thorough business case.

Conclusion

The APSE paper *The Virtuous Circle: Creating a Revolving Fund for Solar Energy* hailed the potential value of this route. Describing it as a 'once in a lifetime opportunity', it said:

"APSE has been involved in direct services for over 25 years and, most of that time, those services have been under threat. It is a very long time indeed, since an opportunity to create some new 'family silver' has come along. An opportunity to enjoy growth as opposed to cuts; to create new skills, as opposed to a brain drain; to have a wider and wholly positive impact on other areas of the council's operation, rather than being a recharged central cost. This proposal offers all of those things."

Since that paper was written, there have been a number of changes to the solar PV regulatory regime, particularly in relation to FITs. As Chapter 8 has demonstrated, the FIT rates have been reduced and re-organised, but the basic principle on which the revolving fund rests, is still as valid today as it was then. It all comes down to the corporate strategy of the authority, its approach to in-house services and the business case.

Those authorities that have gone down this route, such as Swindon Borough Council (via its company Swindon Commercial Services), have benefitted greatly and not just from solar power but across the renewable energy front.

Key Learning Points

- *It is possible to develop the skills in-house to run a solar PV programme*
- *But to do so, an authority needs to have experience of direct services*
- *The supply chain and skills will need research and personnel training up*
- *Funding will be necessary to start the ball rolling*
- *Over time the initiative will become self funding, as income from FITs is applied to the debt and expenditure*
- *This concept will work at both small and larger scale but is a longer term plan, that would see all of the authority's relevant buildings fitted with solar PV*

Our approach

As with any large project where public scrutiny is guaranteed, it can be a challenge to get even the most well thought out project off the ground. Swindon Borough Council's 'Core Strategy' provides a favourable planning framework for the development and use of renewable energy solutions. Swindon Commercial Services (SCS) is a wholly owned company of Swindon Borough Council. SCS tapped into this existing desire by council members to embrace renewables and reduce the carbon footprint of council owned properties by presenting a business case that was robust and provided a healthy return on investment.

Using cautious and realistic financial modelling, developed through the Association for Public Service Excellence (APSE), helped to convince those who were reluctant to take the plunge. Careful pre-surveys using Solmetric 'Suneye' equipment enabled reliable data to be entered into the cost generation model. We also used examples from elsewhere demonstrating proven benefits from both a financial and carbon reduction perspective.

Initially SCS had worked up a grand scheme involving thousands of council owned buildings including social housing, but this 'Big Bang' approach would not have been delivered quickly enough to take advantage of FITs before levels were reduced. Council members decided to approve an initial investment of £900,000 for photovoltaic installations on medium to large sized buildings at five sites. The sites were: Swindon Commercial Services Waterside depot; Thamesdown Transport bus depot; Catherine Wayte School, Swindon Borough Council Civic offices and 23 new build social housing homes.

In just nine weeks, we had promoted the idea, gained council support, acquired all cross-party cabinet approval and funding; dealt with all planning questions; ordered and installed and registered four of the five schemes.

Upon approving the works and funding, the Cabinet stated the importance of the project to contributing to their Sustainable Energy framework and its future benefits to the council and residents of Swindon.

The initial scepticism of the media and public, and fears that the British weather would be a limiting factor in achieving the predicted returns, was soon eliminated by the energy generating results coming through the monitoring mechanism for the installations. Proving the worth of the investment to the wider public has ensured future projects will be viewed favourably

The project

The buildings included in the project provided a fantastic shop window for SCS, displaying a range of potential. The varied range of new build social housing homes, a school, a flat roofed building, a curved and pitched roof profile industrial building and a bus depot created a portfolio for future promotion of similar projects and sites. In every case the predicted returns have either been met or exceeded, making solar photovoltaics a realistic, affordable and sensible solution in reducing carbon emissions in Swindon.

Swindon Commercial Services Waterside site:
Total no. of panels installed   536
Amount of energy produced   **124kWp per annum**
Savings per annum   **£38,504 per annum**
Project payback to council within 10 years

Thamesdown Transport bus depot:
Total no. of panels installed   432
Amount of energy produced   99kWp
Savings per annum   £33,696
Project payback to council within 8 years

Catherine Wayte School:
Total no. of panels installed   217
Amount of energy produced   50kWp
Savings per annum   £16,000
Project payback to council within 8 years

Swindon Borough Council Civic offices:
Total no. of panels installed   168
Amount of energy produced   42kWp
Savings per annum   £14,000
Project payback to council within 11 years

Malmesbury Gardens
13 Houses x 16 panels giving nominally 3.5kW each property
Six two bedroom and six three bedroom and one five bedroom houses in 2 terraces.

Solar Panels were 'Myriad Segen'
Houses were built to code 5 with solar PV and Solar Thermal, central heating, mechanical ventilation, feeding a wet underfloor heating system with weather compensated control from an air source heat pump.

Water saving measures include dual flush cisterns, flow reducing aerated taps and careful selection of sanitary ware, dishwasher and washing machines. Rainwater harvesting system collects roof water into underground tanks.

In the current economic climate there is no greater or safer return in an investment than the ones we will see with photovoltaics.

Paul Jenkins, managing director of Thamesdown Transport, said: "The installation was planned very closely with our engineering team and there was very little disruption to our depot operations, with the electrical supply being off and on within one hour."

Robert Buckland, MP for Swindon, called it, "a demonstration of civic leadership [that] has taken advantage of support available to move solar energy projects off the drawing board and onto installations in Swindon."

The future

SCS, a wholly owned company of Swindon Borough Council, now has a large and diverse skill set specialising in delivering a range of services mainly to housing associations and local authorities across the south of England in locations as far apart as Bristol to Milton Keynes to Margate and Swindon. This reflects an assertive bidding success and a willingness to think beyond the boundaries of its Wiltshire origins. The council's support and commitment has enabled SCS to invest in training and developing relevant areas of its workforce. Continued support will contribute to SCS being required to employ more people to deliver renewable solutions.

SCS has gained Microgeneration Certification Scheme Accreditation and is leading the way in the development of the renewable energy market. Since April 2011, we have installed over 450kw of photovoltaics across privately owned homes, social housing properties, new builds and commercial buildings.

Although the furore over FITs and the industry reaction has caused a decline in the market, SCS is confident that as panel prices fall, the market will return.

By making a brave and bold move, Swindon Borough Council has taken the first steps in turning promises in the Sustainable Energy Framework into a demonstrable reality. SCS is in the forefront of assisting the council in unlocking the huge untapped potential across civic buildings.

Swindon Borough Council's intention is to lead the way in delivering environmental, social and economic benefits through the use of renewable energy.

Bill Fisher
Managing Director
Swindon Commercial Services
(*Swindon BC's inhouse company*)

The Future

16

Introduction

The green agenda in the United Kingdom has now been mapped out for many years to come. There might be debates about whether the Conservative/Liberal Democrat coalition is indeed the 'greenest government ever', but the direction of travel for Government policy is unlikely to change, even if the pace does vary from time to time.

The Climate Change Act 2008 enshrined in law the targets for the UK and this was a truly historic pledge to the world. The work that needs to be done to reach those targets is gaining more momentum, as more people are convinced that climate change is happening and concern grows about its effects.

But what is the role of local government and the public sector? The comments above concern national, central Government policy, derived from its position in the European Union and Intergovernmental arrangements and ties. Local authorities are, however, in a pivotal position to push this agenda forwards. Decentralised energy fits with localism; local empowerment fits with community leadership; asset management fits with energy performance; local Energy Services Companies fits with delivery of wider policy objectives.

This much is now becoming clear, hence the growing recognition of the alignment of the green and wider corporate / regional agendas in local government and the marked increase in action.

But it is still necessary to crystallise down the role of the public sector to actions and strategies. So a good way to do this is to ask what does success look like? **Figure 16.1** offers some ideas.

- *An authority that has adopted a low carbon economy*
- *This means that it has its energy management side very tightly run*
- *That appreciates the carbon impact of all its decisions*
- *That has extensively looked at its use of energy and reduced it*
- *That has extensively looked at its energy efficiency and improved it*
- *That performs well in the CRC but more widely too*
- *That covers areas such as transport*
- *That generates its own electricity and heat*
- *That leads its community by offering a good example in its own operations and encourages similar behaviour in others*
- *An authority that has created local growth from the green agenda,*
- *such as jobs and a local supply chain*
- *An authority that has good alliances and relationships with other public bodies such as the NHS, together with the voluntary / third sector and the private sector*
- *An authority that has taken bold decisions, such as the Community Infrastructure Levy and borrowing to invest in renewables*
- *An authority that has created an Energy Services Company, either alone or in partnership with others, to supply electricity and heat to consumers in its area*
- *And that has developed a good reputation as a result*

Figure 16.1 - What does success look like?

It focuses on the acceptance of a low carbon economy for the area and the key role that a local authority plays in this. The Committee on Climate Change in its report How Local Authorities Can Reduce Emissions and Manage Climate Risk (May 2012) centres on this point: the fact that a large slice of the CO2 emissions that the Government is seeking to combat are actually under local government control. But real action will only start to happen when local authorities really face up to carbon and its consequences. One of the ways the sector can do this is to appreciate the carbon consequences of all of the decisions that it makes. Another is a comprehensive push on energy efficiency, still the 'Cinderella' area of climate change at local level. It is, perhaps, too early to see whether the Green Deal will change this, but it is already apparent that the Green Deal has at least highlighted the need for action, whether the Government's favoured policy solution is acceptable or not.

Turning to renewable energy, success is an authority that understands the necessity to be self sufficient in energy and create as much as it uses (with the use part having been substantially reduced). This is not just something that each council needs to do, but also to work in tandem with other public bodies to help them along the same path. Growth and jobs will surely come from this journey, as already demonstrated by the leading players in the public sector to date.

Many of the decisions need to be long-term thinking, not short term compromises. But every journey starts with the first step and solar PV is an excellent place to begin on the journey to energy self-sufficiency.

A Vision for the Future

What would local government look like in, say, ten years time if it gets the strategy on the green economy right?

The answer, quite simply, is new jobs and a high level of employment available locally. A workforce comprised of quality employment, on a permanent (rather than temporary basis). Workers, with new skill sets in solar PV, solar thermal, ground and air source heat pumps, biomass and other relevant technologies. A supply chain for renewable energy that is essentially local in nature and does not rely too heavily upon others.

In the paper *The New Green Team: local government, sustainable energy, jobs and skills* (October 2011, Unison / TUC) a vision was projected based on solar PV investment. The notional authority was called Barchester Council and its progress is reproduced in **Figure 16.2** opposite.

Barchester has lots of civic buildings. It is an education authority and has a large retained stock of social housing, as well as the normal civic offices, one-stop shops and leisure centres.

It has fitted solar PV to all of its various buildings. It undertook the social housing work first, with the tenants getting the benefit of free electricity generated from the solar panels. This improved relations with tenants and was a leading edge project. It then moved on to schools and ensured that they all had the benefit of this technology. The schools were appreciative of the free power too and this helped soothe an otherwise fractious relationship, as well as enabling the schools to introduce green energy as part of the curriculum, to the delight of the pupils.

The council also set about fitting solar to all of its civic buildings. In the Town Hall it fitted a large monitor showing real time how much power is being created. This was fitted amongst a bit of a fanfare, with the local TV stations, radio and press present. The council received excellent publicity over this and the monitor in the Town Hall still attracts plenty of attention.

But the authority pressed on, determined to ensure that all buildings had the benefit of solar energy. It covered the roofs of the leisure centres, the sports clubs, the walk-in centres and all other relevant buildings. The response was universally positive.

The PV strategy was undertaken using the concept of the APSE Revolving Fund. The council developed its strategy in advance and carefully planned the necessary steps. It redeployed a large number of its employees that were unfortunately going to be made redundant under the spending cuts of 2010/11. It trained them to MCS standards and developed a corporate system to operate the new processes safely and properly. These jobs included electricians, scaffolders, tradespeople and others. On the professional side, the operation employed procurement staff, finance and legal staff, communications and PR people and a policy operation.

The council then started offering the service of fitting solar PV to other public bodies in the area. Many of the smaller voluntary bodies wanted to take advantage of the technology but did not have the capital and know-how to do so. The council entered into arrangements whereby it would finance the purchase of the panels and give the free electricity to the organisation. All surpluses from the operation of the feed in tariffs are ploughed back into the council's wider green programme.

In 10 years, the council has gained significant community respect from this work, has shown community leadership, has created new jobs that are sustainable and valuable, has improved the energy security of the area, and has helped the region to meet the carbon emissions reduction targets in the Climate Change Act 2008. Everyone agrees that it has been a resounding success.

Barchester is fictitious but the scenario outlined here is entirely possible in real authorities across the UK.

Figure 16.2 - Solar PV in Barchester Council, an urban unitary authority

The APSE Energy Vision

The author has worked with the Association for Public Service Excellence (APSE) for many years. In 2010, APSE started to offer local authorities consultancy services to help them devise strategies, identify projects and bring them to fruition. The author is the lead consultant in this operation.

In 2014, APSE decided to set up a new team, APSE Energy, to focus this work and help it to expand. As part of the process, the members of APSE were widely canvassed on the subject of energy and a 'vision' for the new entity was devised.

This vision is very similar to that featured above but goes a little further in ambition. The vision is the municipalisation of energy at local level:

"In simple terms, the vision is a local, publicly controlled organisation that provides not only electricity and heat directly to residential and commercial customers in the area, but also delivers a range of related services, from information and education to design and fitting of energy systems. Such a body would have great influence in the area and therefore would be able to effectively tackle fuel poverty and other social problems at local level."

It is interesting to note that since the author's own comments earlier in this chapter, originally written in 2012, the appetite of local authorities to go the extra mile and provide energy services directly to residents in their area has really taken off. This was seen as a step too far just a few years ago, but now authorities across the country are aspiring to this goal.

Settling of the UK Solar PV Market and the Journey to Grid Parity

In 2011/12, the UK solar PV marketplace went through a period that can only be described as turmoil. This was caused by inexperience in developing and implementing a new financial incentive system in the UK that had not previously existed. In the view of the solar industry, despite its best efforts, the Department for Energy & Climate Change did not get this right. FITs were too generous, insufficient data was available on falling panel prices, the Government had wildly underestimated the appetite for European style solar parks and, accordingly, a 'boom and bust' pattern was created. FIT rates were slashed, the industry was outraged, massive peaks of installation (before deadlines for cuts), were followed by complete slumps in installation numbers. Everyone agreed that it was not sustainable.

The history is largely irrelevant now. As Chapter 8 demonstrates, the Government learned its lessons and introduced a more stable system from 2012. This was based on a regular and planned degression in FITs rates, tied to triggers for actual deployment in the previous period. If less deployment happened, degression was slowed; if more, digression was accelerated, so that Governmental budgets could be maintained. This has had the effect of settling down the solar PV market and whilst not everyone in the solar PV industry agrees with or accepts that way the system has been changed, it is generally regarded that reasonable returns are still available on solar PV projects.

The reason for this is the continual fall in the prices of solar panels. Costs have reduced by over 80% in a short number of years, meaning that a FIT rate of 43 pence could be reduced to a rate of 21 pence and on to 13 pence, without markedly changing the return on capital employed. It is not clear for how long prices can continue to reduce, particularly by those sorts of amounts, but the trend is still firmly downwards.

'Grid parity' is the term used to describe the situation when obtaining electricity from a solar photovoltaic panel is no more expensive than obtaining brown energy from the national grid and therefore the solar PV deployment truly will explode in the UK. Every building will have solar panels and generate its own energy. Why wouldn't it? The slow growth in this technology has been entirely down to the additional cost of having a solar panel, over and above purchasing electricity from the grid and therefore from polluting fossil fuel generation. Once this changes, the temptation of having decentralised, on-site energy from a completely renewable source, will be too great to resist.

Estimates vary from 2017 to 2020, but grid parity in the UK is not far away. A report by Gerard Wynn and Gerard Reid for low carbon think tank Themal, in December 2014, considers this issue. In Sight: Unsubsidised UK Solar claims that in all three sectors (solar farms, commercial roofs and residential roofs) solar PV will be economic without subsidy within the next decade.

This is another reason why local government should invest time and money in solar power now. Rather than wait to see what happens, it should tap into the Government's financial incentives, improve its carbon footprint and create a much-needed fillip to the local economy. Then when grid parity does finally arrive, it will be in an excellent position to take advantage of the benefits it provides.

So to return to the central question – what does success look like? Well, that is completely up to you. Solar PV works at every scale and so it could be one building fitted with PV panels to a replication of the 'vision' featured above. Each authority will decide what is right for it, which is, after all, democracy in action.

Biodiversity benefits on a Sussex solar farm.

In 2013, I had the opportunity to compare the biodiversity of a newly-built solar farm with that of the biodiversity of an ordinary ploughed field under a wheat crop. The solar farm and the wheat field were about the same size, just over 10 hectares each, next to each other in Oving, West Sussex, and each in open countryside with good views to the south. In other words they were exposed to the same sort of environmental conditions, good for scientific research.

At the time, I was interested in comparing the two because the general public and planners were a little sceptical as to whether solar farms could support any wildlife. They still are. Granted, many of the solar farms in England and Wales are usually on species-poor land. They are often on mono-cultures of oilseed rape, winter wheat or field beans – about the worst habitats for wildlife in the country - but they are amongst the best places for solar farms according to Natural England. They have an advisory Technical Information Note (TIN) for this (Natural England, 2011. Technical Information Note TIN101, First Editions 9 September 2011. Solar parks: maximising environmental benefits). So farmers are only following government guidelines – they don't tend to put solars on their best land.

One influencing factor that affected both sites was they were both farmed organically as part of the Woodhorn Farm Estate. The solar farm was erected on part of an original organic field of wheat, and the adjacent wheat field carried on growing organic wheat. So it is fair to say that each site started out under the same management regime, on the same sort of soil.

The solar farm had a small flock of sheep grazing to keep the growth of plants at bay. The wheat field was not subject to any herbicide treatment.

The two sites were visited between July and November in 2013 and the flora and fauna was surveyed each time. The results were a surprise, but not entirely unexpected by this ecologist.

The organic field of wheat produced no mammals, no fungi, no bumblebees and no ferns. What else would you expect when the field was wall- to- wall wheat with precious few habitats for wildlife, except around the margins?

There were actually 18 species of wildflowers present in the wheat field – a relatively high number because it was organic; for a non-organic field of wheat would have much less. There were however 29 species of wildflowers present on the solar farm.

Overall there were 121 species of combined flora and fauna on the solar farm, and 53 in the wheat field. These both relied on species found around the edges of the fields, and within the sites as well.

There were five species of mammal on the solar farm that included badger, mole, muntjac, rat and rabbit, and none in the wheat field.
The reason for this was that there was more useful habitat for foraging in a solar farm than in a wheat field, which is probably why the badger and mole were present. Mole is a fairly unloved species, that conservationists seem to have ignored, yet it is essentially a woodland species that has migrated into open fields.

As for other mammals, the hedgehog was found locally in Oving, but not on either site, as with Brown Hare. Both are Biodiversity Action Species (BAPs) and due consideration has to be taken of these on this site, as on all solar sites allowing free access below the perimeter fences.

Solar farms, with their understory of greenery (or as ecologists like to classify it 'grasslands') seem to be more attractive to wildlife than an agricultural environment, which is focussed on a single crop species, according to this field research work in West Sussex.

Neither reptiles nor amphibians were found on either the solar farm or the wheat field. This was not surprising for the wheat field as it does not have suitable habitat. For the solar farm it was thought to be too early for reptiles to colonise from the hedgerows into the grasslands under the arrays, and, more importantly around the open buffers between the array rows and the perimeter fence.

Buffer zones around the edges of solar farms, and between the array rows are important places where biodiversity is promoted. As with Oving, there are opportunities to develop wildflower meadows, put down log piles for hibernating invertebrates, amphibians and reptiles and the whole area swiftly become a foraging area for bees, true flies and bumblebees.

Butterflies did very well on the solar farm, and poorly on the wheat field. Twelve species of butterfly were recorded on the solar farm with only two on the wheat field (Small white and Small Tortoiseshell) although two others were found around the margins of the wheat field: Comma and Large Skipper.

The presence of such a high number of butterflies on the solar farm was in part due to the presence of stinging nettles and thistles (which act as food sources for the larvae of some species for the former and nectar sources for many species in the latter). By comparison the wheat field is managed so as to reduce these plant species from the standing crop, which no doubt contributed to their decreased biodiversity.

Bumblebees seemed to be in their element on the solar farm as the grasslands were blossoming with nectar sources, thistles, buttercups and clovers, a feature that was lacking in the wheat field. Six species of bumblebee were recorded on the solar farm, none on the wheat field. Solar farms are particularly good for bumblebees (Feltwell, J. 2013. Solar farms for bumblebees. Buzzword, The Bumblebee Conservation Trust's Members Newsletter. November 2013. Issue 23, p.13-14.)

This biodiversity of butterflies and bumblebees is an indication that solar farms are in an increasing position to harbour more of the biodiversity of local areas, helping to bring back the wildlife that has progressively been lost due to agricultural intensification.

With other solar sites, I have already stated that creating a solar farm is like making a nature reserve (Feltwell, J. 2013. Solar Farms and Biodiversity. Guest blog on Solar Power Portal. 16 September 2013.   http://www. solarpowerportal.co.uk/guest_blog/solar_farms_and_biodiversity_2356). It is hard for some antagonists to believe that by stopping agriculture for 30 years (the maximum that solar farms tend to be permitted) it means that wildlife in the surrounding hedgerows and woodlands tends to creep in.

within the first year, let alone 30 years without any help from man. But solar farms hardly get through planning today without a proper package of enhancement measures, often conditioned by the LPA, that boosts the biodiversity of the site immediately and it does not have to rely on natural plant succession.

Enhancements for biodiversity has been a central theme promoted by the Solar Trade Association (STA) (Solar Trade Association, 2014. G. E. Parker and L. Greene (with Feltwell, J. 2014 as co-contributor) BRE (2014) Biodiversity Guidance for Solar Developments. Eds. G. E. Parker and L. Greene. 9pp. Published by the Solar Trade Association) since they brought in the Biodiversity Guidance for solar farms in the spring of 2014, thus introducing Biodiversity Management Plans (BMPs) that have tended to replace the Landscape and Environmental Management Plans (LEMPs). BMPs are important packages for all solar farms now, and they are a platform for LPAs and all stakeholders to have their say.

The physical structure of the solar arrays themselves offer plenty of perches for birds, visiting, or passing through. The top of the panels are perch points and look out spots for local birds, or perches for resting birds of passage, even gulls at high tide, judging by the accumulation of bird mess. Twenty-nine species of bird were recorded on or over this solar site, and only 16 on or over the wheat field. Skylarks (BAP) were recorded in both sites, so to the Buzzard which seems to be increasing in the south east of England over all habitats.

No mortalities of birds were observed at the solar farm, even though it was a few kilometres from the sea and was often overflown by seabirds. It was an initial concern of Natural England that swans might confuse solar farms for bodies of water and alight and get injured or die, but this was investigated in 2011 and found not to be the case for the first large solar farm in south-east England near Sandwich. (Feltwell, J. 2013. Are photovoltaic solar arrays an influencing factor in avian mortality? The Newsletter of The Kent Field Club. February 2013. Number 77, p.18-27.) The concern over adverse effects on invertebrates was also not observed at Oving. (Feltwell, J. 2014 Observations on the effects of photovoltaic solar panels on invertebrates at Ebbsfleet Farm, Sandwich, Kent 2010-2012. The Newsletter of The Kent Field Club. Number 79. February 2014. p.4-17.).

The results from the solar farm at Oving suggested that the solar farm was more biodiverse than the wheat field. This was actually suspected, and confirmed, even though both fields were previously under organic management, giving the wheat field an unusually high level of wildflowers, but even so beaten by the solar farm in terms of species richness.

So the future for solar farms looks very bright for biodiversity, not that this has been fully appreciated by Local Planning Authorities (LPAs). LPAs are still making planning conditions stating that the site has to be returned to its former use. Given the snowballing effect of biodiversity on solar sites due to natural means and BMP enhancements there will be an increasing problem in returning these new nature reserves to their species-poor fields of oilseed rape or winter wheat.

So what other lessons have been learned? Sceptics cannot see the issue with the 'temporary' nature of solar farms. As with this Oving site, the biodiversity of the solar site will get better year- on- year, whereas the wheat field will have to start all over again each year when it is ploughed. The soils on the solar farm will have a complete rest for 30 years and be much improved nutrient wise and for biodiversity. It used to be called 'fallow' when fields were left uncropped for about three years to give them a rest in a process of crop rotation. Now with solars the soils are rested for 10 times longer. (Feltwell, J. 2014. Solar farms: gain or grain? Solar Business Focus UK. Volume 11 – 2014. p.40-41.)

Dr John Feltwell, CBiol, CEnv, CEcol, Dip EC Law of Wildlife Matters Consultancy Unit has been involved with the ecology of over 40 ground-based solar farms in England and Wales. Wildlife Matters Consultancy Unit, Marlham, Henley's Down, Battle, East Sussex, TN33 9BN. Tel. 01424 830566. john@wildlifematters.com.

Appendices

Appendix 1 List of Figures

Case Studies

Term	Definition
Amorphous Solar Cells	One of two main types of solar cells. A thin film of silicon is deposited onto a sheet of another material, such as steel or glass, and sunlight causes the silicon to release electrons, generating an electrical current. Often found in small solar panels such as calculators or garden lamps, but also expanding with technology into larger installations. **See also Crystalline Solar Cells.**
Ampere (Amps)	The standard unit of electrical currents.
Anaerobic Digestion (AD)	AD is a process whereby organic materials such as food and farm waste are broken down by naturally occurring micro-organisms in the absence of air. This process releases methane which can then be used for heat and electricity generation
Area of Outstanding Natural Beauty	An area of England, Wales or Northern Ireland considered to have significant landscape value and specially designated as such by the relevant Government. These areas are given legal protection to conserve and enhance their natural value.
Arms Length Management Organisation (ALMO)	A not for profit company that provides housing services on behalf of a local authority. Essentially, the ALMO will be set up to manage and improve the local authority's housing stock.
Automatic Meter Reading (AMR)	Technology used to automatically collect consumption readings, take diagnostics and send status updates to the relevant utility company.
Bio-energy	A renewable energy made available from materials which derive from a biological source. Bio-energy is the energy extracted from biomass, the fuel.
Biomass	Biomass can be used to describe a broad range of materials derived from living, or recently living biological organisms. On a relatively small domestic scale, biomass fuel usually takes the form of wood pellets, chips or logs which are burnt for heat and energy.
Biomass Boilers	A simple alternative to standard gas or electricity fired boilers: biomass fuels the heating process.

Bonds	A type of debt security used to raise finance and which evidences a promise by the borrower to repay money loaned to an investor, usually with interest. Bonds can be traded on the capital markets.
Building Regulations	Government legislation applying to buildings in England and Wales which promote high standards for most aspects of a building's construction, energy efficiency, access and health and safety requirements.
Capital Expenditure	Financial investment to either purchase new fixed assets (such as plant and machinery) or improve the value of existing fixed assets.
Carbon Capture and Storage/ Sequestration (CCS)	A process whereby carbon is captured during the combustion process of energy generation and then transported to a suitable geological storage location such as a used oil field or saline aquifer. Essentially, carbon is no longer emitted into the atmosphere: it is merely stored below the surface of the Earth.
Carbon Dioxide (CO2)	A natural, colourless greenhouse gas which is emitted as part of the combustion process of fossil fuels. CO2 is widely blamed for climate change and global warming due to its ability to absorb infrared radiation from the sun, preventing its escape from Earth.
Carbon Dioxide Equivalent (CO2e)	A measurement devised to express GHG (other than CO2), in CO2 equivalent terms based on their global warming potential.
Carbon Emissions Reduction Target (CERT)	To help the Government meet its 2020 and 2050 carbon reduction targets, all suppliers with a customer base greater than 250,000 must meet specified carbon savings. **See also Energy Company Obligation (ECO)**.
Carbon Floor Price	A mechanism which aims to attract low carbon investment by making the price of carbon pollution higher. If the market price of carbon under current regimes such as EU ETS and CCL falls below that of the carbon floor price, industries must pay a top-up amount. This mechanism combats uncertainty caused by the trading of carbon allowances on the market which can often fail to incentivise carbon reductions due to the low price of allowances.

Carbon Footprint	The total amount of GHG produced to directly or indirectly support human activities, expressed in equivalent tonnes of CO2.
Carbon Neutral	The concept of a net zero carbon footprint which is achieved by zero carbon emissions when balancing carbon emissions against carbon savings and off-setting.
Carbon Reduction Commitment (CRC)	A mandatory carbon emissions reporting and pricing scheme for non energy-intensive organisations. The scheme aims to reduce carbon emissions in both the public and private sector. **See also CRC Energy Efficiency Scheme.**
Carbon Trust Standard	A standard developed to encourage good practice in carbon measurement, management and reduction by businesses and public sector organisations. The Carbon Trust Standard provides an objective benchmark against which to assess an organisation's commitment to carbon reduction.
Chinese Wall	Arrangements within a business that require information held by a person or department to be withheld from another person or department in an attempt to avoid conflicts of interest.
Climate Change Agreements (CCA)	Given that certain industries are inevitably and unavoidably energy-intensive, DECC has provided for a discount system whereby such industries can benefit from a 65% reduction in its CCL if it meets energy efficiency targets set out in the terms of a CCA.
Climate Change Levy (CCL)	A tax on the use of energy in industry, commerce and the public sector. Energy efficiency schemes and utilisation of renewable sources of energy are rewarded under this system by cuts in the employers' National Insurance Contributions. The levy aims to encourage energy efficiency and in turn reduce emission of greenhouse gases.
Combined Cycle Gas Turbines (CCGT)	A highly efficient energy generation technology combining both gas-fired turbines with steam turbines. The gas turbine generates electricity and the resulting waste heat is captured and used to turn the steam turbines.

Combined Heat and Power (CHP)

The simultaneous generation of electricity and heat, sometimes referred to as "cogeneration". CHP installations can range from simple Micro CHP boilers in an individual domestic property, to large CHP generators housed in an ESCo, distributing electricity and heat through a private electricity network and district heating network to local houses, businesses and public sector buildings.

Community Energy Saving Programme (CESP)

A Government programme which requires all licensed gas and electricity suppliers and electricity generators to deliver energy saving measures to low income areas of Great Britain. As part of this programme, such suppliers and generators must meet carbon emissions reduction targets.
See also Energy Company Obligation (ECO).

Community Infrastructure Levy (CIL)

Following criticism of Section 106 Agreements, the CIL was introduced to clarify the way in which local authorities can impose a levy on new developments in their area for use within the community. Charges under this system have been simplified so that the amount corresponds to the size and type of development and all new Section 106 Agreements must comply with the provisions of CIL.
See also Section 106 Agreements.

Community Interest Companies

Limited companies created for the use of people who want to conduct a business or other activity for community benefit and not purely for private gain.

Contraction and Convergence

A global notion that countries should aim to converge towards an equal level of emissions 'per person' by an agreed date, with the richer and more developed countries contracting at a greater rate, causing a bargain between all countries at different stages of industrial development.

CRC Energy Efficiency Scheme

Formerly the CRC, a mandatory scheme introduced by DECC to improve energy efficiency and cut carbon emissions in large public sector and private organisations. The scheme targets large carbon emitters not already covered by CCAs and the EU ETS and includes a league table based on energy efficiency performance.
See also Carbon Reduction Commitment (CRC).

Crystalline Solar Cells	There are two types of Crystalline Solar Cells: 1) monocrystalline cells that are cut from a single silicon ingot from a single large crystal of silicon; and 2) polycrystalline cells cut from a silicon ingot made up of many smaller silicon crystals. When met with sunlight the silicon cells release electrons creating an electrical current. **See also Amorphous Solar Cells.**
Degression	A mechanism used to reduce tariffs, usually on an annual basis, in order to both reflect and encourage decreases in the costs of certain technologies.
Department for Environment, Food and Rural Affairs (DEFRA)	The Government department responsible for issues such as the natural environment, plants and animals, food, farming and fisheries, environmental protection, pollution control, sustainable development and the green economy.
Department of Energy and Climate Change (DECC)	A Government department with aims including the protection of vulnerable energy consumers and the promotion of a low carbon economy.
Direct Labour Organisation (DLO)	A business unit of a local authority or other public sector body which undertakes day to day service functions.
Distribution Network Operator (DNO)	Companies licensed in the UK by OFGEM to distribute energy from the High Voltage Distribution Network to businesses, local authorities and domestic households. There are currently six DNO's which operate across the fourteen regions of the UK. **See also Local Distribution Network.**
District Heating Network	A system for distributing heat from a centralised generation point to residential and commercial properties for space and water heating.
Ecology	The scientific study of the relationship between living organisms and their environment.
Electric Vehicle (EV) Charging Infrastructure	Infrastructure created to provide charging facilities for electric and plug-in hybrid vehicles.

Electricity Market Reform (EMR)

A wide ranging Government process aimed at reforming the UK's electricity market. As part of this process, a draft Energy Bill has been introduced, together with the ongoing reform of electricity supply licences and the intended introduction of the Green Deal.

Embedded Carbon

The carbon content of an item or product reflecting the total amount of carbon dioxide emitted from every stage of its production and distribution, from source to store. If this figure exceeds the carbon saving of the final installation, emissions will not fall and so the technology is counterproductive.

Emissions Performance Standard

A Government standard proposed to limit the amount of CO_2 the most carbon intensive power stations can emit: in particular new fossil fuel power stations.

Energy Company Obligation (ECO)

The ECO will take over from the existing obligations of the CERT and CESP, which are due to end in December 2012. These obligations are likely to heavily link with the introduction of the Green Deal.
See also Carbon Emissions Reduction Target (CERT) and Community Energy Saving Programme (CESP).

Energy Efficiency

An aim towards reducing the amount of energy required to deliver products and services. This includes better conversion rates in energy production, developed technologies requiring less energy consumption to achieve the same goal and more efficient use by the final consumer to prevent wastage.

Energy Networks Association (ENA)

An industry body in the UK funded by gas and electricity transmission and DNOs. ENA represents its members with the aim of influencing relevant policies on gas and electricity infrastructure by communicating with Government and within the industry.

Energy Performance Certificate (EPC)

All homes bought, sold or rented require an EPC which provides information on energy efficiency within the property. A sliding scale of classifications (A to G) are awarded to properties, with A reflecting the most efficient properties. For some Government energy programmes such as FITs, a minimum EPC rating must be achieved before a house owner can benefit from the full scope of incentives.

Energy Security

The term used to describe a country's access to and availability of natural resources and fuels to continue to meet its energy demands

Energy Services Company (ESCo)

A commercial business which typically provides energy services such as the installation and maintenance of energy efficiency improvements.

Environmental Impact Assessment

A process whereby information about the environmental effects of a project is collected, assessed and taken into account when making a decision as to whether the project can go ahead. A local authority should check with the planning department as to whether this assessment is needed in the given circumstances.

Equity

A method of raising finance in the alternative to debt finance (loans, bonds etc). The investing party will pay money for a stake in the project and in return it will benefit from a corresponding share of any profits.

EU Emissions Trading Scheme (EU ETS)

An EU scheme whereby factories, power stations and other large scale energy generators across the EU must monitor and report their yearly CO_2 emissions. Through CO_2 allowance trading and emission caps, the scheme attempts to manipulate industries and Member States into reducing their overall carbon emissions and to help the EU meet 2020 and 2050 targets.

EU Renewable Energy Directive

One of the key EU Directives which sets all Member States a number of energy efficiency targets, with the overall aim of ensuring that the EU generates at least 20% of its energy from renewable sources by 2020.

Feed-in-Tariff (FIT)

A programme to promote the uptake of small-scale renewable and low-carbon electricity generation technologies across the UK. FITs will usually consist of a payment for renewable energy generation in addition to an actual payment for surplus energy being fed back into the Grid. The level of support received is dependent on the renewable source used.

Feed-in-Tariffs with Contracts for Difference (FIT CfD)

Long-term instruments proposed in the Draft Energy Bill published on 22 May 2012 which aims to provide stable and predictable incentives for companies to invest in low-carbon generation. Essentially, there is a mechanism in place whereby a long-term price is guaranteed for generation from a renewable source, protecting green investors from price reductions in the market. However, to hedge this, any extra income above the market price will be repaid to the relevant counterparty.

Fossil Fuels

Fuels formed from natural processes such as the decomposition of organisms over millions of years. Including coal, oil and natural gas, these fuels are used in the combustion phase of electricity generation and emit large amounts of CO_2 due to their high concentration of carbon.

Fuel Poverty

If a household needs to spend more than 10% of its income on fuel to maintain a satisfactory heating regime, then it is said to be in fuel poverty. A satisfactory heating regime is usually 21 degrees for a main living area and 18 degrees for other occupied rooms. The latest information shows that in 2010 around 4.75 million households in the UK were in fuel poverty.

Geology

The study of the physical material of the Earth.

Geothermal Energy

Thermal energy generated and stored in the Earth from its formation and the decay of minerals. This energy source can be used to heat water for electricity generation and be utilised as a heat source.

Gilts

UK Government bonds used as a form of long-term Government borrowing.

Green Deal

A Government initiative designed to encourage domestic and non-domestic customers to employ green technologies in their properties. Essentially, customers will install green technology at no upfront cost, and then pay back the costs over time through increased energy bills. This initiative is not considered to be a loan as the repayment obligation remains with the property even when the owner vacates.

Green Deal Provider

For the Green Deal to be successful, Green Deal Providers are needed. These will include finance companies, energy companies, accredited advisory companies and other large companies that will carry out property inspections, raise finance and installations. Some companies may decide to act as a 'one stop shop', while others may oversee Green Deal projects, subcontracting installation and inspection elements to other companies.

Green Investment Bank (GIB)

An institution to be established by the Government in order to support investment in 'green', low-carbon technologies.

Greenhouse Gases (GHG)

Gases including CO_2, methane, nitrous oxide and ozone. These gases allow sunlight to enter the Earth's atmosphere freely. Once the sunlight hits the Earth's surface, infrared radiation will reflect back into space. GHG absorb this radiation, trapping the heat within the Earth's atmosphere which is believed to cause the gradual rise of the Earth's temperature: Global Warming.

Grid Parity

The point in time where obtaining electricity from a renewable source is no more expensive than obtaining energy from the Grid. At this point, the renewable production will no longer require a Government subsidy.

Gross Domestic Product (GDP)

A single figure which aims to indicate the health of a country's economy and in the UK this is published by the Office for National Statistics. Growth and recessions are determined by the change of GDP, with a recession being the occurrence of negative growth for two consecutive 3 month periods, expressed as a reduction of GDP. The figure is usually an accumulation of all money earned by the country or all money spent. Both approaches should roughly come to the same figure of GDP.

Ground and Air Source Heat Pumps (GSHP and ASHP respectively)	A GSHP is a low-carbon heat generating system which utilises natural thermal heat from the ground. The process involves pumping a mixture of water and antifreeze around a system of underground pipes. This liquid absorbs heat from the ground which can then be used in radiators and for hot water and under floor heating systems.
	An ASHP uses heat from outside air to warm the inside of a property (and vice versa to cool the property when required). A refrigerant system absorbs the heat from outside for use in space heating and domestic hot water systems.
Hectare (ha)	A unit of measurement used to denote an area of land. One ha is equal to an area of 100 metres by 100 metres.
Her Majesty's Revenue and Customs (HMRC)	The department of the Government responsible for the administration and collection of taxes. HMRC also governs policies on the national minimum wage and pays certain State support credits.
Hertz (Hz)	A unit of frequency equal to one cycle per second.
High Voltage Distribution Network	See National Grid.
Hydropower	Energy in water is captured by the movement of the water from a higher level to a lower level. The flow of the water and its fall between levels is used to convert energy into mechanical energy, which in turn generates electricity.
Indemnities	A promise by one party to reimburse another in respect of loss suffered. This specific loss will be compensated in full when there has been a breach of a specific provision in a contract.
Inflation	The rate of change in the price of goods and services in an economy at a given time.
Infrastructure Planning Commission (IPC)	Abolished in April 2012, the IPC has been superseded by a new National Infrastructure Directorate, which will continue its duties to examine major infrastructure applications.

Internal Rate of Return (IRR)	A rate of return used to calculate the profitability of an investment. A high IRR will suggest that a project will lead to positive growth in returns. IRRs for different renewable projects could be used by a local authority to decide which should be taken through to the next stage.
Inverter	An electrical device that changes direct current to alternating current, ready for use in the home or for entry onto the Grid.
Irradiance	The impact of the sun's rays on the Earth. It is calculated as the power of electromagnetic radiation per unit area of the surface affected. These quantities are typically referred to in W/m2. Irradiance levels will affect the performance of Solar PV installations.
Isolator	A part of the generation installation which enables a circuit to be de-energised for repairs and maintenance.
Kilovolts (Kv)	One Kv is equal to 1,000 volts (a measure of potential energy of a unit charge). Electricity will be transported at different voltages. Transformers initially increase the voltage of generated electricity for transportation across a High Voltage Distribution Network. As the electricity begins to branch down to the end user, transformers will reduce the voltage. The early distribution of electricity is often described in Kv due to the size of the voltage used to prevent loss during the transportation process.
Kilowatt Hour (kwh)	A unit of power typically used by energy providers for the purpose of billing domestic consumers. A typical home in the UK uses around 21,000 kwh (or 21 MWh) of energy per year.
Large Scale Voluntary Transfer	The process by which a local authority will transfer all or part of its housing stock to a new or existing RSL or housing association.
Levy Exemption Certificates (LEC)	Electronic certificates issued to accredited generating stations, for each unit of electricity generated from renewable sources. The certificates are then used to claim exemption from the CCL.

Liquefied Petroleum Gas (LPG)

An abundant product sourced as a by-product of the oil and gas industries. LPG can be used as a fuel alternative for vehicles and causes the emission of lower levels of CO_2.

Local Authority Carbon Management Programme (LACM)

A programme aimed at raising awareness and preparing a local authority to create a strategic plan for carbon management and reductions in its area.

Local Distribution Network

The connection between the Grid and the end user. Once electricity has been transported from the generation source to particular areas of the UK, the relevant DNO will distribute the electricity across individual cities, towns and villages.

Local Enterprise Partnerships

Led by local authorities and businesses across the given natural economy areas, these partnerships provide the vision, knowledge and strategic leadership needed to drive sustainable private sector growth and job creation in the area.

Megawatt Hour (MWh)

One MWh is equal to 1,000 kwh.

Microgeneration

The production of heat and/or electricity on a small-scale from a low carbon source by individuals, small businesses and communities to meet their own needs. Examples include water turbines, ground source heat pumps, solar installations and Micro Combined Heat and Power installations.

Microgeneration Certification Scheme (MCS)

An internationally recognised quality assurance scheme that demonstrates to customers that the companies which install microgeneration technologies to produce electricity and heat from renewable sources are signed up to meeting high levels of tested standards.

National Grid

Also known as the Grid and the High Voltage Distribution Network, the National Grid is the infrastructure involved in transporting electricity from the source of generation, to specific areas of the country. Evidence of this network is clear for all to see, with large 400 Kv pylons crossing the UK countryside.

It should be noted that National Grid specifically relates to the English company which owns and operates the English network, however it is sometimes loosely used interchangeably with the Grid.

Net Present Value (NPV)

The difference between the present value of the cash inflows from a project, and the present value of cash outflows (for example the capital expenditure for the project). A profitable project will need a positive NPV.

Nuclear Energy

The use of nuclear reactions or radioactive decaying to generate electricity and heat. Essentially, the nucleus of an atom is split inside a nuclear reactor to release a large amount of energy. Heat is removed from the core of the reactor and is used to generate steam, which in turn drives the turbines for electricity generation.

Office of Fair Trading (OFT)

A non-ministerial Government department established to enforce consumer protection and fair competition, as regulator of the markets.

Office of Gas and Electricity Markets (OFGEM)

The government body appointed as regulator of the electricity and gas markets in Great Britain.

Office of Government Commerce (OGC)

An arm of the Cabinet Office's Efficiency and Reform Group, the OGC works with central Government and public sector organisations to help with the acquisition, procurement and sustainability policies of Government and public sector spending and project delivery.

Official Journal of the European Union (OJEU)

The official gazette record for the European Union.

Parts per Million (ppm)

A measurement to express the concentration of substances in the atmosphere, water or soil. Greenhouse Gases are measured in ppm in the atmosphere. 1 ppm means that there is one molecule of GHG per million molecules of gases present in the atmosphere. Reports in 2011 suggest that Earth has recently exceeded the 400 ppm barrier for the first time.

Peak Oil

A point in time when the world's peak production rate for oil is reached and thereafter, it can only decline.

Permitted Development Rules

Implied planning consent to carry out certain classes of development to a property. Criteria for any rule must be strictly adhered to if a home owner is to rely on this implied consent without risk.

Power Purchase Agreement (PPA)

An agreement between two parties which sets out the terms upon which one party will generate and sell electricity, which the other will purchase. This agreement will include all terms of the relationship including a schedule of delivery, minimum and maximum off-takes, payment terms, penalties for failure to deliver and termination rights. A local authority that generates surplus electricity from a renewable project could enter into a PPA if it could bargain a better price than feeding the electricity into the Grid.

Private Finance Initiative (PFI)

A Government initiative introduced in 1992 to encourage private businesses to tender for the provision of public infrastructure and services (for example to build schools and hospitals). A local authority will enter into a long-term contract with an SPV which will usually construct and operate the facilities in question. The SPV secures private funding, and receives a monthly payment throughout the term.

Private Finance Initiative (PFI)

The process by which the Government, local authorities and other public sector bodies must follow to award supply and service contracts to the private sector.

Public Works Loans Board (PWLB)

A Government department managed as part of the UK Debt Management Office and tasked with providing loans to local authorities for capital projects and as a lender of last resort.

REAL Assurance Scheme

A scheme created by the Renewable Energy Association, the UK's leading trade organisation for renewable energy producers and suppliers. The scheme requires members to follow a consumer code to ensure that domestic consumers receive high standards of services from energy generators.

Reduced Data Standard Assessment Procedure (RD SAP)

RD SAP is a form of SAP introduced as a lower cost method of assessing the performance of existing dwellings. Both RD SAP and SAP are used to produce EPCs.
See also Standard Assessment Procedure (SAP).

Registered Provider (RP)	Independent housing organisations including housing associations, trusts, cooperatives and companies. RPs provide access to social housing including low cost ownership schemes and support for disabled and vulnerable persons. RPs will also help with housing management, regeneration and development.
Registered Social Landlord (RSL)	Government funded organisations including housing associations, trusts and cooperatives which provide affordable housing in a given area. RSLs will be involved in both the development of homes, and their maintenance thereof: repairing the property and collecting rent in line with its duties as a landlord.
Renewable	A natural resource which has the ability to reproduce through biological or natural processes, replenishing without a finite supply. Examples include the sun, wind and tidal movements.
Renewable Energy Roadmap	DECC's overarching action plan setting out the Government's ambition for renewable deployment to meet 2020 targets for renewable energy generation.
Renewable Heat Incentive (RHI)	The RHI is a Government incentivised policy similar to the FIT system, but in respect of heat generation from renewable sources. The RHI regime hopes to increase heat generation in a wide range of renewable technologies, balancing between expenditure of public money and subsidising innovative and costly generation installations.
Renewable Heat Premium Payments	A Government scheme which gives money to householders to help them buy renewable heating technology such as solar thermal panels, heat pumps and biomass boilers. At the time of writing, this scheme is intended to be short-term with the effectiveness of these grants being assessed.
Renewables Obligation (RO)	An obligation placed on UK electricity suppliers to source an increasing proportion of their electricity from renewable sources.
Renewables Obligation Certificates (ROCs)	Issued to accredited electricity generators and suppliers for the production of eligible renewable energy as part of the RO.
Requests for Information	In accordance with the Freedom of Information Act 2000, in certain circumstances public bodies must comply with a public request for information.

Restrictive Covenants	A term often found in a property deed or other agreement whereby the house owner promises to do or not to do something with his land.
Retail Price Index (RPI)	A measure of Inflation, published in the UK by the Office for National Statistics. This is calculated using a virtual shopping basket of standard purchases on goods and services in the UK. The average price will show a rate of change from previous quarters or years. RPI differs from the Consumer Prices Index as it includes housing costs such as the effect of mortgage rates and council tax.
Retrofit	The addition of new technology to adapt and improve older systems already in existence.
Return on Investment (ROI)	A performance measure evaluating the efficiency of an investment. This is expressed as the net benefit of the investment over its total cost.
Salix Funding	Salix Finance is a not for profit company funded by DECC. Interest free loans are offered to public sector bodies aiming to improve energy efficiency in public sector buildings.
Section 106 Agreements	Section 106 of the Town and Country Planning Act 1990 empowers a local authority to impose planning obligations on a land owner so as to influence the manner in which it can build a new development, intend to use the property and may even require a financial contribution to be made by the land owner. **See also Community Infrastructure Levy (CIL).**
Small Scale Embedded Generators (SSEG)	A generation source of electrical energy typically of around 16 amps per phase and of 230/400 volts of alternating current, often operated in parallel to a DNO's Local Distribution Network.
Solar Farms	A large Solar PV system with numerous Solar PV installations, often used for the supply of electricity into the Grid under a PPA or otherwise.
Solar Photovoltaics (Solar PV)	Solar PV panels are made from a semiconducting material such as silicone. Solar PV systems are usually installed on the roofs of buildings and generate electricity by capturing energy from sunlight **(but see Solar Farms above)**. The panels do not require intense, direct exposure to the sun so electricity can still be generated from regular daylight.

United Kingdom Accreditation Service (UKAS)	The UK's national accreditation body for the assessment of organisations providing certification, testing and inspection and calibration services.
VAT	Value Added Tax.
Warranties	A contractual statement of fact made by one party to another. If the statement later turns out to be untrue, the innocent party can sue the offending party for damages.
Watts per square metre (W/m2)	A standard unit of measurement for levels of Irradiance on Earth.
Wave Energy	Although not yet in full commercial use, current inventions work around the idea of floating installations capturing the energy released from breaking waves and converting this for electrical use.
Wayleave	A right given to a service provider to install pipes or cabling on, through or above a person's land.
Wind Energy	Wind turbines can vary in scale from large, free-standing mast mounted structures to small domestic roof mounted systems. The turbines work by harnessing the wind to drive large propellers, which in turn drive a turbine to generate electricity. Turbines can be connected to feed unused power into the Grid.
Worldwide Fund for Nature	An international, non-governmental organisation promoting a sustainable environment and good conservation.

Bibliography, further reading and references

Books

- Sustainable Energy Without the Hot Air
  Professor David MacKay

- Renewable Energy – Power for a
  Sustainable Future
  Godfrey Boyle

- How bad are bananas? The carbon
  footprint of everything
  Mike Berners-Lee

- The Hockey Stick Illusion
  AW Montford

- The Solar Century
  Jeremy Leggett

- Choosing Solar Electricity – A Guide to
  Photovoltaic Systems
  Brian Goss

- Solar Power for Everyone – Solar Praxis

- The Revenge of Gaia *James Lovelock*

- Six Degrees *Mark Lynas*

- *Al Gore* An Inconvenient Truth

- How to Go Carbon Neutral
  Mark Bressington

- Its Not Easy Being Green
  Dick Strawbridge

- Renewable Energy and the Grid
  Godfrey Boyle

- Sustainability in Austerity
  Philip Monaghan

- Prosperity Without Growth
  Tim Jackson

Government Papers

- The Coalition: Our Programme for
  Government

- The Renewable Energy Strategy *DECC*

- The Low Carbon Transition Plan *DECC*

- The Low Carbon Industrial Strategy
  HM Government

- The UK Renewable Energy Roadmap

- The Carbon Plan: Delivering Our Low
  Carbon Future

- The Plan for Growth

- The National Planning Policy Framework

- Renewable Heat Incentive – Consultation
  on the Proposed RHI Financial Support
  Scheme (DECC)

- Consultation on Renewable Electricity
  Financial Incentives 2009

- Feed in Tariffs Scheme: Government
  Response to Consultation on
  Comprehensive Review Phase
  2A: Solar Cost Control (May 2012)

- Feed in Tariffs Scheme:
  Government Response to Consultation
  on Comprehensive Review Phase 2A:
  Solar Cost Control (May 2012)

- Electricity Market Reform (December
  2011)

- Planning Our Electric Future: A White
  Paper for Secure, Affordable and Low
  Carbon Electricity (White Paper July
  2011)

Other Reports

- Zero Carbon Britain 2030 – Centre for Alternative Technology

- The Greenest Government Ever: One Year On – Jonathan Porritt - Friends of the Earth 2011

- Local Government's Offer on Climate Change – LGA

- Energy: Grow your Own – National Trust

- More Bang for the Public Buck (APSE – February 2010)

- Birmingham City Council - Birmingham Declaration

- Power in Numbers – the Benefits and Potential of Distributed Energy at the Small Community Scale (EST - 2009)

- Renewable And Low Carbon Energy Supplementary Planning Document (June 2010 – Cornwall Council)

- How Local Authorities Can Reduce Emissions and Manage Climate Risk – Committee on Climate Change May 2012Papers by the Association for Public Service Excellence

- Insourcing: A guide to bringing local authority services back in house

- The Virtuous Circle: Creating a Revolving Fund for Solar Energy

- The New Green Team: local government, sustainable energy, jobs and skills (October 2011, Unison / TUC)